FATE KEEPS ON HAPPENING

ANITA LOOS

FATE KEEPS ON HAPPENING

*Adventures of Lorelei Lee
and Other Writings*

Edited by
Ray Pierre Corsini

DODD, MEAD & COMPANY
New York

Library of Congress Cataloging in Publication Data

Loos, Anita, 1888-1981
Fate keeps on happening.

I. Corsini, Ray Pierre. II. Title.
PS3523.O557F3   1984   813'.52   84-13497
ISBN 0-396-08398-6

Editor's Note

Anita Loos had begun to prepare a collection of her writings, when her death in 1981 cut her work short. In the past few years she had written new pieces which she planned to include in this omnibus, and had sent copies to the editor. Never satisfied with her own work, she kept revising the new material in between lengthier stints on her plays and books.

Among Miss Loos's papers were found manuscripts in various stages, some in rough draft, others in finished form. They have been edited carefully to retain her inimitable style and viewpoint. Titles of the pieces first published in this book follow:

"Memoirs of a Best-Selling Blonde," "A Bachelor's Dilemma," "A Girl Can't Go On Laughing All the Time," "What's Better Than Sex?," "The Joys of Money," "A Meal to Remember," "Why Not Try a Little ESP?," "Beating the Rap," "Hollywood Now and Then," "Fashions in Faces," "Anatomy of a Siren," and "Roman Holiday."

The editor and publisher are grateful for permission to reprint writings that appeared in diverse publications. If their titles differ, they are listed in parentheses after the original titles used in this volume.

"Liquor Makes You Smart," International *Cosmopolitan,* June 1927. Copyright (c) 1927 by International Cosmopolitan. Reprinted by permission of *Cosmopolitan Magazine.*

"It's All a Plot of the Hairdressers," *The New York Times Magazine,* November 27, 1949. Copyright (c) 1949 by The New York Times Company. Reprinted by permission.

"Gossip that Speeds over the Hairwaves," *The New York Times Magazine,* March 19, 1950. Copyright (c) 1950 by The New York Times Company. Reprinted by permission.

N.Y.C. Excerpted from Twice Over Lightly. Copyright (c) 1972 by Helen Hayes and Anita Loos; Harcourt Brace Jovanovich, Inc., New York.

"Dear Noël," *Vogue,* February 1973. Copyright (c) by The Condé Nast Publications Inc. Courtesy *Vogue.*

"Those Were the Days," *Saturday Review,* May 13, 1961. Copyright (c) 1961 by Saturday Review Magazine Co. Reprinted by permission.

"A Poet In Love" ("Vachel, Mae and Me"), *Saturday Review,* August 26, 1961. Copyright (c) 1961 by Saturday Review Magazine Co. Reprinted by permission.

"M G M Makes Room for a Genius." Excerpt in revised form from *Kiss Hollywood Good-by.* Copyright (c) 1974 by Anita Loos; The Viking Press, Inc., New York, and W. H. Allen, London. (See further Acknowledgment following this list.)

"About 'San Francisco,' " Afterword to *San Francisco,* Screenplay by Anita Loos. Copyright (c) 1974 by Southern Illinois University Press. Reprinted by permission.

"Lillian Gish—A Tribute to a Trouper," *The New York Times,* September 14, 1980. Copyright (c) 1980 by The New York Times Company. Reprinted by permission.

"Lulu Baby" ("Greatest Actress in Moving Pictures"), *Vogue,* October 1981. Copyright (c) 1981 by The Condé Nast Publications Inc. Courtesy *Vogue.*

"Harlow's Hollywood," *Cosmopolitan* Magazine, May 1974. Excerpted from *Kiss Hollywood Good-by.* Copyright (c) 1974 by Anita Loos; The Viking Press, Inc., New York, and W. H. Allen, London. Reprinted by permission.

"The Italians Have a Word for It," *Town & Country* magazine, May 1980. Copyright (c) 1980 by Town & Country. Courtesy *Town & Country.*

"Why Girls Go South," *Harper's Bazaar,* January-March 1926. Copyright (c) 1926 by Harper's Bazaar. Courtesy *Harper's Bazaar.*

Grateful acknowledgment is made for permission to quote the following material:

Excerpt of "Reflections from Anita Loos" by William Empson, from *Collected Poems.* Reprinted by permission of the author.

Letter from William Faulkner. Published with permission from Mrs. Jill Faulkner Summers, Executrix of William Faulkner.

Letter from H. L. Mencken. Reprinted by permission from the Enoch Pratt Free Library collection, Baltimore, Md., in accordance with the terms of the will of H. L. Mencken.

Excerpts from *The Letters of Aldous Huxley,* edited by Grover Smith. Reprinted by permission from Harper & Row, Publishers, Mrs. Laura Huxley, Grover Smith, and Chatto & Windus. Quoted from *Kiss Hollywood Good-by* by Anita Loos.

Excerpts of letters from Vachel Lindsay. Reprinted by permission of Nicholas C. Lindsay. Quoted in *A Girl Like I.* Copyright (c) 1966 by Anita Loos; The Viking Press, Inc., New York, and Hamish Hamilton, London.

Contents

PART
ONE

A Lifetime
with Lorelei Lee

by Lorelei Lee

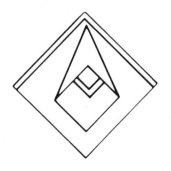

Memoirs of a
Best-Selling Blonde

◆

*L*AST week I was laying on the sofa in my boodoire, reading one of those startling biographies of a famous film star, when the telephone rang. Well it turned out to be Mr. Bugsie Lazarus, the famous littirary agent, who said he wanted to see me about writing a book. I mean I wrote one years ago called *Gentlemen Prefer Blondes,* and it sold like the preverbial hotcakes. So I gave Mr. Lazarus an appointment and then, when my girlfriend Dorothy called up, I mentioned what had happened. But Dorothy said, "Don't get tangled up with Bugsie Lazarus because that rat will get you to tell everything and then wind up with all your royalties in his own pocket."

Well, Dorothy knows what she is talking about because she socializes with the Bugsie Lazarus set and her advice is straight from the so-called Horse's Mouth. So when Mr. Lazarus arrived the next day I put on quite a formal house-gown and went downstairs to decline his offer.

The first thing Mr. Lazarus asked was "Why?"

Well, I was quick to think of a polite excuse and I told him I did not know how to write a book about sex and vialents that people read today. I mean if I wrote a biography it would be as clean as the preverbial hound's teeth.

But Mr. Lazarus is the kind of an agent who will not take "No" for an answer. And he said, "Don't give me that, honey, because when you were sixteen down in Little Rock you were put on trial for attempt to murder some Arkansas yokel."

Well, I began to get annoyed with Mr. Lazarus, so I informed him that his information was not true. And that the gentleman he called a "yokel" was a wealthy member of the Arkansas legislature. And the reason I shot him was because of my high ideals, because I always considered that matrimony was sacred and when Senator Jenkins refused to even consider it at all, I suddenly realized that there was a revolver in my purse. And the revolver had shot Senator Jenkins.

Mr. Lazarus didn't seem to be convinced, so I went on to inform him that everything turned out for the best. I mean that when the accident took place, the Senator was trying to get through the doorway. So the bullit only made a small size wound that couldn't even be noticed when the Senator had his trousers on.

And I enformed Mr. Lazarus that in those days it was a novelty for a blonde to go on trial. I mean, the Honorable Judge Peabody said I brought a ray of sunshine into the courtroom, and it only took two minutes for the jury to acquit me. But the best thing of all was that I had learnt a lesson. I mean that a girl's personality is more important than any firearms. So I have never purchased any more revolvers.

Well, after the whole thing blew over, I went North and married the aristocratic Mr. Henry Spoffard-The-Third of the wealthy Philadelphia family. So my autobiography was out of the question.

But my refusal only squelched Mr. Lazarus for a moment. I mean he said, "Okay, sugar, but if that's the way you feel I'll get some authoress like Rona Barrett to take on the assignment."

After Mr. Lazarus went away, I began to worry so I phoned the news to Dorothy. And to say that she was disturbed is to put it mildly. I mean Dorothy said, "If Bugsie gets one of his authors to do a hatchet job on you, she won't leave you with a single leg to stand on."

Well, Dorothy became even more alarming when she enquired, "How would that Presbeterian suitor of yours feel about such a book?" And while I was squirming she went right on to ask, "And what about his *mother*?"

So I had to admit that Mrs. Peoples is even more Presbeterian than her son. And then I mentioned the Board of Trade that he's the chairman of. But I only added tinder to Dorothy's flames. I mean she said, "What's even worse is that the public exagerates everything. Like it did down in Washington when the Speaker of the House was ruined because he merely hired a stenographer who never learnt how to type."

And then Dorothy said the only way out of my predictament was for me to contack Bugsie and tell him I'd write my own biography. And she picked up the phone and got him at his office. Well, my change of heart delighted Mr. Lazarus and he said he'd bring the contrack to my place the first thing in the morning.

But by the next day I had time to think things over. So when Mr. Lazarus handed me the contrack I told him I would only sign it if the royalties were paid directly to me in person.

Well, Mr. Lazarus looked at me for a little while and then he enquired where his own percentige would come from. And I told him he could trust in me for that. Well Mr. Lazarus looked at me in silents and then he went to pick up both the contrack and his hat. And he said, "So long sweetheart. It was good to meet you. Have a nice day." But when he went out, he slammed the door.

I mean I was quite depressed because I feared he was on his way to one of his authoresses who writes smutt. So I phoned Dorothy to tell her the bad news. But Dorothy said, "Well, old pal, it was just a case of Greek meeting Greek, but it looks like Bugsie's won the Olympic Games." But Dorothy is never pestamistic for long. And she had made a date to go to a cocktail party. So she went.

But something happened at that party that was almost like fate. After all, fate keeps on happening. So when Dorothy was climbing the staircase to the second floor she encountered Mr. Lazarus who was escorting one of his most obnoxious authoresses. I mean, by that time, Dorothy must of had a cocktail because she pulled him aside and said in quite a loud voice, *"Bugsie, you're a dunce!"*

Well, Mr. Lazarus only smirked and asked her, "Where did *you* find that out?" And Dorothy said, "Everybody knows that those filthy books you push are beginning to make the public yawn. So what do *you* do? You turn down an author like Lorelei who can squirt perfume on a garbage dump and give you a *genuine* best smeller!"

Mr. Lazarus gasped. And Dorothy might have gone right on and gotten rude except that she lost control of her knees and suddenly fell all the way down a spiral staircase.

Well, Dorothy was picked up by a friendly chorus-boy who found a taxi and escorted her safely to the nearest diskoteck to calm down.

But the most delightful thing of all took place next morning when Mr. Lazarus sent my contrack back for my signiture and it was smothered in a box of orchids.

But the sweetest thing of all was Mr. Lazarus'es card, for he wrote, "Good luck to *our* book, sugar. But don't forget my percentages are in your hands."

So it makes me feel quite proud to know that my tack-ticks are just as sound as any agent's.

Liquor Makes
You Smart

*W*ELL, Dorothy and I were spending a delightful winter at
Palm Beach but we decided that society gets on a girl's nerves. So
we decided to get away from everything and take a trip to Cuba. I
telegraphed my husband at New York to send us the money but he
became economical and said stay where we were.

So, then, we counted up our money and we had enough fare to
get to Cuba, but we did not have so much left to pay high price
hotel bills. But I am always of the optamistic nature. So I said, "Lets
go anyway and maybe everything will all turn out for the best."
Dorothy said, "If you are game to face the sheriff of Cuba, I guess I
can take a chance." So, then we went to Cuba.

But when we got there I had to realize that Cuba is no city for a
girl like Dorothy. Because Dorothy makes friends very, very easily.
And Cuban gentlemen on the street do even more. So insted of
pretending that she did not notice them like I always do, Dorothy
would pass remarks right back, even if they did not understand the
English landguage. And it only encouraged them, so by the time we
would get back to our hotel it was practically a parade. And
speaking to an officer does less than no good because Havanan
policemen go even longer lengths than gentlemen in a business suit.

So I told Dorothy if she did not stop I would insist on spending all our time in bars where we would be with Americans. So Dorothy said that was a threat that could not make her quale. So, then, we went to the most famous bar at Cuba, called Sloppy Joes. And it was given the nickname of Sloppy Joes bar by a big Congressman's wife who was at Cuba quite a few years ago and seemed to notice that the gentleman called Joe who ran it was not so well groomed. So he has not done anything about it since, and he is practically an example of what happens to gentlemen who stop grooming. But his bar is really a delightful spot.

I mean the walls are full of more different kind of bottles than any spot in the world. And Americans can sit there and drink their choice and gaze at bottles that they have not seen for years. And some of the bottles they have never seen at all, so that it is practically like a wonderful old libery full of unusual books. And if we Americans would improve our time at Sloppy Joes bar by reading all the labels it would be an education. But most Americans who sit in bars do not want to learn anything. And Dorothy says, "What American could read after he hit Sloppy Joes anyway?"

So I ordered a cute drink of foreign emported liquor out of a quaint bottle, but Dorothy did nothing but drink large size glasses of beer and hold conversations with bartenders. And I finally had to realize that even Sloppy Joes bar was no place for a girl like Dorothy. So when we got back to our hotel I told Dorothy that I would not stay in Cuba with a girl like her unless we spent more time with the upper classes.

Then it turned out that Dorothy had met quite a lot of delightful native gentlemen of the upper classes that very morning in the Union Club of Havana, which is a male club for gentlemen only. But Dorothy went in because she thought it was a hotel and she was looking for a bar as usual. So quite a few of the Havanan gentlemen she met in the Union Club tried to make her see her mistake, but they did it in the Havanan landguage so Dorothy did not understand them until she reached the third floor where she met one who was quite educated in English.

But by the time she learned of her mistake she had made dozens of dozens of Cuban gentlemen friends, because there is nothing that a Cuban enjoys more than the aquaintence of we American girls. So by the time Dorothy started back and got to the main floor going out, she had collected practically a whole deck of calling cards from Cuban gentlemen.

So Dorothy told me to cut the deck, and she would call up the loser and give him an introduction to me. So I asked Dorothy how she would be able to talk to him on the telephone if he did not know the English landguage. But Dorothy said that all a girl had to do in Havana was to say "Sevilla Biltmore Hotel" over the telephone in a female American voice and the Havanan would be there by the shortest possible direct root.

I told Dorothy not to call them up until tea time when we were ready. Because it was only 2 oclock and we had to go shopping. But Dorothy said "Let him come and wait. What is time to a Cuban?" So she called him up. And he was in the lobby of the Sevilla Biltmore by the time we got downstairs.

So Dorothy said lets take him shopping but I said No, because we were only going to a wholesale Phillipinos to buy perfume which is very very cheap in Havana and I do not like to take gentlemen shopping for small size nicknacks and give them a false sense of values. So we left him sitting in the lobby. But when we got back to the hotel we were quite late from loitering and we did not know if he would still be there. But we did not really care so much because Cuban gentlemen who are wealthy are quite prolific at Havana on account of all of the sugar that comes out of the sugar cane. So it is always easy to find another.

But he was still sitting in the lobby and when Dorothy came up he was quite delighted. So then Dorothy introduced him to me and he was even more delighted because girls of the blonde coloring are quite novel to a Cuban.

So we sat down to have delicious Backardi cocktails and he started breaking out into Cuban. Whenever I hold a conversation with some gentleman in his own landguage I like to always be on the safe side when he stops to wait for an answer. So I always give a smile and say yes. Because I think that politeness comes first. But after a little while Dorothy began to get quite restless. And finally she could not stand it any longer. So Dorothy got up from the table and said, "I'm going to hunt up an interperator, because the last time you said yes, I think you promised him something illegal." I told Dorothy to hurry back because girls are not really safe with Cubans even in a lobby.

So Dorothy went over to a table full of American gentlemen who were of the gambling perfession. I mean Dorothy had met one of them in an elevator so she knew that she would be among friends.

So she asked them if one of them knew the native landguage and would be an interperator and protect two American girls from a Cuban who looked like he was full of evil intentions.

There was one gambler there who was of practically no social position. I mean he did not even make use of a name, but only went by the nickname of the Frisco Flash. So he told Dorothy he would interperate for us because he understood several Cuban words and what he did not understand he could fake. So when I saw Dorothy start to bring him over to the table, I was quite delighted because he was of the middle age generation and looked quite fatherly. And he and Dorothy arrived at the table just in time to save me from having to give a Cuban a push.

But when he sat down, insted of interperating other peoples thoughts, he started right in to tell us how famous he was all over the world for his motto, which was

"Any man from any land
At any game that he can name
For any amount that he can count."

So I really began to be nervous and I told him that I thought he was quite dangerous and I would be afraid to leave my Cuban gentleman friend alone with anyone like he. So he said "That's all right girlie. I pay my commissions and you'll get your 10 per cent." So I did not make any reply to such a mersenary remark but I held my dignity. So then he went on to tell Dorothy that he could always tell by the look on a "sucker's" face what he was good for in dollars and cents. So he looked over my Cuban friends expression and he said it would be about $30,000. And I really have to admire his training, after all, because that was what it turned out to be.

Then we all decided to go to the Gambling Casino for dinner. So Dorothy and I went to our rooms to dress and we had quite a little quarrel. Because I told Dorothy that I did not seem to care for an interperator who not only made his living at cards, but could not even talk Cuban. But Dorothy said I should have reverants for the elder generation that had to use cards because my own game might go out of date some time. So then I only gave Dorothy a look, because the law of nature always teaches that the feeling gentlemen have for girls goes on forever. But then I decided that if it was going to be rivalery between an elderly gambler and I over a Cuban, we would see who got 10 per cent at the finish.

When we went downstairs to meet our escorts they were in the barroom of the hotel playing dice and my Cuban gentleman friend had won practically every time, which made him feel very very good.

So we all went to the National Casino of Gambling for dinner and it is really very very unusual to see a gambling Casino with policemen at all of the doorways to protect the gamblers, insted of visa versa as policemen do in America. I mean in America policemen are always smashing in the door with an axe. So life in Cuba is really much more restful.

And the Casino at Cuba is very very beautiful with quite a lot of Art and marbel statuary and windows that look out on the scenery, which is quite novel because in Casinos at America all the windows have to have blinds to cover it up.

So after we had quite a delicious dinner we all went into the gambling rooms and my Cuban gentleman friend bought Dorothy and I $100 worth of checks each to gamble with. So of course Dorothy gambled with them. But I do not believe in gambling. So I put my checks in my hand bag, because our Cuban gentleman friend was very very busy gambling himself so he did not notice what we were doing.

When he came over to Dorothy and I to buy us some more checks, I could not tell him I was apposed to gambling on account of not being able to talk Cuban. So when it came time to go back to our hotel Dorothy had lost everything, but all I had to do was to cash in my checks for $500. And I think that is the only refined way girls can act at Casinos and hold their dignity.

But the Frisco Flash did not gamble either, because he said he was apposed to any kind of gambling which could not be controlled. So he spent the evening holding a conversation with a croupier to see what he could find out about our Cuban friend. And this croupier knew the histry of Havana so he told him that our Cuban friend could never get any money from his family, but he had just sold some horses for $30,000 and had it in cash.

On the way home I became quite indignent at our interperator because he made an engagement with my Cuban aquaintence to come up to his room and play a game of piquay, which was the only game of cards the Cuban gentleman knew how to play. So the Frisco Flash told Dorothy that when she saw him in the lobby in the morning he hoped she would show proper respect due a newly rich man. So we said goodnight, but after they started away he had an afterthought and he came back and got Dorothy off on one side and said, "Say how does that game of piquay go, anyway?" Dorothy did not know but the Flash told her not to worry because he was always prepared for any emergency.

So Dorothy said, "Good luck. Don't let him freeze his fingers on a cold deck." But the Frisco Flash answered back with another one of his mottos which was

"A good horse never stumbles
And a sucker never tumbles."

And the last Dorothy and I saw of them they were going down the hall into the room of the Frisco Flash which was nothing but a gambling den in disguise.

So then we went to our room and we had quite a little quarrel. Because I told Dorothy that she should not mix the upper classes with the lower classes in our aquaintenceship, especially when one of them was likely to take all the money away from the other one and practically spoil everybody's enjoyment. But then Dorothy said why didn't I study the Flash's methods and learn something new. And I told Dorothy that I did not see what anybody could learn from someone who had to sit up all night and work hard to win money at a game he did not know.

Well, when Dorothy and I went down in the lobby in the morning, the Frisco Flash was sitting at a table drinking champagne alone to celebrate winning $30,000 at piquay. And he had $15,000 of it right in his pocket, because that was all of the cash the Cuban had the night before. So he asked us to sit down and have a bottle of champagne and celebrate to. But I told him I did not care to drink, because I had a luncheon engagement with my Cuban gentleman friend and I did not want my brains to be unstrung. So then he said that I was foolish because liquor makes you smart. So then Dorothy said that she always noticed that liquor made her smart to. So they had a few drinks.

And the more drinks they had, the more smart they decided they were becoming. And Dorothy finally got to feeling so smart that she made a suggestion that they go out to the Casino and win back the money she had lost because she said that if the Flash added his smartness to her smartness they would wipe out the joint. But the

Flash could not go, because he had an engagement to meet his Cuban aquaintence and get the rest of the $30,000. And he was afraid to leave him loose around Havana with all that cash when he had such an open hearted Cuban nature.

So Dorothy and the Flash had some more champagne and Dorothy finally got to feeling so smart that she said she had decided she could buck the Casino single handed. So she started off alone with all of the money she had in the world.

Then the Flash had more champagne and decided that he ought to do something more than a commission for a little girl like I who had brought him all that good luck. So I told him that if he really wanted to do something he could do it at the jewelry shop next door.

So we went into the jewelry shop and he was feeling so full of exileration that he told me to select my own choice. So my own choice turned out to be quite a cute bracelet for $10,000. So he paid the money and we went back to the lobby to wait for the Cuban to arrive and pay the Flash his $15,000.

Finally our Cuban aquaintence came in and he brought a gentleman friend of his own along to be his interperator, because of the ineficiency of the Flash in talking Cuban.

Then the Flash ordered some more champagne and while they were all drinking it I really began to feel very very sorry that my Cuban aquaintence had to give up $15,000 more to a gambler that I had really been responsable for introducing to him. So while they were all drinking champagne I began to think up ideas.

I finally thought up one and I opened my pocketbook and I took out my box from the jewelers with the bracelet in it and I showed it to the Cuban gentlemen. So they admired it very very much and finally my Cuban aquaintence asked his interperator to ask me where I got it. So then I told the interperator to tell him that the jewelry store next door sent it in to me on approval, but it was much too expensive for a girl like I to pay for, so I would have to send it back.

So then quite a look of askance seemed to come into the countenance of the Frisco Flash. And he kept right on looking at me and looking at me. So then my Cuban aquaintence wanted to know how much the bracelet cost. So I said it cost $15,000. So when my Cuban aquaintence heard it he took out his wallit and he started in to count his $15,000 out. And by that time the expression on the face of the Frisco Flash seemed to be practically paralized.

So my Cuban aquaintence gave me the money to pay for my bracelet and I thanked him very very much, because, after all, it was all he had. But he promised the Flash that he would get $15,000 for him as soon as he could ask for it from his family. So then the Flash said, "Gentlemen, if you will pardon me, I'll pay my respects to this little lady and go out for air." So he kissed my hand with reverants and went away.

Finally Dorothy arrived back from the Gambling Casino and I had to lend her $3 of my money to pay for her taxicab.

Then we all had luncheon, but at luncheon I decided that I had really seen enough of Cuba because when an honest interperator got to interperating my Cuban aquaintence it turned out that he was nothing but a bore. So we told them we would see them at dinner, but we really took a boat at 4 oclock for Miami and the next morning we were quite delighted to be back where a girl speaks her own landguage and knows what is going on around her.

It's All a Plot
of the Hairdressers

*B*EING very scientifically minded, it is my purpose to trace
the basic causes, which have caused our present return to the
fashions of the Twentys and to find out for *The New York Times*
whether or not there is going to be a return of the Flapper. And, the
best way to find out is to go to the root of the matter, and
concentrate on Histry.

So it seems that back in Nineteen Nineteen the road was first
paved for the entrance of the Flapper into our form of Civilization.
Because that was when our Fedral Goverment made the Historic
Decision that it could repress people's thirst. So between the years
of January 12, 1920 to November 2, 1932, they went to work and
did it. But, looking back from the vantage point of Today, the only
refreshing thing that grew out of those historical twelve years of
Prohibition was termed the Flapper, which was a young girl in her
teens who was developed through the use of bootleg Gin.

And the choice of Gin as a means of forming a girl's character,
was the result of Economic efficiency. Because up to the time that
Prohibition became the most promanent Law of our Nation, there
were very few bootleggers in existence, so when the need for them
suddenly grew acute, they had to be recruited from every walk of life
and they really were not very efficient. But bootleggers of no
previous experience at all could manufacture quite a potent drink in

one simple operation by placing flavor made out of analine dye in a bathtub full of raw alcohol and term it Gin. And, since bootleggers were largely drawn from the ranks that had no additional need for bathtubs anyway, it did not even discomode the Household.

And the use of Gin also had another virtue, which was that it could also be made nutriciously in the Home and thus avoid ingredients which were not pure, such as wood alcohol, which was a favorite among bootleggers of the Period and resulted in quite an epidemic of total blindness.

And the use of bootleg Gin had an even further advantage, because the Flapper was able to drink it publicly in a water glass without causing the members of the Police Force, who were always peeping in and out of Speakeasies, to suspect anything. I mean the Officers who were carrying out our Country's laws could take one quick glance around the Speakeasy, make a hasty observation that everybody's glass was full of something that had all the earmarks of water, and withdraw without creating the indignity or the annoyance of a raid. And I always think that cooperation between the Police and the Citizen makes for the Highest Form of Civilization.

So now let us come to the Behavior Pattern which was evolved by the Economic Trends of the Nineteen Twentys. And this pattern had its basic foundation in the fact that young girls who became addicted to bootleg Gin were enclined to develop quite high spirits, particularly in the Speakeasies, where most of a young girl's time was whiled away.

And now we come to the observation that these high spirits had a tendency to cause disarrangement of both the garments and the coiffeur. And, since Fashion is invaritably influenced by a girl's Mode of living, a Flapper, in order to always appear modish while badly groomed, solved the problem by going to the root of the matter and getting herself dishevelled on purpose before she ever started out, which resulted in the Birth of the Wind-Blown Bob.

And to show how Nature can always be counted on to do the Right Thing, we have only to conjure up a picture of a young lady of, let us say, the Era of the Great King Edward VII of Great Britain, becoming full of grain alcohol while garbed in a straight-front corset, eight to ten petticoats, to say nothing of an umbrella foundation garment, and had her head marcelled into a pompadour with a "rat" in it. The result would be so inconsistent with Harmony that Nature would really rebell at such a thing. But the Economic Structure of the Edwardian days was so prosperous that the fashionable girls of that period could always drink champagne, which produced a refined form of exhileration which was in accordance with all the clothes they had on. So they were never in danger of any disarrangement of the garments, except in cases where a young lady might remove one of her slippers in order for some very gallant gentleman to substitute it for his wine glass.

But, con-versely, we find that in the Twentys, a young lady full of grain alcohol had no corset to confine her, her skirt was above her knees normally, her stockings were rolled down, and her hair Wind Blown, so that she was at all times in complete Harmony with the natural activities of the Period.

And in order to demonstrate how Civilization can always be counted on to improve, we have only to go further back into Histry and study the previous Period in which Gin was in general use by the female elimint of a nation. And this Period seemed to be in the 18th Century of England. I mean we can get quite an accurate record of this period by looking at pictures of a bevy of girls who used to model for an artist named Mr. Hogarth.

But these girls were invaritably ending up in some Mental Institution and were not the kind of girls that anyone would care to invite into their Home. While the girls of the Nineteen Twentys were of the best families and were depicted by a much more optomistic artist called John Held.

And further-more, the use of Gin in the Twentys was not condusive to Mental Institutions, but broke out in the much more attractive environments of the Speakeasies where the inmates developed activities such as the "Charleston" and the "Black Bottom" with their attendant slogans, such as "Hay, Hay" and "Vo-de-o-do" which were far more cheerful than the type of mental unbalance of the 18th Century.

But at the very moment when the Behavior Pattern of the Nineteen Twentys had reached its apex, the Fedral Goverment of the United States finally reached the point where they really couldn't be bothered any longer with Prohibition. I mean after twelve years of doing it, they learned that it couldn't be done. So I think it was a very, very great advance in thinking to think that it only took twelve years for the Legal Minds of the U.S. Goverment to learn something. Which goes to prove that their brains must really be getting brighter.

And one of the things that was most condusive to our Legal Institutions learning something, was the Flapper. Because practically every legal Mind in the United States had at least one of them in his own family and the strain finally reached the point where it broke the camels back. So I think that really the biggest feather in the cap of the Flapper was to think that a bevy of young girls in their teens could teach something to the Fedral Goverment of our Nation.

And now that we are nearing 1950 and can look around in every direction and note that the fashions of the Twentys are returning, I would really like to examine the Sociological reason back of it.

But, studying the World Economy of 1950, I really seem to notice that it is quite different. Because, to the young girl of 1950 bootleg Gin is no longer an Economic Necessity. Because the cocktail bars of today are as prevalent as the air we breathe and are no longer invaded by Enforcement Officers, which has resulted in alcohol of any form being no longer a novelty. So the girls of the Fiftys will have lost the impetus of trying to drink all they can hold, just in case some unforseen catastrophy happens to the source of supply.

So naturally, the result is that girls do not indulge so much in drinking. And thus, the subsequent need of appearing dishevelled on purpose has disappeared, which leads us to the fact that there is really no Sociological reason for a return of the Wind Blown Bob.

But using sound scientific research as a means of finding something out, I have finally discovered the reason why our present day Modes have returned to the past. And the reason seems to lay in the hands of a Body of Men who are invaritably constructive in directing Social Trends—meaning Hairdressers.

Because it seems that during the past ten years, Civilization developed a thing called the "Home Permanent" which started to remove clientelle from the jurisdiction of the Beauty Shoppe and placed it in the confines of the personal bathroom. So all over this great Nation of ours, husbands of no previous experience were beginning to give permanent waves to their wives at a minimum cost. And finally, the Mass Desertion of Beauty Parlors began to hit at the very foundation of Human Intercourse. Because Beauticians are noted for being quite a source of private information. And in some instances our most important columnists would miss their most sensational squibs, if it were not for the fact that the very girls who are trying to keep their private lives out of the press, have a tendency to become voluble the moment some Beautician starts working on their head.

So with the decline of the Beauty Parlor, repercussions followed that were reaching into the very confines of Hedda Hopper and Dorothy Kilgallen and Cobina Wright . . . the circulation of Newspapers was being kerbed . . . advertising began to shrink . . . conversation throughout the homes of the Country began to lack luster . . . the very mental welfare of the Nation really seemed to be endangered.

But, as in the case of any Historical Emergency, it was not the Economists who came to the rescue, but other kinds of experts who seemed to know what they were doing. And these experts were the bevy of gentlemen in charge of the Welfare of Beauticians.

And their solution was the return of the Wind Blown Bob. Because no matter how adroyt a girl is, she can never reach around with a pair of scissors and shingle her own head. And any husband would balk at attempting a job which requires a full four months course in a Barber's Colledge and, in case of a failure, putting his wife in a tantrim that would last until her back hair grew in again.

And then, following this Decision of the Beauticians, the Dress-Making-Trades went to work with a will, because the minute a girl's head is bobbed, all her previous garmints are out of Harmony. And the repercussions have been quite stimulating to everything except the personal pocket book of people who have to pay for them.

And so we find that the basis of the Return of the Wind Blown Flapper is not Alcoholic but Industrial. And the emotionalism of Gin has been replaced by the exigencies of the Business World which are not provocative of so many thrills.

And so, looking forward towards the Future, it is obvious that the girls of the Fiftys will really be a far, far cry from the Flapper of the old days. Because with no reason for an over-consumption of alcohol just because it is contra-banned, the girls of today sit in Cocktail Bars in a comparative state of sobriety. And instead of indulging in the conversation of the Twentys, which consisted of cheery catch phrases on the order of 'Boop-boop-a-doop' or 'So's your old man,' they spend their time conversing about topics like the Passing of Democracy and the Future of the Soviet Republic, which do not really inspire gaiety.

But I really think that the good old Flappers of the Twentys were best after all. Because the girls of the Present Era are only wasting a lot of time brooding about a thing called Security, which is really not a thing at all because it has become non-existent.

Gossip That Speeds
Over the Hairwaves

*I*T seems that I have been approached by *The New York Times* to write an article on the subjeck of Hairdressers, which I am quite pleased to do. I mean there is nothing about girls that is more promanent than their hair.

And it seems that whether we have it cut off, or get a permanint, or become a blonde, or let it grow out again, is a question which will always be moot, not only among we girls and our escorts (encluding husbands) but even to *The New York Times* which reveals the great importance of the subjeck.

But for every moment that girls spend in looking their best, they have always had to spend a previous ammount of time getting ready for it in the hands of some Hairdresser, who really becomes the unsung hero of the occasion. So I feel that a great deal of Justice ought to be done to Hairdressers. And, in order to find everything out along the lines of the subjeck, the best thing to do was to go to some large Publick Librery for research.

But browsing around the Non-Fiction Departmint in a Librery really causes a girl to think that Hairdressers have become neglected. I mean there is really such a dearth of volumns on the subjeck that a girl begins to feel that Authors are either of the Male Sex (without any knowledge of the subject) or else they are literary ladies who never go near a Hairdresser in the first place. So I am afraid that we girls who really frequent our Hairdresser and know how to appreciate their contribution, seldom take our pen in hand to write about it.

But on the other hand, the Publick Librery seems to be clogged with quite a few books by people who, instead of being Authors, are meerly Generals or Military persons, who's experience has been limited by war. And the shelfs are also permeated by other Authors who are Medical, and only write books about 'The Psychy-atric.'

But I think that Authors who concentrate on the contents of the Brain to the neglect of the coifeures that cover it, do not even understand the contents. Because I believe in the viewpoint of the Early Greeks who pointed out that everything ought to be in Moderation. And Early Greeks would not think of foistering so many books on the Reading Publick by Authors who's viewpoints have become warped through being overly-informed on their own subjeck.

For instants, I think that Authors who are writing books about such subjecks as 'Atomic Fissure,' for instants, ought to realize that quite a large ammount of Fissure was created one time in the British Iles by the well-groomed apearance of Mrs. Wallis Simpson with the ade of some Hairdresser who shall be nameless because of the neglect of Authors who are only conscious of the technical aspick of a thing and neglect the artistic side which encludes Hairdressers.

And I also think that, while the 'so-called' Brains of the Nation may think it is highly important to discover some new Secret Weapon, they should never forget that, sooner or later, some well-groomed girl will always crop up to inveegle the secret away and give it to some Enemy Nation. And at some of the Spy Trials there have been indications that the inveeglemint can even be accomplished by boys, because of the heter-o-genius times we seem to live in now-a-days. So it finally turns out that the whole acheevement is cancelled by some attractive young person who has never had the advantage of any technical proficiency. And I really feel that Authors who only deal, for instants, with the Hydrogen Bomb, to the exclusion of Peroxide-of-the-Same-Name, are over-looking one of the most pertinent branches of chemistry.

And so, on looking through the books at the Librery for some write-up that would pay a tribute to Hairdressers to no avale, a girl is finally forced to leave and write it herself without the ade of research.

But even though the Librery seems to be quite un-rewarding, it is quite a comfort to always know that the Readers who read the works of all those 'Experts' really form a meer percentage of the Publick.

For instants, any time something like the Modren new Version of the 'Carol Channing' coifeure, with its dearth of short hair, can intreege a larger amount of Publick Interest than the United Nations, it really shows that the Publick prefers to read about we girls than about a large body of Political Persons who do not know where they are getting to. Because the Publick knows that when we girls start for the Hairdressers, we really get there. And when the Hairdressers get something done, the result is definate.

But anybody who thinks that the Hairdressers' is a meer place to get your hair dressed, shows even more ignorance than Experts.

Because among we girls it is a well known fact that Beauty Shoppes have a special tendincy toward provoking confessions. And these confessions are enduced by an unusual form of an anesthetic, which is caused by the damp atmosphere of Beauty Shoppes, combined with quite a dank perfume from the shampoos of days gone by, and augminted by the mild sound of scalp-vibrators. And this anesthetic was invented by Hairdressers many years before the Russian Nation ever thought they had invented it theirselves. But insted of using the confessions like they do in Russia, to give people guilt-complexes, Hairdressers use them to create a delightful form of chit-chat.

And, insted of dropping Iron Curtains to shut all the rumors in, the Hairdressers give it every assistance to leak out, by recounting it, one by one, to all their verious clienteles. With the result that some of the most intimant relations soon filter into the Gossip Colloms where they can be read by every man, woman and child, forming one of the most delightful examples of Free Speech and Democracy in Operation.

And then, sometimes the relationship between Hair and the Person Who Elects to cut it off, is even supposed to be Mystic. Because Cecil B. DeMille has produced a Film to prove that back in the Bibical Days, a girl called Delila gave a gentleman called Sampson a trimming that destroyed his Power. But I am a girl who is more enclined to explane everything along more rational lines. So

I believe that while Delila was doing it, she really worked along the same lines used by Hairdressers and extracted some confession, which she was able to use later, and destroy his Power more along the lines of what the lawyers of today term 'Blackmail.'

Well—when a girl like I decides to dwelve into the Histry of the Past, there is another girl who heaves into view, who was famous for being in the enviromint of the well-known King, called Henry the Eighth. So this girl went by the name of Ann Bullen and it is quite aparent she must of had something extra-ordinary along the lines of publick apeal. Because she not only caused Henry-the-Eighth to poise in his Royal Progress and single her out from all his wife's other Lady-in-Waitings, but she caused the British Nation to split away from the denomination of an Italian Pope and break up a Holy Roman Empire.

Well, I am a girl that is always dwelving into the root of some matter in order to get helpful suggestions. So one day in London I went to Tate's Picture Gallery to see if I could find out what Ann Bullen had that could break a Govermint Contract between two famous Nations. Because any girl of today who could aproxamate the same thing should really be able to at least secure the Junker Diamond. But it was quite difficult to note that Ann Bullen had any greater apeal than all the other Lady-in-Waitings, who all seemed to employ the same Hairdresser who gave all of them the same type of a cute apearance, which is quite distinctly portrayed by a painter (and I quote) called Holbein.

Well, such a great Historical Mystry was bound to intreege a girl like I. So on enquiry, I was directed to a place called the British Museum where, on closer study, it turned out that the other Lady-in-Waitings were just as astrounded as I was about her. But they even went so far as to accuse Ann Bullen of having be-witched her Monarch through witch-craftery.

But I refused to be apeased by such an ignorant explanation, so I searched and searched until one day it was rewarded. And in a quite dusty tome the mystry became solved. So it seems that in the Court of Henry the Eighth there was a Court Hairdresser of French extraction by the name of Gaspar de Mauvissiere. And, on learning that Ann Bullen was a girl who was interested in always making the most of herself, Gaspar went and told her he had evolved a secret that (and I quote from the research of the period) "would infinately enhance her youthfulness and, at the same time, be so indetectable that no human mind could figure out the mystick process it envolved."

So (and I still am quoting) "the Lady Ann entered into a contrivance with Gaspar de Mauvissiere firmly believing that his secret had some connexion with divers charms and mystic amulets to be introduced into the structure of the head-gear every six or eight months when it was dresst."

But (and I am now un-quoting) it turned out that the idear of Mons. de Mauvissiere, like many other great idears, was really quite simple. Because all he did was to secretly, every week, shampoo her hair and remove from it the 'smog' of London, which has its counter-part today in Los Angeles, where each and every small-salary Stenographer can have a Hairdresser do the same thing which was once the hidden Beauty Secret of an Incipient Queen.

How to Win a
Fur Coat

$\mathcal{E}$very year, when the Fall Weather arrives and the air becomes brisk and Nature begins to have tangs, one of the most delightful pastimes is to get your Fur Coat out of storage. Because I always feel it is just like meeting a girl's Best Friends once again, to spread them around the room, and look them over, and decide to get some new ones.

And this year, the Furriers have designed so many new animals that girls can hesitate between no less than 106 diferent kinds of coveradge, which is a far cry from the Olden Times, before Minks got mutated, and when Ermine grew tails. Because in those days a girl had to hang onto her Ermine Wrap until it grew yellow and she grew gray, together. But such a combination is seldom seen today, except at a Concert, or the Meteropolitan Opera, where the owner is present to meerly listen to music.

And I always seem to think that the most delightful part of a shopping tour is to frequintly change your mind. So with 106 fresh opertunities, we girls can haggle longer with Clerks over our decision, this Fall, than we have ever haggled before. And it sometimes makes me smile to think that we girls can probably make Clerks in Fur Stores turn just as gray as the mutated Minks they are trying to get rid of.

But even a healthier sign of the new Fall Season is the statistics, which learn all we Students of Economics that the fastest selling animal in the whole United States is a Mink. So I think we should all feel very proud of the Stamina of American Girls who can go through sevral World-Wars, and all the Social Insecurity instigated by Democrats (who were not secure enough to get elected by other means) and still ensist on Mink.

Because I have heard that over in Europe, most of the girls gave up their Ideels long ago, and settled for a winter coat made of a rough woolen texture, along practicle lines, with a heavy intra-lineing. And I have even heard that quite a few girls in the suburbs of Europe have retreeted to the statis of a shawl.

But the most depressing aspeck of the Fur situation is to look at the News-Shots on Television, which reveel the mass photography of girls who live in the Soviet of Europe. Because those girls could look quite cute (in a muscular sort of way) if it was legal to be well-groomed in the U.S.S.R. But they do not even seem to own the Original Model of their garment, which is a Sport-Coat, made of Second-Hand sheep, that has been worn out by sevral generations of the male members of a girl's family, who got fed up with it first.

And those Models have also gone through Revolutions, so they do not even come out in one piece, which instigates patches that do not even hold to the original color scheems. And the resulting wrap would only be worn in our Country by Milton Berle who will do anything for laughs. But it really makes a lump come in a person's throat to think what has happened to the girls of the U.S.S.R. who were born on the very Ground Floor of the Nation that gives so many Minks to Humanity.

For the girls of Moscow never get to wear the Minks of their own nationality, because their Government likes to disrupt World-Peace by making the girls of other nations as attractive as possible. So the Soviet exports all their Minks to the enemy countries of England, America, and France.

And I can remember one time in Paris when Walter Duranty (the famed Russian Correspondent) asked me to buy a fur-piece for him to take back to a Soviet Girl-Friend, which would pervide warmth and at the same time look repulsive enough to keep her from being ostracized as a Caputolist and purged.

So I searched high and low for some accessory that could safely add nothing to any Soviet onsemble. But even in the bargain stores of Paris everything seemed to be flattering, so one day I dropped into Mainbocher's (which is noted for being the World's most Exclusive Coutouriay) for a breath of fresh air. Well Mr. Main

Bocher was far from the right person to solve a Leftist garment problem, but it was quite lucky I told it to him, for he preceeded to design an unobstrusive neck-piece made of imitation fur which accorded to the specifications of the U.S.S.R. But if he had not made Mr. Duranty a present of it, as his contribution to intranational Harmeny, that Mainbocher Fur Piece would have cost about 85 years of a Soviet Salary. And I do not think Goverments ought to concoct laws that burden citizens with so much expense for any meer imitation fur piece.

But on the other hand, shopping has also got its problems even among we Democrats. For although there are now 106 modren incentives to buy another new Fur Coat, Nature always believes in the Preservation of the Species, so it also prevides gentlemen with new motovations for trying to prevent shopping. And in New York this Fall, the preventative measure has turned out to be Korea. So we girls have had to set and listen, for hours, while gentlemen, and Escorts, and husbands recount how North Koreans have turned Victory into a rout, by making Financial Security extinct, because of augmented taxes.

And listening to such deefeatist conversation sometimes makes a girl's mind wander away from New York, and dwell on the States of Texas and Nevada, which have remained outside the jurisdicktion of Communists, by only demanding 33 and 1/3 percent of the same taxes that are paid in other locales. Because in the State of Nevada, for instants, our Goverment likes to encouradge Beef, in order to feed our G.I.'s the delicious Sirloin Steaks which are stewed in the skillits of the Army Cooks. While Texas is famous for Oil, which is required by airoplanes and tanks in their trips to and from the war. So our Goverment refaines from putting a sur-tax on the Beef and Fewel Professions, which removes the obstruction from shopping for Minks with the gentlemen of Texas and Nevada.

But, after all, every girl in the East can't follow the advise of Mr. Horice Greeley, and follow every young man who goes West. And I have heard that the native Texans and Nevadans haven't got faith in we New Yorkers, and escribe a mercenary motovation to every girl that sets foot off a train. So my advise to girls is to put their mind on how to meet the requirements of their own locality. And I would like to give girls hints on how to get Mink Coats in the New York area.

And so now we come to the subjeck of sales resistance on the part of gentlemen required to pay for Mink. For very few persons of the masculine gender can understand what Minks do for the Moralle of we girls. So they will often try to swerve a girl towards the kind of fur found in bargain basements, which is called by some deceeving term (such as 'lappin') which has been trumpted up to disguise the fact that it is nothing more than rabbits. But it gives a girl quite a lot of self confidents to toss on some garment which costs more than an entire house-and-lot occupied by the kind of a girl who wears lappin.

But when girls start out to get a new Mink, Etiquette should teach us to, first of all, previde the gentlemen of our choice with a sound motovation for spending money. And when Times are as astringent as they seem to be this Fall, any type of shopping that can be put in the cattagory of non-essentials (like jewellery) has almost become extinct. Because it is quite dificult for gentlemen to vizualize the type of warmth which is enduced in we girls by a Diamond Clip, for instants. But a Fur Coat has the advantadge of easeing their conscience, because they can always feel that, if they didn't buy a girl a new one, she would be chilly. For motovations of this type are quite basic, because they date back to the Pre-Historical Times, when Cave-Men had to fell animals with a Club, in order to get the Cave-Girl of their choice a new tippet. And so, the very self-same gentlemen who would lay awake nights and worry over spending quite a lot of money at Cartiers, will make the same identical expenditure at Gunthers and sleep like a baby.

But just the same, it is adviseable for girls to carefully work their techneeque out in advance. And the quickest techneeque I have worked out for getting a new Mink Wrap, is to first make an engagement with some Escort to meet you downstairs in the Lobby. And then, before stepping out of your apartment, step to the faucet, allowing the cold water to run on the fingers for sevral moments (or until thoroughly chilled). After which, a girl should quickly preceed to the Lobby and shake hands, previding an Escort with a very protective thrill, especially if a girl wears a light-weight wrap, and at the same time shudders.

So the next step is then taken by the Escort who inverriably suggests a cocktail to keep himself from catching Newmonia after shaking hands in that Lobby.

And then, over Cocktails-for-Two, an opening soon opens up to make the suggestion of an all-purpose Mink, as more economic than being compelled to buy sevral other Fur Coats which would be required to take the place of one mere Mink. For the strongest motovation gentlemen have for buying Mink, is previded by the little Minks themselves, who are born durable enough to be worn to a Football Game (for warmth) and at the same time, expensive enough to be worn to the Stork Club, with dignity.

And so, many a gentleman who has failed to see anything good in any fur-bearing animal what-so-ever, can be won over to Minks when forced to take a pencil and paper and add up the cost of buying a girl a Shaved Racoon (for Football), plus a Beaver (for Shopping), plus a Sealskin (for Cocktails), plus an Ermine Wrap (for Formal).

Well, after an Escort has listened to Logic long enough to give in, the next preceedure is to get rid of him and do the shopping alone. Or better still, to take along the type of a Girl-Friend to which gentlemen have adversions, so she is eager to take advantage of them, by egging you on. And it is very unadviseable to take along any Shopper like a friend of mine called Dorothy, who has such a weakness for Escorts that she will come fairly skipping out of a store, in a small neck-piece made of imitation rat.

Which now brings up the most important reason for girls to never take gentlemen into Fur Shops this Fall. Because while honest Furriers have been busy mutating the plain, normal Ranch Minks into all the lovely abnormal shades called 'Silver-Blu,' 'Star-light,' 'Kohinoor,' 'Heather,' 'White,' 'Breath-of-Spring,' and even 'Black,' the dishonest ones have been dying Muskrat into the same identicle variations. And they are so diabolic in their cleverness that sometimes the only way a gentleman can tell real fur from imita-tion, is to ask the price. So an Escort might get false idears of economy from seeing some man-made Mink that sells at 1/10 the cost, and looks so identicle it would fool anybody except women (who are born with the instinct for self preservation and can tell a Fake by intuition).

But I always think it is the lowest depths of deceet to play a trick on little, small, defenseless Minks by counterfitting them for a mercenary purpose. And I would never think of wearing such a garment, for I have always been quite a lover of Wild Animal Life.

History of the
Preferred Blonde

*T*HE painful approach of a birthday has led me into reminiscences of my youth and some of the girls I knew who gave color and character to the Twenties. For that period will always live in our memories as a giddy montage of their short skirts, bobbed hair, long cigarette holders and rolled stockings. And when, on New Year's morn of 1930, the last gentleman of the old decade snapped the last garter of its final blonde, we started a descent into the horrors of scientific (I might almost say "institutionalized") sex. Today the mortifying couch of the psychoanalyst has replaced the pink satin chaise-longue of the Twenties, with its cushions outlined in marabou or fashioned in the shape of dolls.

So what of those blondes whom gentlemen preferred when they were younger? Do gentlemen still prefer them? Have they been able to weather the Fifties? Is the flash of their diamonds obscured by dust from the atom bomb? Should I invade the privacy of a blonde I knew quite well and ask her what she is up to at the moment?

I learned that her present address is a suburb of Detroit where she has been living for several years. So I dispatched a letter to her and here is Lorelei's reply—for what it is worth:

Dear Miss Loos:
    Your letter of inquery about my present statis has just reached me at my estate in Grosse Point. So evadently, Miss Loos, you have not

read the book of Ettaquette or learned that girls who reach a more advanced stage of youth should not ask impertenent questions of one another.

I mean, why should I tell an authoress like you the secrets of how to be happy dwelling in Grosse Point, Michigan? For nobody ever came to my ade along these lines, or I would have found out that the most prosperous suberb in the U.S.A. is Greenwich, Connecticut. And those are the facks of Life which are only learned by the 'blood, sweat and tears' of Randolph Churchill's father.

So my first impulse, Miss Loos, was to not accord you a reply. Because twenty-five years ago, when your book about we blondes appeared, I was quite desturbed. And I said to myself, 'That authoress has gone and given we girls away and the first thing we know, gentlemen will read that book and find things out. And we blondes will be left severally alone.'

But I soon begun to note that gentlemen were reading that book in droves and then laying it down and going right over to pick up the telephone and make another date with a blonde. And when a book of the same ilk was written by Mr. Hitler, who called it 'My Kampf', where he, hisself, told everything he was up to, his admirers went right on associating with him. And it seems apperent that most persons never really learn anything. So if you want to go ahead and give away my secrets of success, I may as well let you do it.

Well, Miss Loos, the first marriadge I made (to a wealthy Philadelphiam) was termenated by having to live with him in Philadelphia. After which, I felt I deserved to be pampered a little, so I packed up and moved my Securities to New York. And then I decided that every girl should allow herself the privilege of making one mistake, so I became engaged to an Argentine whose only visible means of support was sex appeal. So on the day of the ceremony, while our wedding guests were waiting for the honorable mayor to arrive at the Ritz and tie the knot, I coaxed Camillo to sign a paper which reduced his claims to merely room and board and pocket money. But even so, it was a releef to learn how quickly he became obnoxious.

Well, to celebrate my new divorce I took my girl friend, Dorothy, on a world tour of Europe. And while we were in Italy, I was able to put to good use the lesson I learned from Camillo. Because the principle comoditty of the Italians is the sex appeal of their Signors. And while Dorothy and I were boating in the gondolas of Venice, it was sometimes quite difficult (even for a girl like I) to remove my gaze from a gondoleer and concentrate on a palazzio. While Dorothy didn't even try. And I really hate to think how frequintly she went boating in the moonlight and not only paid for the ride, but tipped the gondoleer with her last centissimo and claimed it was a bargain.

And the only safe thing we girls incountered in Italy was at our hotel in Florenzi, where I noted Mr. Peoples, the General Motors Magnate from Detroit, sitting alone in a vestibulio.

Well, Miss Loos, to be married to a Detroit General Motors Magnate might become quite tedious these days when occupation for a wealthy wife is sparce in any locale. And as soon as I found myself in such a predicament, my first impulse was to study the habbets of other wives who were in the same fix. But when I found them out, I was aghasted. Because most wealthy wives of our epock now seem to be occupied in develleping a condition caused by laying on weight around the center of the torso by means of Martini cocktails. And this is a condition which Dorothy (who is noted for not watching her words) has termed a 'Martini Barrel'. And Dorothy even boasts that she has 'rolled up a whopper without being wealthy.'

So I am beginning to fear that Dorothy never will be wealthy. For when she first arrived in Michigan to be my Maid of Honor, she was slender enough to have married the entire Detroit Athletic Club. Insted of which she eloped with the propiator of the garage who supplied the limousines for my marital cortege.

Well, Miss Loos, the worst thing about adding girth to the waist line, is the conversation which accompanies it. Because those wives of wealth do nothing but hold arguements about their unapetizing diets and the pains resulting from massage and the iritating types of their new girdles. And the only form of action they all seem to agree on is, that if one will drink enough Martinis on awakening, one will ultimately reach a state where one will feel just as good as if one had not had too many Martinis before one retired. And it seemed to require a girl with brains like I, to work out a solution which consisted in not starting to drink them in the first place.

So while my co-temperies seemed to be boreing everybody within earshot in bars, I began to sip tomato juice and talk about matters of interest to their husbands and, in many cases, their sons.

For Mr. Peoples seems to always sense that he can trust me. Because a girl who has had a few romances in early life, seldem starts to grow romantick when it is too late to do so with dignity. While the marriadge I underwent with poor Camillo cancelled any doubt I ever had on the inadaquincy of the 'love of a girl's lifetime'.

And I think it is really pathetic, Miss Loos, the way most husbands have to search for something about wives of which they can be proud of. And poor Wesley was so delighted when I began to have listeners that he started comparing me to a brainy blonde of early Greece and termed me the 'Aphasia' of Detroit.

So then I began to thrash around and see what I could do to sway the opinions of a few more others. And it did not take me very long to recollect that Wesley was paying $650,000 every week for an hour on TV. So I went to work and foemilated the plan of sending our private plane to New York every week, and having it pick up all Wesley's Advertising Executives and whisk them out here to Detroit, where I preceed to tell them what to put on Wesley's programs.

Well, Miss Loos, those Executives are delighted, because of not knowing what to put on programs theirselves. I mean I even empress Dorothy who says that I not only pervide them with a script, but also with its alibi. And with thirty million listeners every week, Wesley can now term me the 'Aphasia' of the entire U.S.A.

So I hope you realize, Miss Loos, that the firmness of character and integritty that was avinced by girls like I in 1900 is still at work. I mean I almost have to smile about those who live in the past and think that the acquasition of jewellry can indacate we girl's importants today. For in this era, costume jewellry fools anyone and the wearing of diamonds has lost its victory.

And you will note that one of the most gorgeous blondes of the Nation is going to represent Our Government in Italy, and another beautiful blonde will represent us at the British Coronation. So it is time for us to realize that girls have entered a new epock. And I quote:

> Wives of rich men all remind us
> We can make our lives sublime
> And departing leave behind us
> Feetsteps on the sand of time.

And now, I hope you can see that times have changed quite a lot since I was a "so-called" flapper in the twenties, when we girls were not required to be promanent because gentlemen took a propietory interest in us. I mean they wanted to see we girls in a lovely apartment, and sometimes even in a whole brownstone house, surrounded by gilt furniture, encluding a piano and, in some instances, a bookcase. And they loved to give we girls delightful presents of brick-a-brack, such as solid gold picture frames, or a clock made out of genuine Rose Quarts from Cartiers. For nothing really gives gentlemen as big a thrill as letting we girls wheedle things out of them.

So my heart really aches for the gentlemen of today who have to pay Our Government so much income tax that they can only afford to see a girl from time to time, and have to be contented to meerly take a blonde to dine at the Little Club once a week. And then, for the remainder of the week, the blonde herself has got to get to her next six meals by allowing six other gentlemen to take her to dine at the Little Club. Or else she has got to foist for herself by the more arderous method of posing for *Vogue* (in clothes) or being a show girl (without).

And so today, when nothing is expected of gentlemen beyond a girl's meer entertainment for one evening, they seem to have lost their sense of hospitality. And it is no wonder that gentlemen with nothing better to support than a war in Korea, become crass. And my heart really bleeds for the blondes of this epock who never knew the time when the Man-of-the-Year was inveritably the gentlemanly and humorous Wilson Mizner insted of the caddish Menot Jelke of 1953.

So, Miss Loos, I hope your curiosity on all these matters is releeved.

Fondly yours,
Lorelei Lee Peoples

But Dr. Kinsey,
What About Romance?

*A*N imperturbable blonde partisan of soft lights and soft touches addresses a letter to the doctor and asks a few questions of her own.

Dear Dr. Kinsey:

To say that I am horrowfied at your new book called "Sexual Behavior in the Human Femail" is really putting it mildly. For I am not only horrowfied at you and the cohorts who abetted you in interviewing those Femails but most of all I am horrowfied at the Femails you interrigated. And all I can say is that you have manadged to incounter 5,940 Femails who will never get anywheres.

Because, if there is one thing I have learned by being a Human Femail, it is that the most necessary ingreedient to Human Behavior is Romance. And nowhere in your whole book do those Femails of yours allude to Romance, except as an insult to the Human Mail. I mean, the only mention they make of it is where they indicate that they are emotionally effected (and I quote) "by romantic fiction and romantic movies." In other words, at a time when those Femails you interrigated should have been thinking about the Human Mail with who they happened to be at the moment, they were either concentrating on some best seller like *From Here to Eternity* or on Gregory Peck.

So, I am beginning to really fear, Dr. Kinsey, that students who glance through your book might get the idea that the Human Femails of the United States are incapabil of concocting romances of their own and are relying on the Book of the Month Club and the script writers of Hollywood to supply their needs.

But I am quite idealistic about we American girls, Dr. Kinsey, so all I can do is hope that those Human Femails of yours are not representitive of girls like I who seem to think that Femails who substitute a novel or a film for reality are not only cheating the Human Mails of their acquaintance but are also giving them inferiority complexes, which, in these modren times, are the most horrowfying things that Human Beens can do to one another.

And to give you an example of the romantic behavior of girls like I, Dr. Kinsey, I would like to recount an ideal evening I recently underwent with a Human Mail of my own acquaintance. I mean, if I had been a laggard, like those 5,940 heroines of your book, it might have been quite a releef to have closed my eyes while dancing with him at the El Morocco and conjured up a mental picture of Marlon Brando. For this Human Mail in question had been born over sixty years previous and had spent much of the interim gaining weight and suffering the loss of his hair.

Well, to turn an evening of that type into a Romance, Dr. Kinsey, was really not an easy task for an ideelist like I. I mean, for conversation, I could have merely repeated the lyric of the song the band was playing and whispered "Be My Life's Companion and You'll Never Grow Old" in Mr. Wolpus' ear.

But my method of handeling an ordeal of the above type, Dr. Kinsey, is to always concoct some romantic dialogue of my own that is peartinent to the occasion and, at the same time, fits the personality of the Human Mail in question.

So while dancing that night, I said to him (and I quote):

"Mr. Wolpus," I said. "Last Sunday afternoon when there was nothing to do of any interest, my girl friend Dorothy and I went to an Art Museum."

So he remarked with pleasure,

"Did you, Lorelei?"

So I knew I was on the right track, because there is nothing that releeves any Human Mail so much as to have a Human Femail provide an indication of brains as an alibi for enjoying our company.

So I continued along the same lines (and I quote):

"And do you know what happened to me, Mr. Wolpus?" I said. "I saw an antient Greek statue of an early Roman Emperor and he looked *just like you!*"

Well, to say that it flattered Mr. Wolpus to resemble a Roman Emperor was putting it mildly. I mean he blushed all the way up from his chin to the back of his collar.

So then I continued and said,

"Doesn't it thrill you, Mr. Wolpus, to know that, far away in antient Greek, you were the center of everybody's admiration?"

Well, Mr. Wolpus felt he had to apologize for counteraddicting me, but he never-the-less said,

"Now, Lorelei, I think you're exaggerating."

So then I said,

"I mean every word of it, Mr. Wolpus. And if I had been born in antient times I would have followed the custom of the country and put a wreath of flowers on your head. But since both of us seem to be modren," I said to him, "I will give back one of the orchids you sent me. Only I will place it in your buttonhole, because if I put it on top of your head, it would slide off."

So he laughed at my little joke and I laughed too. Which goes to prove that comidey releef is also quite condusive to Romance.

So I really think, Dr. Kinsey, that you would have learned a lot more scientific facks if you had questioned a few of we girls who do not have to resort to either films or fiction to become amotional. I mean, I did not even have to use fiction in my dialogue with Mr. Wolpus. Because the Roman Emperor I compared him to was as fat as a porcupus and he looked even more like Mr. Wolpus than Mr. Wolpus looks like hisself.

And so it is my theory, Dr. Kinsey, that those Human Femails who prefer to day dream about fictionary characters or Hollywood Film actors in preference to a cute type of genuine Human Mail like Mr. Wolpus are wasting their opportunities for a real romance. Because the heroes of a good novel only exist in cold type, while on the other hand, those Hollywood Film actors are too hot to handle. For quite a lot of them are neither Mail nor Femail and their Human Behavior is atrocious, as every Night Club from the East to the West Coast can verify.

And while I am on the subjeck of Romance, I may as well recount the end of my romance with Mr. Wolpus. Because the time came, as it inveritably does, when someone of more Romantic impact hoved into my view. So one day in order to get rid of Mr. Wolpus by the same romantic methods that I picked him up, I bursted into tears and remarked that we would not be seeing one another any more.

And when Mr. Wolpus wanted to know what motivated our rupture, I told him that a girl like I was not of sufficient background for a gentleman of such distinction as him. But I had assertained previously that his taxes had been mounting up to a point where Mr. Wolpus' life had become almost a burden, so my decision previded him with a releef that made the end of our romance just as delightful as the beginning.

And we parted the best of friends, which is the ideel way to bring things about. For a girl's reputation can be greatly augumented by having some Human Mail publicly crying into his highballs at bars where other Human Mails can overhear him remark that you gave him up because of having such nobility.

So it is my feeling, Dr. Kinsey, that sex appeal which is applied with romance, is really what makes the world go round. And the absents of romance in those Human Femails of yours augers very bad for the sentimental status of our nation. For girls of that ilk are likely to turn Human Mails away from the Human Femails of the U.S.A.

So, if your statisticks are correct, Dr. Kinsey, it is high time for those Femails to discover the romantic approach of girls like I, who are able to attach Romance to anybody who even remotely resembles a Human Mail.

But Dr. Kinsey, I would like to accord you credit for anything good that has really come out of your book. So I would like to admit that there is a certain group of Human Femails that will be benefitted by it. I mean the type of Femails whose Human Behavior, up to now, has been of no interest what-so-ever to the Human Mail. And for Femails of that bracket to realize that they have become heroines of a book that is longer than *Anthony's Adverse* and full of epasodes that would make *Forever Amber* blush, must really give them quite a thrill. I mean, when walking down the street on the day of the press releese, I noted quite a few Femails of that type walking around with quite a lot of pride.

But I really hope they make hay while the sun shines because, as soon as everybody reads those 843 pages, they are going to be so fed up on sex that they will very quickly revert to Human Femails of the sentimental type like I.

And so, until the time when Romance enters your statisticks, Dr. Kinsey, I will turn away from all such books as yours. Because they are not only krass but furthermore unscientific.

And when it comes to the real truth about such things, I will give my readers two choices of who they want to believe. A group of unromantic middle-western professors or a girl like I.

And furthermore, if I should ever wish to demeen myself by writing about sex, my script would not have to be locked up and guarded against Peeping Toms by the police, but it would be sufficiently refined that anyone could safely let it lay loose around the kindergartens of the U.S.A.

If you are ever in New York, Dr. Kinsey, look me up. In the mean time, I remain

Fondly yours,
Lorelei Lee

The Decline and Fall of Modern Blondes

*A*LONG with all the changes that have changed every-thing for everybody in the last decads we girls also had to go through a Great Sexual Revolution. This is very significkent, even more than politickal revolutions, because if girls revolt and stop having babies what will happen to the human race? The Sexual Revolution has happened all over the world excep perhaps in Arabian terratories where girls don't count and gentlemen force them to cover up from head to toe in black shrouds so their sex can't show at all.

In the Middle Twentys when my book about a blonde like I was printed (against my better judgmint), American gentlemen had a very diffrent atitude towards femails. They liked to support them in a better style than they were ever acustomed to, present them with gifts way above the catigory of flowers, perfume and candy, and never in any circamstances to go out and find them a job.

At that time, for instants, Mr. Powers never even thought of starting a Model Agency whose only objeck was to put girls to work. Some girls did take a job sometimes with Mr. Ziegfeld but this was meerly for the sake of glamour, because in those days Mr. Ziegfeld's *Follies* was the best showcase for beautiful girls. And the work only consisted in wearing delightful costumes of ostrich plumes or roses or artificial diamonds and taking a few short walks across the stage of the New Amsterdam Theatre, or posing in elaborite tableaus, which was not hard labor either.

The showgirls knew that, sitting out front, were row after row of exclusive members of the Racket Club or even the Union League whose members were enclined to be more elderly and therefore of even greater wealth. So, that added to the glamour.

After their work was over the girls would get into their jewelry and ermin wraps and orchids, and be picked up at the stage door by gentlemen who owned their own limousines, which had silver vases to put a rose in, fringed shades, and fur lap robes. Then they were escorted to a Champagne supper at Texas Guinan's or the Casino in the Park. And then a girl would be taken home to her own delightful apartment where anything in the shape of an alarm clock was absent.

But now the selfsame kind of girls are forced to take a job with Mr. Bergdorf Goodman and stay on their feet, changing from one dress to another and walking up and down the floor all day long. And the sad part is, they parade in front of audiences which consist of Park Avenue house-wives whose husbands as well as other members of the male sex wouldn't be caught dead there.

At six P.M. when work of that ilk is over, the gentlemen waiting for the girls outside the employee's entrance on 58th Street may possibly be salesclerks from the shoe department and CIO pickets who are striking the shoe department, all of whose feet are as fatigued as those of the girls who had walked the floor all day. And these escorts procede to walk them to some economacal spot for hamburgers or chow mein, perhaps. Then they walk them home to the Barbizon Plaza where no male is allowed anywheres above the ground floor. And they go to bed at nine P.M. both on account of their feet and because the alarm clock is set to wake them up at seven A.M. so they can go out and pose in front of the Plaza Hotel in hot fur coats (providing it is summertime) or in chilly low-cut evening gowns (providing it is winter), because fashions of the moment have got to be fotographed a season ahead of time.

Nowadays even the theatrecal profession has lost its glamour because, due to the rise of a new element called coreographers (like Jerome Robbins and Agnes de Mille), girls who dance in musical comedy must learn how to dance and even after they've learned, they have to go on practising day in and day out. And the only social contacks they have the time or opertunity to make are with the gentlemen of the chorus, who are dis-interested. For the secret has come out that many gentlemen prefer gentlemen.

Back in the early Twentys girls could take a perfeckly normal attitude toward work of any kind and dislike it. I mean it was quite normal for me to rejeck even a glamorous offer of a million dollar contrack to star in Hollywood films. Because that meant hard work and losing beauty sleep to get up at the crack of dawn and rush out to the studio and be all made up to face the cameras and a tyrant of a director barking orders. That is why movie stars become old before their time and get so many divorces. Because they are too fatigued to attend to their husbands and treat them like nothings if they are not somebodies.

So, a career of that type held no appeal for a girl whose personal apearance made it unecessary to work for a living. On the other hand, my girlfriend Dorothy Shaw, who enjoyed providing gentlemen with money, was really considered abnormal. And most of our quarrels were because of Dorothy's perverted atitude toward Sex.

For many years the shadow of a gentleman by the name of Marx kept spreading over the horizen of the World's Economy. And I do not mean Groucho or even Harpo who could have suplied our Economy with some laughter.

The name of this Marx was Karl. And he was of German extraction of the gloomy type that looked down his beard on every gentleman who enjoyed life, and who ever had the means and opertunity to be generous.

As a student of Politackal Economy I have worked out a scientifick theory which explains why Herr Marx decided to put a stop to the practise of giving expensive presents to we girls. And the theory is that Herr Marx could have given the Crown Jewels of Great Britain (where he took refudge from his own country) to some girl that looked like Lizzie Tish and never got anywheres with her. And if he had ever met a girl like I, he would have run a mile the other way, perhaps toward the British Librerry where he spent most of his time burrowing through books like a bookworm.

And I am sure that Karl Marx would not even have enjoyed accepting things from a girl like Dorothy, even when he was flat broke. Because Dorothy is a girl who loves to laugh more than anything else. And I have gone through the well-known Historical Book of Marx called *Das Kapital* with a fine tooth comb and have not even found a smile.

It seems that this Herr Marx became even gloomier than usual over the wage slaves who toiled at the cloth mills of an English town called Birmingham. And so, in order to fix everything he started a movement called Commonism which finally wound up driving everybody into slavery all over a very large-size country named Russia.

And after they shot the Russian King, who they called a Tsarr, and his family, and had a bloody Revolution and a Civilian War and a Great Famine (which was a starvation diet), the people were worse off than ever. Because then they had a headman by the name of Stalin, called a Dictator, who shipped off millions to the salt mines of Siberia, where they expired. And then everybody all over the world had to fight wars and endure Hitler and Stalin and have pogroms and Bookenwald and Iron Curtains and Atomick Bombs and Income Taxes and become wage slaves.

Perhaps if Herr Marx had realized what he got started he would not have started it. With all his visions he could not visualise the consiquences. And he did not forsee another thing because he was born too soon, and that is the Femail Revolution, which libarated lots of women from house-work to take other jobs.

Well, anytime we girls go to work the results can be forseen: that is, we do things better than the opposite sex. I mean men will go to all the trouble of keeping office hours and holding Board Meetings and getting Mr. Gallop to make a pole, and sending their Public Relations to Washington and traveling to Atlantic City for a convention in order to reach a decision which we could reach while refurbeshing our lipstick. I mean our brains are so much brighter than theirs that men, in order to keep comparasons from being odius, have given our mentality a diffrent name and termed it "femail intuition." But whatever they term it, it is nothing but pure brain power which begins where their brains leave off and take a holiday.

So, the great danger to Political Economy in such a Trend (according to the historical writer called Mr. Gibbons) is that any time gentlemen allow we girls to reveal in public that our brain power is stronger than theirs, the same historick tragedy happens that happened to the ancient Roman Empire and Rome started to decline and fall. But instead of the latest Decline and Fall happening to one Empire, as it did in the case of Rome, it is now happening to the whole world at large, because as Mr. Wilkie once said, we have become One World.

But during our own Decline and Fall there is one hope for we girls. Which is that, as soon as the Great Technical Revolution we are in the midst of gets a chance to stableize, and the gentlemen who lead the party started by Mr. Marx get used to all the vast new opertunities which are opening up for them and begin to have things and buy themselves Cadilacs and drop in to Van Cleef and Arpels Jewelry Shop to shop for some expensive presents for their girlfriends or wives, they will begin to cast their eyes around and notice blondes. And as there will never be enough to go round, compatition will be revived. And with Free Compatition the world can once more go back to normaltsy. And girls will be able to resign from their jobs and accept the atentions of gentlemen who will fix things so that, once again, they can spend money on something that has more sex appeal than the Social Security Tax.

And in many ways it will be even a better world, because it is always healthy to have new blood and the gentlemen who will posses the money in the future will waste it all the more vigerously because they never had the opertunity to waste it before.

And even girls like Dorothy Shaw will be able to lead a better life. Because instead of spending their money on gentlemen who are uncooth, as they did in the olden times, they can get hold of old copies of Dunn and Broadstreets and look up numberless names of gentlemen who have been relegated to the receiving end in matters of Romance. And so, the Dorothys of this world will be spending their money on the kind of gentlemen who have colledge educations.

So, my advice to girls is to never despair, because gentlemen like Herr Marx and Comrade Stalin could get front page publicity to their heart's content, but inside their hearts they must have known there would never be a Hope Diamond for every girl's necklace or a hand-painted Renoir painting for her boudoire. And so, every time the time comes for some High Commissare to decide whether he is going to put them into some Great Public Museum for everybody to look at, or whether to be swayed against it in favor of some delightful blonde, it would be beneath the dignity of his own red blood corpusles if he even stopped to hesitate. And I am sure that Comrade Stalin would never have approved of any anemic leaders such as that.

And, since it is the custom to always follow the Commonist Party Line, the Vice Commissares will follow the example of the Chief Commissares and begin to hold things out in order to present them to lesser blondes and so on, ad finitum, until the whole Commonistic Party will have stopped working for Humanity and begin to do something for human beings.

And so, sooner or later, blondes will once again resume their normal statis in this great Political Economy of ours and, in the words of that gentleman who rescued the poetess Elizabeth Barrett Browning from her father and married her, it will once more seem as if "God's in His Heaven. All's right with the World."

A Bachelor's Dilemma

A book of auto-biography that I once wrote about the subjeck of my life seems to have brought up the question of what gentlemen really prefer. And the Editor of "Lectures Pour Tous" thinks I ought to answer this significkent question so that the case can be put to rest, and things can go on again. I am not sure exactly what he meant by that, for the only time I ever had a case was back in Little Rock, and the defense rested while the jury went out and decided that I was innocent.

Well, when my friend Dorothy dropped by, I told her about the question I had to answer, which was not so easy. And Dorothy said, why rack your brains? The best way to answer any question, she thinks, is to pop one right back. So then, while the inkwisitive party is fishing for an answer, he forgets what he asked you in the first place. "And that lets you off the hook," says Dorothy. "Never give a smart aleck like an editor a chance to think you don't know all the answers."

Well, Dorothy doesn't know all the answers either. If she did, she would not get into one pickle after another. And she would have feathered her nest, instead of letting her feathers fly every which way. But Dorothy and I don't agree about most things, and I think it is rude to ignore a perfeckly legitimate question.

So, I will try to reply by telling the case history of a gentleman friend of my acquaintance called Mr. Gillespie, which is apro-pos. Mr. Gillespie got into quite a prediciment trying to make a decision betwix a light girl and a dark girl in his own case. And I seem to think the story of Mr. Gillespie's Romance will practically answer the question of "who gentlemen really prefer" for one and all.

I suppose that nearly all bachelors who do not avoid the society of girls, and are viril, are almost sure to have love affairs. I am afraid that was the case with Mr. Gillespie. And, when he was madly in love with a blonde, he always enjoyed himself a great deal because it made him feel so masterfull in comparason. And when he went head over heels for a brunette, he dearly loved her admiring glances. So, he really felt very satisfied with himself in both cases.

But my girl friend, who is also acquainted with this gentleman, said, "Mr. Gillespie is a chump! Don't let him pull the wool over your eyelashes. A guy who's in love with himself doesn't give a hoot about anybody else. And how can he be in love with two people at the same time—or three, including himself?" Well, why not? That has happened to me, at times when I was torn betwix two gentlemen with similar assets.

Well, finally Mr. Gillespie reached the age of 45 years and decided that he had become marriageable. I mean his health colapsed, and he had to give up enjoying himself and going to disco tecks, and imbibing beveridges with alcoholick content. And when the doctor told him that he even had to give up women, he realized the time had come for him to make some nice girl happy. But Dorothy thought the only kind of wife he could really make happy was some girl in a collar and necktie who would bring along a girl friend. This silly remark diserved no answer, and got none.

Well, Mr. Gillespie's life was complickated, because he was having romances with two different girls, both of them satisfactory. One of them was a very, very blonde girl by the name of Kay who was always ready with a "yes" to everything Mr. Gillespie remarked. And he liked nothing better than being agreed with. The only trouble was that he began to suspeck Kay had a bad habit of agreeing with every gentleman of her acquaintance. And Dorothy said he was right, because Kay could never say "no" to a boy friend. Which made her very popular with everyone except girl friends.

Mr. Gillespie's other girl was a more intelectuel type, a brunette called Winona. For women of brunette coloration have to do something to make themselves well-come. So, Winona put in all her spare time cultavating her brains. And Mr. Gillespie felt that her conversation took up quite a lot of his valuable time. But at least, her talk was a resumay of the latest books, so he didn't have to take time to read them himself, and his friends would complament him on being so "well read."

Now, Mr. Gillespie had never invited either Kay or Winona to his apartment, so he had no opertunity to see either one of them in the presents of his own invirament. For, when it came to a question of girls, Mr. Gillespie was very thoughtful of appearances, and he did not like to have whispers about women coming to his private home. So, he always went to visit them instead.

But now that his objeck was matrimony he thought it would be quite a good idea to take a look at each of them in the invirament of his own surroundings. So he invited Kay for luncheon and Winona for dinner, on the selfsame day, so that the comparason of Kay would be fresh in his mind when it came to "taking an inventory" (as he said) of Winona.

And then he decided to allow Fate to make the choice because, in his heart, he was quite a believer in the Universal Mind. And he seemed to believe that if he relaksed and let things take their own rhythm, the Universal Mind would take it off his shoulders and give him a sign to guide him on his pathway to the "Right Mrs. Gillespie."

Well, Kay walked into his apartment at luncheon time, and she was really like a ray of sunshine, for the first word she uttered on opening her mouth was to pay him a complament. Because it seems that Kay had always known that he was marvelous, but she did not really know how far he extended until she saw what a large amount of good taste he displayed in his marvelous anteek family heir-looms.

The only little fault that Kay could seem to find in Mr. Gillespie's flat was that the mirrors were conspicuous by being absent. Well, he remarked that one mirror in his bedroom was all that an "ugly bachelor" like he needed to look into.

And that brought up quite a well known argument about his personal apearance that Mr. Gillespie always liked to stir up. For it seems that Kay thought he was very, very attractive. Mr. Gillespie's mind was so open that he was always willing to let in her ideas on the subjeck, even if he did not coinside.

Well, Kay finally said that not having any mirrors in his flat was as if he had a whole flat-full of beautiful oil-painted portraits of himself, and then covered them all up. At that remark he seemed to think the Finger of Fate was pointing at his future bride.

But he held his tongue. For he really wanted to be fair to Winona and play the game as a gentlemen ought to do when it is a question of giving two girls an even chance.

During luncheon Kay watched every bite he ate to make sure he would preserve his devine physick. So she made him renounce rolls for melba toast, rejeck baked potato soaked with butter, and refuse pecan pie a-la-mode. While picking at her entray, Kay asked him to cut up her lamb chop, because she couldn't wield a knife and fork like a great big strong man like he. One complament led to another until he really became more and more enamured every moment.

When it was time to say goodbye, he made an engagement to escort Kay to the theatre the very next evening. And his mind was made up to let his feelings go in a taxi-cab after the show and pop the question.

By the time Winona arrived for dinner his insides had mixed feelings. His heart ached for Winona because she was losing her chance, and his stomick felt stabs of hunger on account of Kay restraining his luncheon.

Just at that moment the butler came to the rescue with a large plate full of apetizers. And Winona did nothing to stop Mr. Gillespie because she was so absorbed in his mentality that she did not even care if he lost his shape.

Winona had brought a book with her. But she said Mr. Gillespie would not have to bother to read it, because she would tell him what it was about. So he held his tongue while she did it, and at the finish she paid him the complament that he was the only man she knew who had the genius to understand the author's talent.

Then Winona asked if she could have a cocktale in order to stimulate her brain to a point where it could keep up with his mentality. So, he began to wonder if Winona was not quite a worthy rival of Kay's, after all.

Well, the dinner was delicious and he ate to his heart's content. But he knew that Winona expected to hear a few of his opinions as an extra treat.

Now, Mr. Gillespie had two full sets of opinions. One set was on the subjeck of the New York Stock Exchange and its ups and downs, while the other was on politicks and that man in the White House.

By this time Winona knew his opinions by heart, so she did not have to concentrate, except on her food. And Mr. Gillespie enjoyed listening to himself so heartily that he never had any desire to stop. Finally, he began to feel that it would be very romantic if his little tate-a-tate with Winona would go on forever.

Well, after she had gone through quite a bit of listening, she uttered an opinion of her own. Mr. Gillespie ought to buy himself a dick-to-graph, she thought. So, when he felt a brilliant idea coming on he could have it recorded, and people in after life could turn it on and let it unwind.

She even remarked that, if he ever had any kiddies, what a treat it would be for them. Only Dorothy says that when a type like Mr. Gillespie has kiddies, the treat is generally enjoyed by some other fellow.

But anyway, after dinner was over Mr. Gillespie felt so satisfied with himself that he decided it really must be Winona who bowled him over. But he escorted her home uncommitted, for he needed time to think things over. Because he felt the Universal Mind had not yet come to a definite decision. If he waited another month, perhaps it would point him in the right direction.

During that month he took Kay's advice and had quite a few mirrors hung up on the various walls of his apartment. And he was quite pleased to note how it brightened up the home to have something attractive to look at. I mean Kay herself was really very beautiful, and he loved to gaze at the admiring expression on her face. But after all, it was quite satisfactory to be able to look at the origenal objeck that gave her such a pleased expression.

Mr. Gillespie also followed up Winona's idea and purchased a dick-to-graph. When he had no engagement to go out for the evening, he got into the habit of making records of the little speeches he liked to hear. And he was very surprised to note that he could listen to himself quite enjoyably without the company of a second party.

Well, by the end of the month his home had become so cheerfull that he decided not to get married to anyone. So Dorothy said, "That guy married a machine. It sure is cheaper than a wife. Now he can save more money and invest it in the stock market. That's not as risky as a marital venture."

But I do not agree the least bit with Dorothy. She is enclined to be cinical in her viewpoint. When I reminded her that Mr. Gillespie left two nice girls like Kay and Winona in the lurch, she just said, "He's done them a favor, if you ask me." But I felt sorry for both of them, because they lost their chances by being too smart for their own good. And Mr. Gillespie never had a chance to find out who it was he really cared for.

So, I seem to feel that the tragedy of Mr. Gillespie answers the question of more than one gentleman in this world. I mean they go all through their life-times and never find out who it is they really care for.

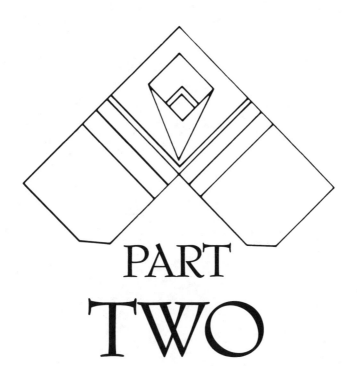

PART
TWO

The Biography of
a Book

*T*HERE was a time in the summer of 1923 when I found myself on a train, the deluxe Santa Fe Chief, traveling from New York to Los Angeles. We were a party of co-workers in the movies, going regretfully back to our studio after a cherished holiday in New York; for we belonged to the elite of the cinema which has never been fond of Hollywood. There were Douglas Fairbanks, Sr., then at the beginning of his career in films but already a nation's idol, my husband, John Emerson, who directed the scenarios I wrote for Doug, and a number of others, such as our publicity man, an assistant director, Doug's valet and Doug's trainer. In those carefree days of the silent movie, we traveled in large and exuberant groups.

Also among us was a blonde who was being imported to Hollywood to be Doug's leading lady in his forthcoming picture. Now this girl, although she towered above me (I weighed about ninety pounds) and was of rather a hearty type, was being waited on, catered to and cajoled by the entire male assemblage. If she happened to drop the novel she was reading, several men jumped to retrieve it; whereas I was allowed to lug heavy suitcases from their racks while men sat about and failed to note my efforts.

Obviously there was some radical difference between that girl and me. But what was it? We were both in the pristine years of early youth; we were of about the same degree of comeliness; as to our mental acumen, there was nothing to discuss: I was the smarter. Then why did that girl so far outdistance me in feminine allure? Could her strength possibly be rooted (like that of Samson) in her hair? She was a natural blonde and I was a brunette.

In view of the reception which was to greet *Gentlemen Prefer Blondes* a couple of years later, it appears I had stumbled onto an important scientific fact which had never before been pinpointed. The light that dawned on me with that first revelation began to illuminate an entire phase of my youthful experiences. I proceeded to go over the various blondes I knew. They were a very special group, for my lot had fallen in with the beauties of the films and the girls of the Ziegfeld Follies from which movie starlets constantly were recruited. And, in going over the list, I presently singled out the dumbest blonde of all, a girl who had bewitched one of the keenest minds of our era—H. L. Mencken.

Menck was my idol and a good friend too. He often took me to Luchow's for dinner; I was even included among his inner circle of beer lovers when they trekked over to Jersey City in those Prohibition days to drink a brew that was uncontaminated by ether. Menck liked me very much indeed; but in the matter of sentiment, he preferred a witless blonde.

The situation was palpably unjust. I thought it over as our train raced across the plains of the Midwest, until finally I was prompted to reach for one of the large yellow pads on which I composed Doug's scenarios, and I began to write down my thoughts; not bitterly, as I might have done had I been a real novelist, but with an amusement which was, on the whole, rather childish. I have always considered grown-ups to be figures of fun, as children generally do, and have never been deceived by their hypocrisies. In those days I had a friend, Rayne Adams, who used to say that my slant on life was that of a child of ten, chortling with excitement over a disaster.

In fact, if one examines the plot of *Gentlemen Prefer Blondes* it is almost as gloomy as a novel by Dostoievski. When the book reached Russia, this was recognized, and it was embraced by Soviet authorities as evidence of the exploitation of helpless female blondes. by predatory magnates of the Capitalistic System. The Russians, with their native love of grief, stripped *Gentlemen Prefer Blondes* of all its fun and the plot which they uncovered was dire. It concerns early rape of its idiot heroine, an attempt by her to commit murder (only unsuccessful because she is clumsy with a gun), the heroine's being cast adrift in the gangster-infested New York of Prohibition days, her relentless pursuit by predatory males (the foremost of whom constantly tries to pay her off at bargain rates), her renunciation of the only man who ever stirred her inner soul of a woman, her nauseous connection with a male who is repulsive to her physically, mentally and emotionally, and her final engulfment in the grim monotony of suburban Philadelphia.

Given the above material, any real novelist such as Sherwood Anderson, Dreiser, Faulkner or Hemingway probably would have curdled his readers' blood with massive indignation. Scott Fitzgerald would have, and indeed he did make his readers shed bitter-sweet tears over such sad eventualities. But I, with my infantile cruelty, have never been able to view even the most impressive human behavior as anything but foolish. When, for instance, Albert Einstein evolved his world-shaking Theory and then admonished fellow scientists not to use it for the elimination of the species, it seemed to me the same joke as when a certain character in *Little Women* told a group of children not to stuff beans up their noses; with the consequence they could not wait to find some beans and stuff them up their noses.

As I began to put Lorelei's story on my yellow pad, it became a mixture of fact and fiction. My heroine's real name was Mabel Minnow. Her birthplace, however, was invented and H. L. Mencken himself had a hand in the procedure. For I wanted Lorelei to be a symbol of the lowest possible mentality of our nation, and Menck had written an essay on American culture in which he branded the State of Arkansas as "the Sahara of the Beaux Arts" (which he spelled Bozarts). Therefore, I chose Little Rock for my heroine's early years; Little Rock, which even today lives up to Mencken's choice as the nadir in shortsighted human stupidity.

I finished the few pages of what I considered to be merely a short sketch as our train was nearing Pasadena; it was time to pack up and get back to the frantic chores of the studio. I stuck the manuscript into the flap of a suitcase and forgot all about it for six months or more.

I might never have thought of Lorelei again, for I was a movie writer and wouldn't have dreamed that my heroine had any place on celluloid. But back in New York one day, I ran across the rumpled and smudged pages of my little critique and, in order to give Menck a laugh at his own expense (this being several blondes later than the one who had first inspired me) I mailed it to him.

Menck enjoyed my sketch, saw the point of it and, although it hit close to home and was an intrusion on his sentimental life, he suggested that the manuscript be published.

The story of its publication can best be told by quoting from the autobiography of Carmel Snow:*

"When *Gentlemen Prefer Blondes* burst on a delighted world," wrote Carmel, "I took Anita Loos under my wing. She was literally under the wing of her tall, thin husband, John Emerson (she reached barely to his chest) and she claims that she held onto his coat tails when I took her around to parties, but our click was immediate and it extended even to our clothes. We were both dressed by Chanel, later by Mainbocher and most recently by Balenciaga.

"When I met her, her Lorelei Lee was appearing serially in the magazine that was to become the impersonal love of my life. How we waited for each new installment in *Harper's Bazaar*! We didn't realize how nearly there were no further installments to follow the first one. Anita wrote *Gentlemen Prefer Blondes* as a short story and sent it to H. L. Mencken, that other great editor of the twenties. He had just left *Smart Set,* where he would gladly have published it, but he didn't think it was right for *The American Mercury* which he now edited. 'Little girl,' he now warned Anita, 'you're making fun of sex and that's never been done before in the U.S.A. I suggest you send it to *Harper's Bazaar,* where it'll be lost among the ads and won't offend anybody.'

"Henry Sell was the editor in charge and fortunately saw the story first. 'Why do you stop?' he asked Anita. 'You've started this girl on a trip, go on.' So, as Lorelei appeared one month in *Harper's Bazaar,* Anita was frantically writing the next month's installment. By the third month, ads for men's apparel, cars, and sporting goods began pouring into the magazine. This was the first time men had ever read the *Bazaar*—the newstand sales doubled, then tripled. James Joyce, who had begun to lose his eyesight, saved his reading for Lorelei Lee. And George Santayana, when asked what was the best book of philosophy written by an American, answered, 'Gentle-men Prefer Blondes.' "

*The World of Carmel Snow, co-authored by Mary Louise Aswell, © 1962, McGraw-Hill Book Co., Inc.

After Lorelei's story ended in *Harper's Bazaar,* a friend of mine, Tom Smith, who was on the staff of the Liveright Publishing Company, asked if I would like to have a few copies of my story in book form to give my friends as Christmas presents. I thought it an excellent idea and Tom thereupon had his firm print a sort of "vanity" edition of a mere fifteen hundred copies (which accounts for the fact that those first few copies became collectors' items).

The first edition was sold out on the day it reached the bookshops and, although the second edition was of sixty thousand copies, it was exhausted almost as quickly. I believe the book ran into forty-five editions before the early demand had ceased. Naturally, there have been a number of soft-cover editions through the years. But I feel that Lorelei's accomplishments reached a peak when she became one of the few contemporary authors to be represented in the *Oxford Book of Quotations.*

Following its American publication, *Gentlemen Prefer Blondes* became a bestseller in thirteen languages. (Note to Khrushchev: Where are my royalties, Tovarich?) In China the story ran as a serial in the newspaper edited by Lin Yutang, who assured me that Lorelei's prose went quite normally into the vernacular of the Sing Song girls.

The world and its ways have changed a great deal since Lorelei made her first appearance on the scene. Later during a television interview in London, the question was put to me: "Miss Loos, your book was based on an economic situation, the unparalleled prosperity of the Twenties. If you were to write such a book today, what would be your theme?" And without hesitation, I was forced to answer, "Gentlemen Prefer Gentlemen" (a statement which brought the session abruptly to a close). But if that fact is true, as it very well seems to be, it too is based on economics, the criminally senseless population explosion which a beneficent Nature is trying to curb by more pleasant means than war.

So now my little book passes on as a period piece to the grandchildren of its first readers. And if their spirits should need bolstering, as they cower in the bomb shelters of the sixties, may they be diverted by the adventures of Lorelei Lee and take courage in the words of her favorite philosopher: "Smile, smile, smile."

A Musical Is Born

*T*HE Dramatic Editor of *The New York Times* thought it might intrigue people to hear about the trials and tribulations that *Gentlemen Prefer Blondes* went through before it finally became a musical show.

It all started in the mid-Twenties, when my book was in the throes of being printed throughout the world in many different languages. And the first one to get the idea of making it into a musical was Florenz Ziegfeld, whose idea was really quite novel because the musical producers of that period were not addicted to the use of books which are best sellers as they are today.

But when Mr. Ziegfeld thought of it, I was in Palm Beach and by the time he reached there from New York to talk it over with me, I had concluded a contract with Edgar Selwyn to make it into a straight comedy.

To say that I was disappointed would really be putting it mildly, because anything Mr. Ziegfeld ever touched had a great deal of glamor. And moreover, his idea was to have my heroine (Lorelei Lee) played by a blonde who was the ideal of all Broadway—namely Marilyn Miller.

But I swallowed my disappointment and went to work with my husband, John Emerson, to dramatize it into a stage play which was put on with Lorelei being played by June Walker (who, being a brunette, had to wear a wig). And the brunette character of my book (named Dorothy) was played by a very delightful comedienne called Edna Hibbard. And the Henry Spoffard of that day was a young actor named Frank Morgan who, as soon as the run of the play was over, was made a large offer by Hollywood which he accepted.

We opened *Gentlemen Prefer Blondes* in Detroit and it was a great success. And I shall always have quite a memento of that opening. Because a girl friend of mine called Jeanne Eagels was also playing there in *Rain*. And one day, we two girls were taken by the District Attorney of Detroit, who was called Mr. Frank Murphy, to hear a Historical trial which was being conducted at the City Hall by a famous lawyer called Mr. Clarence Darrow. And recently, when they built a new City Hall in Detroit, the artist who painted the murals on the walls, painted all of us into his picture. So that, when I got to Detroit and looked at it, I became quite misty. Because Mr. Murphy and Mr. Darrow were gentlemen who were headed for history and Jeanne Eagels was a blonde who can't be forgotten.

When *Gentlemen Prefer Blondes* finally opened in New York it had quite a long run. And Mr. Selwyn also put three companies of it on the road which covered all the territory.

And, the next thing that happened to it, theatrically, was to have it made into a motion picture. And every company in Hollywood put in their bid, but finally Paramount Pictures secured it. And then they decided to find some unknown actress to play the part of Lorelei and make a new Paramount star of her. So after they had tested all the blondes in Hollywood they decided on a girl named Ruth Taylor, who was so ideal in the role that she even played it off-screen and married a wealthy broker. And Miss Taylor is now a prominent Park Avenue hostess called Mrs. Zuckerman.

But after *Gentlemen Prefer Blondes* got produced in the cinema, there didn't seem anything more to do with it. I mean it had been done in book form and serialized in magazines and syndicated in newspapers and designed into dress material and printed into wall paper and made into a comic strip and had even had a song by Irving Berlin.

But some years later, while I was in Hollywood working at Metro-Goldwyn-Mayer, Mr. John C. Wilson used to frequently come out to the studio from New York to confer with Mr. Louis B.

Mayer, who was trying to lure him into directing for the cinema. And Mr. Wilson and I, in our carefree moments, had a habit of contacting each other in a small refreshment parlor located in the alley just outside the Studio gate. And while we were drinking our cup of coffee, Mr. Wilson used to bring up the subject of *Gentlemen Prefer Blondes* and remark that he thought it was finally time to make it into a musical, which intrigued me very much, except that I was busy writing movie scripts and couldn't seem to find the time to get around to it.

But by the time I had worked my way out of my contract at MGM I had become side-tracked by a girl friend of mine called Helen Hayes who was fed up with playing the heroic sort of leading roles they were always giving her, and desired a change. So I moved to New York and wrote a play for her called *Happy Birthday* which took place in the locale of a saloon and accomplished Miss Hayes' ambition to be unheroic very fully.

But every time I encountered Mr. Wilson at a party in New York, he would get me into a corner and ask when we were going to make a musical out of *Gentlemen Prefer Blondes*.

So time went on until one summer when two young producers named Herman Levin and Oliver Smith were sailing home from a trip abroad. And one day on the deck they met a musical publisher friend of mine named Mr. Jack Robbins. And on hearing that these two young producers had nothing to produce, it occurred to Mr. Robbins to mention *Gentlemen Prefer Blondes*. So they got a copy of it out of the ship's library and were delighted at the idea.

And as soon as they reached New York they contacted me at a luncheon in the Plaza. So I told them I really couldn't do anything about it without talking to Mr. Wilson. But when I went to consult him, he was too busy directing *Kiss Me, Kate* to even listen to anything else at the moment. So I decided to let Mr. Levin and Mr. Smith go ahead with it.

So then they contracted Jule Styne to write the music and Leo Robin to do the lyrics. And they immediately went to work to get themselves into the mood of Nineteen Twenty-five, so as to make the musical score authentic. And by the time they had finished the score and I had written the book, John C. Wilson had completed his production of *Kiss Me, Kate* and was ready to undertake the job of directing the show. So everything seemed to work out for the best.

So the next thing our producers did was to engage Agnes de Mille to do the choreography. And in order for her routines to be authentic, Miss de Mille spent all one summer interviewing old-fashioned vaudeville acts that had been prominent in the Twenties. And it was Oliver Smith himself who set about to do the stage settings of the period. And Miles White, who was secured to do the costumes, spent most of his time studying all the fashion magazines of twenty-five years before.

But while all of us were very busy trying to throw ourselves back into the period of the Twenties, a very peculiar thing began to happen. I mean, the period of the Twenties began to come back into style. And so, the musical of *Gentlemen Prefer Blondes,* which began as a costume piece, turned out to be so fashionable that Mr. White's costumes were being copied by dress factories for the girls of Nineteen-Fifty.

A Girl Can't Go on
Laughing All the Time

———◆———

*T*HERE was a time when one could wake up laughing almost
every morning. During the Twenties men were intoxicated by the
mere fact that they were men; boys seldom engaged in pranks that
led to murder; girls gave in to being frivolous; and just to be alive
was fun.

In those days most people earned their daily bread in active
pursuits; comparatively few made a way of life out of spinning the
flimsy legends of Madison Avenue. Business had not yet passed out
of human hands onto the push buttons of computers, which de-
mean us by knowing so much more than we do; even in making
errors a computer can gum up the works so colossally that human
mistakes, in comparison, seem puny. And, during that period,
nobody was required to betray his manhood by inventing tax
dodges.

Then, along came Freud, bent on destroying the virility of man;
trumping up the notion that everyone was sick; turning people into
hypochrondriacs and claiming illness as an alibi through which they
might escape blame for any aberrations a sick mind could devise.
Unable to have any fun, those invalids resorted to self-indulgence,
which was not a very gay substitute.

Love affairs of the Twenties used to contain an element of tenderness; men considered that women were endearing and looked on them with a Jovian amusement that came from thinking they weren't very smart. But when the trend of economics forced women to compete with men, they found out that, in the aggregate, women are smarter than they are and, as far as tenderness was concerned, the jig was up. Today's love affairs begin compulsively, as always, but they tend to be short because men are preoccupied with escape from a situation that downgrades their egos and, no matter how enjoyable a love affair, a man feels that the sooner it ends, the better.

An affair of the heart used to have only one satisfactory end, marriage. And for a girl to marry well required a degree of femininity. But today, when a man's spending money is requisitioned by the Treasury Department, a girl is better off earning her own; in which case her feminine charm descends to the level of Madison Avenue and becomes a matter of public relations, which she exercises to outsmart men in the business world.

The girls of the Twenties used to provoke mash notes; love letters were prevalent and men were even known to request a lock of hair, seduced by the fact that in those days hair could be fondled, and men were not put off by the rigidity of hair spray, the snarls of teasing, or the rigor mortis of wigs.

As a combination of flapper and authoress I used to get fan mail that was more exciting than any letters I ever received.

William Empson wrote me a poem one stanza of which affirms:

> *No man is sure he does not need to climb,*
> *It is not human to feel safely placed.*
> *A girl can't go on laughing all the time.*

From William Faulkner came:

I have just read the Blonde book, Bill's copy. So I galloped out and got myself one. Please accept my envious congratulations on Dorothy—the way you did her through the (intelligence?) of that elegant moron of a cornflower. Only you have played a rotten trick on your admiring public. How many of them, do you think, will ever know that Dorothy really has something, that the dancing man, le gigolo, was really somebody? My God, it's charming. . . .

I am still rather Victorian in my prejudices regarding the intelligence of woman, despite Elinor Wylie and Willa Cather and all the balance of them. But I wish I had thought of Dorothy first.

Sincerely,
William Faulkner.

And Henry Mencken wrote in the vernacular of my own heroine, Lorelei Lee:

Dear Miss Anita:

Well, a woman with a husband who lolls around with actresses and has his picture taken showing him smirking at them with his necktie half way around to his ear certainly deserves to be allowed to take a look herself at a handsome man once in a while and if she sends him a pitcher of herself and he gets mashed on it then certainly no one has got any call to remark on it so long as he behaves like a gentleman and don't call her up and try to get her to make a date with him in some tea-room or other where all you can see is a lot of women that ought to be home getting their husbands' meals sitting there with a lot of bums wasting their time.

Mit evangelischen Gruss,
The Bavarian costume is superb. It makes me yodel.

The tea-rooms referred to in Mencken's letter were fashionable spots that featured an institution called a "thé dansant." This was a misnomer because during prohibition drinks were strictly alcoholic. The music was sentimental and the orchestra played softly so that people could hear each other talk. The fashionable dance, called the Bunny Hug, required men and women to embrace; there was none of the rejection one suffers dancing, far apart, in noisy discotheques with all means of communication cut off.

In the Twenties we used to take time out for practical jokes, some of which required long preparation. They provided relaxation from more serious endeavors, and brains were racked to devise ingenious and elaborate pranks. The victims took them with good grace, or pretended to, laughing at their own humiliation or embarrassment. But then, they turned tables on the pranksters and subjected them to even more imaginative or devious jokes. Any loss of dignity had to be disguised with a properly *sang froid* air.

Have the Eighties nothing at all to offer us in terms of fun? In all truth, I must grant that they do, and furthermore, that it is possibly the most intense pleasure of which human beings are capable: the elation that follows a reprieve; the joy of a condemned prisoner who hears at the last minute that the noose will not replace his collar in the morning. And we denizens of the Eighties don't even have to go to jail in order to enjoy it.

Today, we may not exactly wake up laughing but if, on opening our eyes, we are able to look about, pinch ourselves and say, "Up to now I've escaped being murdered, raped, drugged, mugged, robbed, asphyxiated by foul air, bombed by hydrogen, cracked up in a car or plane accident, killed in Vietnam, or incarcerated for tax evasion," we have experienced the most poignant emotion life has to offer, based on that self-preservation which is the first law of Nature. Our reprieves are, of necessity, quite short because, after all, we face a new day when any of the above calamities can happen at any moment. But even so, the escape from so many different accidents or fatalities all in one colossal instant is a thrill unmatched at any other period in the history of the world.

What's Better
Than Sex?

$\mathcal{T}$HAT question, in my viewpoint, might best be answered by the word "illusion." And may I say that, as a denizen of Hollywood, I was briefed on the subject by some of the world's most renowned sexpots, beginning with Theda Bara, on through Mae West, Jean Harlow, and Marilyn Monroe. I learned at first hand that their personal experiences never added to the value of sex or succeeded in giving it a very high rating. The most glamorous creature of all was Marilyn Monroe who eventually took to suicide as a means of escaping her destiny as an enchantress.

Jean Harlow died in her early thirties, disheartened by four marriages in which she was a four times' loser. But the impact of Mae West hit her audience below the belt and turned sex into a subject for low comedy throughout an entire generation.

Only one of those four sirens was able to beat the sex rap: Theda Bara who, having amassed a fortune through her lurid movies, was able to retire at her peak. Then, as Mrs. Charles Brabin, she got herself listed in the Southern California Blue Book and chose to become a leader of Los Angeles society, which is the least sexy of any group one might possibly conceive. After a timely escape from sex, Theda lived happily ever after.

Sex, which has been acclaimed by too many misguided poets as an utopian activity, seldom attains that status in the human race.

Among human beings it is too often degraded by anxiety, fear, nervousness over getting caught by a legal mate, or causing an illegal pregnancy; most of all, sex is so venalized by motives of gain that at least one participant has to be a hypocrite if not a downright liar.

Actually, in matters of sex the human race ranks well below the level of the animals. Who could even imagine, among our dumb friends, a chimpanzee resorting to venery for a banana? Or a Great Dane giving a pretense of adulation for a bone? Only among the feline species does one find a member that will meaow amorously with its mind on a sardine. (Which may be one reason why the cat has lent her name to the basest type of human female.)

Moreover, sex in the animal kingdom is a seasonal sport of comparatively short duration. But among humans it has been turned into an affair for all seasons, to be indulged in throughout the year with no rest periods for gaining perspective or getting one's mind back to all the other matters of daily life.

I doubt that any thinking person would ever dispute that one of the greatest humanists was Shakespeare, or that the most mixed-up of any character in literature was Hamlet. So, when he admonished Ophelia to "Get thee to a nunnery," Hamlet's advice should give anybody pause for thought.

And what, for instance, would have happened had Romeo and Juliet lived to middle age, their silhouettes broadened by pasta? A memory of their single act of childish zeal would have caused almost unbearable regret. Mercifully, Shakespeare killed off those two lovers in their teens.

In the historic case of that greatest of all lovers, Abelard, dalliance was cut short forever by an act of surgery; so he remained faithful to Heloise as long as they lived, a record the most vaunted of today's lovers fail to match.

The only erotic pair that ever really made it were the Brownings, largely because Elizabeth Barrett had to take to their bed to nurse an ailment, after her elopement with her fellow poet Robert Browning. They celebrated their love in immortal verse while enjoying it in private—unlike a certain modern couple who rashly invited the public to pass in review at their honeymoon bedside.

When Shakespeare, in a sizzling moment, caused Venus to admonish Adonis that "to get it is thy duty," the word "duty" indicates imposition, not enjoyment. And in Shakespeare's time a "duty to beget" had a milder implication than it does today, when we provide children with such dangerous opportunities for mischief as drugs and inexpensive firearms. Parenthood has now become a disaster area.

At the present time Nature is trying its best to reduce the dangers of overpopulation by producing boys who care for boys, and girls who prefer girls. But Nature is being hectored at every turn by antigay laws and penalties against abortion. We have gone a long way since Margaret Sanger was prosecuted for spreading the gospel about birth control. Yet a high court decision legalizing abortion is being fought by Right-to-Lifers, who in turn are vociferously opposed by Right-to-Choose adherents. Where will it all end? Certainly in a rise in the decibel level of noisy argument, if not in a reduction of the birth rate.

There are special joys in romantic illusion that carry one far beyond the reach of disaster. Suppose, for example, that on a certain evening in the nineteenth century, the poet Keats had wasted a lot of erotic energy in seducing an adored one? Keats would then have deprived the world, most likely, of that lovely poem, "The Eve of Saint Agnes," which became an item of beautiful illusion for all eternity. It is also manifest to anyone who reads his sonnet that Keats took major satisfaction in reporting the incident.

If one belongs to that brainless hoi polloi that is incapable of illusion, there is small chance for any sex affair to avoid calamity. But with a modicum of invention anyone can trump up a romance that will last forever, and have no regrets. Just hold hands and cool it.

The Joys of Money

I wonder who invented the old saws that we keep applying to money. They must have been boneheads or dodoes burying their heads in the golden sands of yesteryear. Tell somebody who is falling through a hole in President Reagan's safety net that money isn't everything, and he'll think you are cracked. Say that money is the root of all evil to an unemployed worker, and he or she might respond, the lack of it is surely evil.

One hoary adage is still valid nowadays. The rich are getting richer, as always, and the poor, poorer. But how can a well-heeled twosome not feel guilty if, on their way home from a fancy bistro to a luxurious bed, they pass homeless people wrapped in rags sleeping on the sidewalks of New York? These poor folk can go to shelters, we are told, but apparently they feel safer on the streets.

How can anyone wholly enjoy even the best-gotten gains today? But there was once a time when we could take real pleasure in money, as I did in the days when a few dollars seemed like a huge, heaven-sent bonanza.

It was purely through a series of chance circumstances that I, as a child, was introduced to a practical grounding in matters of finance. At the age of seven I began to earn fifteen dollars a week as a child actress in a San Francisco stock company. The salary was paid in those old-fashioned California silver dollars which were so enormous they made me feel very rich.

But further prosperity was on the way; through acting in plays I gained an insight into theatrical technique, and it soon crossed my mind that to write a play might be more rewarding than acting in it. So, as a teenager I tried my hand at authorship. My plot failed to interest the impresario of the Alcazar Stock Company where I worked, so I mailed it to the Biograph Moving Picture Company in New York. By return mail came a check signed D. W. Griffith, and it was for twenty-five dollars, almost twice as much as I earned for an entire week of acting. I immediately quit the acting profession to become an authoress. And, as such I wrote more than two hundred silent movie plots before the advent of sound.

I was in business. I had struck gold—or something that was just as valuable—ink.

During 1925 I switched from movies to write a book, and after it became a best seller I was able to quit work altogether; to allow royalties to roll in automatically without any further scribbling on my part.

As a rich literary figure I happened to be spending the winter of 1929 in Palm Beach where being an authoress of a best-selling novel gave me a unique position among the Wall Street brokers vacationing in Florida. It was true that other best sellers had recently been written by Fannie Hurst and Edna Ferber, but Fannie was fat and Edna too thin to interest the financiers. And I, who weighed in at ninety-two pounds, became the Egeria of the Wall Street boys. It was then that my education in the esoterica of high finance began. I learned all about money from *them*.

At that time Wall Street values had hit an all-time peak. Everybody played the stock market but me. Why bother when all those royalties were flowing without any effort?

Finally, the Palm Beach season approached its end. It was time to head North, and I was invited to make the trip in the palatial railroad car of a leading financial expert, Otto Kahn, along with his stockbroker friend, Thomas Chadburn. Now, those two had very little literary small talk; the only subject on which they were expert was Wall Street. So, they took it on themselves to advise this ingenuous little authoress on what to do with her royalties, which up to that time had been dribbling into Van Cleef & Arpels or Cartier on knickknacks.

Otto and Tom devised a list of securities for me to buy, but their advice was delivered on the eve of the stock market crash of '29. If

I'd had time to put their information into practice, my money would have brought me no other joy than the glamour of going down the drain with the millions of Otto Kahn and Tom Chadburn.

The stock market crash gave me a low opinion of the mentality of financiers, who had started jumping out of their Park Avenue windows and dashing their brains out on hard pavements. Why had I been so modest as not to believe my own advice, already stated in print: that diamonds are a girl's best friend? At any rate, it marked a beginning of my own self-confidence and keen disbelief in money in the form of stocks, bonds, and parchment securities.

Since those days of disillusion my way through life has led me among some of the best financial brains of various countries. And I never knew but one who had true expertise. I happened to run into him soon after World War II in the casino at Baden Baden. He was His Excellency Herr Hjalmar Schacht, former head of the Reichsbank and German Minister of Economy.

Herr Schacht was a nationalist, but not a Nazi. For taking part in a plot to murder Hitler, he wound up in a concentration camp. At the Nuremberg trails he was acquitted of any war crime.

When Herr Schacht first went into office, Germany was in such dire financial straits that only a miracle could restore world confidence in it. The German monetary system was based on a gold standard, and the gold had been gobbled up by the cost of its First World War defeat. But Schacht, who was wise to human ways, realized that confidence would only be revived by something tangible. He looked about the countryside and noted the bumper crops of German rye. So, by a simple change in the monetary system he replaced the gold standard with the golden rye which all the world could see. Confidence was restored, the German mark was saved, and so was Germany (until Hitler ruined it)—just as our own metropolitan crisis was solved, years later, by the bonds of Big Mac, which evoked the universal joy we Americans take in hamburgers.

On the subject of money one could turn to the pronouncements of Maynard Keynes, who was supreme among European monetary experts. But in his autobiography Keynes confessed the superior joy he experienced by falling madly in love with a middle-aged, balding fatty of male persuasion. This fact damaged the prestige of money per se in the estimate of this humble observer.

As a joke-writer I don't expect to be taken seriously. But I can paraphrase from a letter of that critic of genius, Edmund Wilson, recording *his* slant on the subject of money. In a letter written to a friend in 1964, Edmund described a glamorous event he had recently attended, as follows:

> The guests were all very rich, heaps of well-dressed ladies in an apartment furnished in what Oscar Wilde would have called "impeccable bad taste". Lots of brains among the guests, Arthur Schlesinger, Saul Steinberg who is solid, dogmatic and so serious he never allows himself to smile. John Galbraith, an equally dogmatic Canadian Scot, spent the whole evening listening to Jackie Kennedy and smiling even more rarely than Steinberg. I never knew why I was there or what it was all about. But you can see what you gained by not being among the rich.

But that 1964 crop of millionaires was on the way out even then. The *in* millionaires are rock singers and movie stars, mostly in their teens. They drive their Rolls-Royces and Bentleys in their bare feet and seldom, if ever, wash their jeans. Dirty feet and dirty blue jeans are easily acquired. You can look and feel like a millionaire without even making the effort to sing ditties, such as "Short People." But the new rich don't rely on money for their entertainment. They get it out of small cellophane bags in the form of white powder.

I have begun to feel that money is going out of fashion because it produces too little joy. The most one can say for it is that, when it became chic to be tatty, you didn't need any. At any Park Avenue cocktail party female guests were redolent of Alumni Day at the Poorhouse. A lady, true, may have paid several thousand dollars for a caftan that was inspired by a sack of flour with the contents missing. But any girl, at no cost to herself, could wear grandma's identical Mother Hubbard wrapper and be right in style.

Money can only fool you if you let it. So, just disregard the experts such as Maynard Keynes, John Galbraith, et al. Their pronouncements sound like gibberish to most of us laymen, anyway. Only by rising above money, as an anonymous pundit said, can we appreciate its real perquisites. Help yourself to some disco or rock music, faded jeans, and a Big Mac and Coke to fill the void left by caviar and champagne. You might as well live it up, doing your own "thing"—if it doesn't land you in jail.

As money loses its value, hardly worth the paper it's printed on, why not enjoy the best of worst times? Let's remember another ancient adage: The best things in life are free.

A Meal to Remember

*M*Y rating as a gourmet hovers around zero, so I can never provide recipes to clip into a cookbook. But I do remember some outstanding meals, not so much for the food but who ate it. The company at table makes all the difference, to my mind, between a so-so meal, no matter how sumptuous, and a memorable repast.

One dinner that lingered in my memory for many years took place in Palm Beach, Florida. The host was Addison Mizner, the founding father of that winter playground for the rich. It was 1926, the peak of the glamorous Twenties and the social season was at its height.

Addison's home, a treasury of museum pieces, featured the self-portrait of his ancestor Sir Joshua Reynolds, who looked down on the party rather quizzically. The dinner guests included several titled Europeans, while the Americans were presumably of matching quality. Addison's British butler and serving man were exceedingly snobbish. The guest of honor was the well-known writer Joseph Hergesheimer, whose novel *The Bright Shawl* headed the current list of best sellers.

But the party was outstanding for the lowest of all possible motives—pure, unadulterated sadism. So, this account had better start off with a pretty good excuse, or none of us who took part in the affair could be forgiven.

Joe Hergesheimer's character has to be understood to begin with, if our excuse is to have any validity. Joe was a born figure of fun, a self-made patsy who practically begged for the humiliations that dogged his footsteps. He was crowding sixty, fat, semibald and married, but nothing interfered with his ambitions as a Casanova. Every girl who came into Joe's ken was a target for his pitch.

At a party one night I had an experience that tells a lot about Joe as a Lothario. The month was June (which was then more provocative for romance that it is now). I was to leave for Europe the following day, and Joe had spent a good part of the evening maneuvering to get me into the dark. Alone at last, he asked in a tense whisper, "When are you coming home?" I told him, "In August." "Do you know what I'm going to do, young lady?" he demanded, by this time breathing hard. "I'm going to kiss you—*in August!*" After which he led me, unkissed, back into the light.

But girls didn't resent Joe's fumbles, which never reached anything like a climax in an actual affair. We treasured him all the more as an unfailing source of amusement. Joe was a dear old pussycat.

Being a man of real talent, he was popular with other distinguished writers, such as H. L. Mencken, Ernest Boyd (the Irish essayist), and George Jean Nathan (the Broadway critic), a group that should have adorned any thinking man's personal life. But in the case of Joe, it failed. He yearned to be received by society, to see his name in the gossip columns.

The trouble was that Joe used to tell the plots of his novels at social affairs, which caused listeners to scamper out on him like today's addicts of rock and roll when someone starts to play "The Beautiful Blue Danube."

But the main alibi for that shameful dinner party was a fear Joe had of dentistry. The result was unfortunate. One can overlook almost any facial blemish except a scarcity of front teeth, and Joe's were almost gone. But he so completely ignored their absence that no one had the heart to suggest he should go to a dentist.

The prelude to Addison's dinner began one afternoon when a group of us was having tea in his drawing room. Addie, a wit and an iconoclast, was surrounded by a bevy of favorite people. There was the beautiful Marjorie Oelrichs, a self-made reject from the Social Register; a French Vicomte whose ancestors would have pulled a chair from under Louis XVI just for the fun of it; an Austrian Prince who excelled in the pursuit of pleasure as only the Viennese can; and myself, who would do anything for a laugh, which included writing *Gentlemen Prefer Blondes*.

In the midst of the tea-table chatter, a telegram arrived from Joe Hergesheimer. It appeared he had once wangled an introduction to Addison, and now he announced his imminent descent on Palm Beach society. Addie's first reaction was to hope that the old boy had seen a dentist. But, be that as it may, Addie decided to welcome him with a dinner party. And to lay it on thick for Joe, it should be highly formal.

Addie jokingly suggested that the titled members of his group wear some medals, if they could find any. Our Vicomte, who had left his medals in Paris, suggested that he and his Vicomtesse could wear ribbons across their chests as decorations. And, as the joke snowballed, the Prince's American bride ventured that she might even dig up a fake tiara in West Palm Beach.

When Joe arrived among us, it was at once apparent that he had *not* been to a dentist. His situation had even worsened, if possible. And then, as the date for the party drew near, Addie made an unfortunate move by asking Marge, the dropout debutante, to plan his menu. "It's got to be food that Joe's front teeth can handle," Addie warned.

This warning gave Marge an idea, bold enough to please the most confirmed prankster. And, discussing the menu with me one day, she remarked, "Let's give Addie's friend a dinner that will teach him a lesson."

"What sort of lesson?" I inquired.

"One that will finally get him into a dentist's chair!" said Marge.

"Like what?"

Marge thought for only a moment. "One of the hardest jobs the toothless ever have to tackle has got to be an artichoke."

"Wonderful!" said I.

Having settled on an hors d'oeuvre of artichokes, we proceeded with our menu; naturally, we omitted soup which would pose no difficulty for Joe. As a substitute we chose corn-on-the-cob. Then, for an entrée what could be better than filet mignon? At its best filet mignon tends to be tough, but we argued Addie's butcher into supplying us with fresh steaks, before they'd had time to hang and be chewable. Salad was easy. It could be hearts of raw celery.

Dessert posed a bit of a problem until Marge came through with an excellent idea: "Walnut ice cream with a topping of stringy caramel."

The party started off with our guest of honor all aglow from the sparkle cast by the Princess' fake tiara. At the table we pranksters took satisfaction in Joe's struggle with the first leaf of artichoke. After a defeat, he cancelled the remainder of it. Joe bypassed his corn-on-the-cob, which remained unbitten in its little plate. A single mouthful of tough filet mignon caused him to skip the entrée; likewise the hearts of celery. And he deserted the dessert after one clinging mouthful of the strings from the caramel sauce.

But, barred from eating, Joe took advantage of a rare opportunity to tell us the plot of his forthcoming novel in great detail. So, now it was the turn of his captive audience to suffer in silence. We had to lend an ear while we continued to chew the food we had so cruelly forced poor Joe to neglect. All the same, he had the time of his life, completely oblivious to the glazed look of his table mates as he spun out his narrative.

Joe Hergesheimer didn't learn a thing from that lesson we attempted to teach him. For he never did get to a dentist in the years that followed. On the contrary, it was Joe who taught us smart alecks a much-needed lesson: Pearly teeth are not a requisite for happiness, and man does not live by food alone.

Why Not Try a
Little ESP?

ONLY of late did my friend Paulette and I realize that the extraordinary good luck we'd had throughout our careers had a lot to do with extrasensory perception. We stumbled onto that force at an early age, when the term was not yet in vogue; even if it had been, we wouldn't have known exactly what it meant or how powerful its influence could be.

It may even have been ESP that brought about our encounter with Aldous Huxley in Hollywood. Although deeply interested in parapsychology, Aldous seldom discussed it with us. Our friendship with him was sparked by his penetrating wit and sense of humor; we enjoyed his viewpoint on all the ridiculous things that went on under the sun of Southern California. But we may have learned something about ESP from Aldous by osmosis. It is almost as if we were channels through which the subject flowed quite naturally. And by more or less unconscious use of it we have both gotten everything out of life we ever really wanted.

Back in San Diego when I was in my teens, terribly poor and absorbed in girlish daydreams about riches, I came across a book in the public library titled *The History and Power of Mind*. The author's name was Ingalese and he was widely read by the screwball population of Southern California.

At that time I was a child actress in my father's stock company. But show business had been hit by hard times and our theatre was doomed to close, leaving all of us stranded.

One evening in the dressing room of our leading lady, Sue Iles, we were discussing our chances for survival, when I happened to mention my discovery of Mr. Ingalese and suggested we try out his plan.

"But how?" asked Sue.

"Well, let's just visualize you acting in a sketch that's playing the Orpheum Circuit."

"Where do I get a sketch?" Sue inquired.

"I'll write it for you."

"Are you kidding?" Sue asked. For in the field of entertainment Sue and I were very small potatoes, and to be booked on the Orpheum Circuit would place us in competition with international stars such as Sarah Bernhardt, Houdini, and Sir Harry Lauder.

Lolling on Sue's dressing-room couch, I began to visualize a sketch that would make use of Sue's own characteristics. She had been a big success as Camille because of her fragile type of beauty. So my heroine would be a helpless young woman, married to a brutal husband; the hero a young attorney to whom she applies for legal protection.

The lawyer, instantly smitten with his pretty client, begins to extract her story which reveals that the husband's latest atrocity had been to throw an inkwell at her. She has brought the inkwell along as evidence; it proves to be about the size of a thimble. And then, continuing her story, the persecuted wife displays a stupidity, egomania and ineptness of such monstrous proportions that, after twenty minutes of seething irritation, the lawyer picks up his large brass inkwell and lets her have it right in the face. (When I conjured up that plot at fourteen I'd already become rather cynical about my own sex.)

At any rate, I wrote that sketch and then, continuing to rely on Mr. Ingalese, mailed it to the manager of the Orpheum Theatre in San Francisco.

The Inkwell, starring Sue Iles, began its regular annual tour of the Orpheum Circuit. My royalties were one hundred and fifty dollars a week which, in those days, provided the Loos family with sirloin steak for three successive years.

Whereas I had visualized my objective in terms of a job, Paulette's method was more direct. When she began to earn a living at fourteen by modeling dresses for a Seventh Avenue wholesale house, her daydreams were of diamonds from Van Cleef & Arpels, Balenciaga dresses, Revillon furs, Renoir paintings, Dom Perignon champagne, and Persian caviar. She always seemed to bypass the labor which would bring them about.

Paulette has never given much credit to economics. One day in Rome during the market tumble of '51, she encountered a gloomy stockbroker on the Via Veneto who asked where she was going. "To pick out a diamond necklace," she said. "What else should a girl do at a time like this?"

She showed a breadth of vision that is altogether missing from Wall Street. "If all the stock markets of the world were to collapse, diamonds would still survive," she declared. "So what's all the panic about?"

At a later date Paulette felt it incumbent to own a large-sized pigeon's blood ruby. At that time she was Mrs. Erich Remarque. Now Paulette always made it a rule never to ask for anything, but she may have hinted something like this: "Somewhere there's a great big ruby that, by rights, belongs to me. Don't you think it's about time for it to come home, Erich dear?"

Always happy to be doing something for his pretty wife, Erich scoured Paris to find a big ruby, but none filled the specifications. Presently news filtered out of Iran that the Shah had decided to sell a few of the Imperial jewels. Among them was an eighty-five-carat ruby. At once Erich got on the phone, and the deal was made inside an hour.

Some time later in New York, I asked Paulette, "Aren't you afraid to wear that ruby on these mugger-infested streets?"

"But why?" she inquired. "It doesn't belong to a mugger. It belongs on me!"

Then, as an afterthought, she mentioned that recently, when venturing forth to a party, she found her limousine hadn't yet arrived. While waiting for it she noticed an evil-looking character lurching toward her from a dark alley.

Paralyzed with fright, she was getting ready to scream for help, when a patrol car turned the corner and was stopped by the flash of her ruby in the glare of its car lights.

"Why, there's Paulette Goddard!" exclaimed one dazzled cop.

"How're you doin', Paulette?" asked the other.

By which time the evil character had decamped, and she escaped with ruby intact. "It was as simple as ABC," she declared, "or rather—ESP."

Another manifestation of that force evolved after Erich first took her to live at Porto Ronco, Switzerland, on the shore of Lake Maggiore. She wasn't entirely sold on that place; it was peopled by vulgar rich German businessmen. But Casa Remarque was an ideal retreat for Erich: a quiet place for writing. So his wife kept her mouth shut.

Only later did she realize that ESP transplanted her from her old haunts of Paris, Rome, and New York. For living in Porto Ronco was a world-renowned teacher of Zen Buddhism, and before long she was studying Zen with him. The truth is, though I'm not supposed to expose it, she is a compulsive student of practically any subject. In any locality she is apt to find a teacher in no time. And no matter what his subject, she plunges into it: political science, languages, exercises, diction, acting, anything. Perhaps Zen made her even more receptive to ESP. Whether the two are compatible I don't know.

About a year after Erich's death, thieves broke into Casa Remarque and took off with a fortune in Picassos, Monets, Renoirs, Egyptian bronzes, and other valuables. Paulette immediately flew to Porto Ronco to investigate. Soon after her arrival the Swiss Chef de Sureté phoned her from Berne to say they'd caught the thieves, her treasures were safe, and could she motor to Berne to pick them up.

On examining the loot she found a certain item was missing: a tiny clock of mainly sentimental value. It had been a birthday gift to Erich from Paulette. He loved it, even after it was broken and stopped telling time. She returned home with her restored treasures but disappointed to lose Erich's little clock.

About a week later the Police Chief called again. He had found the clock in a repair shop where the burglars left it to be fixed. So, when that clock was returned it had more value than when it was stolen. Once more the perils of Paulette were averted and inflicted instead on those who tried to take advantage of her.

Back in New York, she was walking along Madison Avenue one day, when she saw in a shop window a new model of a miniature radio in a favorite shade of red. "That radio *belongs* to me," she thought, without going into the shop to make the purchase. "Never pay for anything that belongs to you," she says.

Paulette completed her morning walk meditating on that little red radio. But she rather overdid the process. Within the next few days she was presented with not one but three red radios.

"Did you happen to mention it to anyone?" asked a skeptical friend. "Well, yes," she admitted. "I happened to mention it to three gentlemen friends. But I never *asked* for one. I just gave ESP a little mild assistance."

Then, there was an even humbler instance of this power. On that occasion we were en route somewhere from Grand Central Station, when Paulette paused to make an important phone call. In those days a phone call only required a nickel. The two of us searched our pocketbooks but couldn't find one. We felt frustrated until a very ragged old tramp, emerging from nowhere, approached and held out a nickel to Paulette. She thanked him and made her call.

When she finished, I remarked, "Really, Paulette, you shouldn't have accepted that poor old tramp's nickel."

Gazing at me wide-eyed, she said, "But it was all he *had*." Then her orbs smiled with mischief. "After all, I couldn't insult him by refusing his offer, could I?"

ESP at work again? There we were thinking "nickel" and suddenly our need was met. Of course we were standing beside a phone booth, rummaging in our bags, so anybody could tell what we were hunting for. Yet none of the double-breasted men rushing by to catch the 5:23 to Larchmont or wherever, thought of stopping, while the generous tramp was wafted toward us as if by magic.

How to Keep from Having a Nervous Breakdown

I worked for many years in the nerve-racking atmosphere of Hollywood and, later on, in the equally frantic environs of Broadway. But I have yet to visit a psychoanalyst or even take my first tranquilizing pill.

This is due, I'm sure, to having stumbled across a treatment for unstrung nerves a long time ago. The treatment costs much less than a single session with an analyst and is a quicker tranquilizer than any of the so-called miracle drugs.

This medical discovery of mine took place one summer when my husband John and I were in Europe. I had remained in Paris while he had gone to London on business. He planned to take a plane back on a certain day.

Those were the early years of plane travel when any flight was a hazard. The plane was due at 5 P.M. at an airport about an hour from our hotel. So 6 o'clock found me in our suite waiting for John.

But he didn't come. Never mind—possibly traffic from the airport was heavy. Six-thirty came; still no John. Beginning to be apprehensive, I called the reception desk and asked whether it was usual for the flights from London to be late. I was assured that, as a rule, the planes arrived on schedule.

It may only have been imagination, but I sensed that the reception clerk shared my alarm. At any rate, he said he would phone the airline. While waiting for his report, I began to visualize any number of catastrophes. I could almost hear John's airplane smacking the waters of the Channel.

Finally I called the reception desk again. The receptionist said that he had been trying to get the airport but the lines were jammed—possibly flooded with other calls of the same nature as mine.

His line of reasoning only increased my fears. I now began rapidly to disintegrate, to feel I'd never see my husband again. Had I been a smoker, I would have spent the following hour lighting one cigarette after another. But I don't smoke. Also, I don't drink—else I'd have ordered up a double martini or two. I was alone in Paris; there was no friend with whom I could share my alarm. Should I call up the American Embassy?

While deep in thought, I found my gaze fixed on a piece of needlepoint I had bought at the Galerie Lafayette. I picked it up, still in a daze, and started automatically to work on it, my hands shaking so violently that it was hard to get the stitches into line.

Little by little, it began to seem very important that the row of small crosses should be straight. I was forced to steady my hand, to concentrate on the needle—*in and out it went . . . the line began to straighten . . . good . . . now the little crosses were uniform.*

Almost hypnotized by that row of even stitches, I reached a point where it was necessary to change to another color of yarn. *It must be just the right nuance . . . not too light . . . not too dark.*

I found the proper shade, went on with a blotch of yellow that would soon turn into a daisy, and was going great guns when I was rudely interrupted by John walking in. He said that his plane had been delayed in taking off from London—after which he had enjoyed a perfect flight.

Without realizing it, I had conducted a successful experiment in the control of nervous tension. That piece of needlepoint did duty for years. I can't remember when, or if, it ever got finished, which is just as well because the pattern was pretty banal, and I came to look down my nose on it as a work of art. But as therapy it never failed.

During the 1930s I went to California, where I spent 18 years in the scenario department at Metro-Goldwyn-Mayer. It was a period when MGM dominated the entire Hollywood scene because of the genius of Irving Thalberg, who headed the organization.

Irving was so great a perfectionist that we often used to work on a movie script for as long as five years. Most of the time was spent waiting for conferences with Irving, whose duties, both as executive head of the great studio and as inspiration to a waiting staff of more than 100 authors, were staggering.

Sometimes a writer would be forced to wait for months before Irving was available for a conference. Such periods were frustrating, and, sitting outside Irving's office, other writers used to chafe with impatience or gradually disintegrate through boredom.

I, however, put my previous medical discovery to good use. But because needlepoint required too large an assortment of yarn, I took to knitting. While waiting for conferences on a script I wrote for Jean Harlow titled "The Red-Headed Woman," I knitted a scarf which, when you consider the time I put in on it and the $3,500-a-week salary I was being paid by MGM, could have been valued at about $85,000. But as long-range therapy it was worth that sum.

There were two other girls on the old MGM lot who had stumbled onto the therapeutic value of handiwork—although I'm sure they had done so as unconsciously as I had. They were Joan Crawford and Paulette Goddard.

The most common complaint of any film actress is that acting occupies a very small portion of a day's work. The majority of time is spent in waiting: waiting for huge, clumsy lights to be arranged, for cameras to be adjusted, for make-up to be freshened, for costumes to be changed, for endless technical details. Nothing ages a girl so much as boredom. It dulls the eyes, brings on wrinkles, and deadens the spirit.

But both Joan and Paulette looked years younger than their age. Could this partly be due to the fact that during long periods of boredom on studio stages, Paulette did acres of needlepoint and that Joan, during World War II, knitted enough socks to outfit a regiment? (One can only wish that poor little Marilyn Monroe, instead of getting hooked on sleeping pills, had become addicted to needlework or sought tranquility in a pair of knitting needles.)

Any sort of manual activity can be a substitute for needlework. I can cite the experience of a friend of mine who some time ago lost her adored husband of many years. It was one of those losses so tragic that it would have been understandable had she taken to drink.

For many years she had been a pampered wife living among the most exciting people of both her own country and Europe. She had had no other occupation than that of being hostess for her famous husband. At the time of his death it was appalling to think of what her future might be. She was totally unequipped for loneliness.

Her friends came forward with suggestions. She had always been a witty letter writer. Why couldn't she write professionally? Or take up decorating as a career? At any rate, see an analyst!

To all this advice our friend had very sound objections. "I'd be only an amateur writer," she said. "As to the decorating business, it's already too full of women who have no equipment except their own imagined good taste."

As for an analyst, she explained that she had found an excellent substitute. She had discharged her servants and was doing all her own housework. She took the occupation very seriously, made a very precise schedule for dusting, scrubbing, vacuuming, and ironing. It was a schedule from which nothing short of doomsday would ever jolt her.

The schedule not only assured her physical and mental health but enabled her to do away once and for all with the servant problem. And she saved much more money on servants' salaries and food than she could ever have earned as a phony professional.

There is, of course, a great deal of housework being done in America by overburdened wives, but, in the majority of cases, it is done inexpertly and produces as much confusion, frustration, illness, and fatigue as does idleness. But it is easy to keep house efficiently by adhering to a schedule. A job that doesn't have to be rushed is never tiring, and with its accomplishment comes a glow of well-being that's practically a beauty treatment.

If you take to handiwork instead of to an analyst, it will not only save you the wear and tear of self-pity—it will also save the high cost of therapy.

It has long been my ambition to hear of a case where an analyst has said to some patient, "I will now tell you good-bye, dear lady, because you won't have to come back here any more."

After all, analysts like to keep busy, too.

If I Were Husband-Hunting Today

*T*HE main requirements of an ideal husband, 30 or 40 years ago, were that he be a good provider and could face the issue of having a family without dismay.

There was an abundance of such material, and good husbands really were not too hard to catch.

First of all, men found certain advantages being married—wives were conditioned to do housework, homes were sufficiently roomy so that children could be stashed away out of sight and hearing.

Although children, under our native methods of upbringing, always have been little sybarites, one could scarcely call them spend-thrifts in the '20s. Toys and gadgets were of the five-and-ten-cent variety; children were not connoisseurs of record albums; they never ran up phone bills nor demanded anything as expensive as color TV sets.

A theme song for family life in those days might well be "Home Sweet Home," sung without any hint of irony.

The qualities that made a good husband at that time haven't changed in the least, *but* the available number of such males has been reduced greatly. The disadvantages of being a husband these days have come to outweigh the gains by far. The cost of living has risen astronomically, the taxes have become so high that young men balk at financing a household singlehandedly.

Now, even though expenses may be shared by wives who hold down jobs of their own, the difficulties of catching a husband have steadily mounted. The same brand of "push-button" housekeeping that released wives to the marts of trade has made it all too easy for a bachelor to keep house for himself. His only female requirements can be supplied by a part-time maid.

By the time he returns home from the office, his housekeeping, sketchy as it is, has been completed. There is nothing to interfere with the blessings of solitude or prevent an evening of the most delightful selfishness—no hindrance to reading the sport pages, no listening to a wife recount her frustrations of a day at her own office.

Moreover, a bachelor can provide himself with much the same dinner that would be put forth by a working wife.

Today the business of fathering a family is beset with frustrations other than the high cost of living. That pleasant "lull in the day's occupation" that used to be known as "the children's hour" has gone the way of other family delights. A daddy of our present world returns home at the end of the day to face the unfair competition of TV. As an amateur entertainer, what parent can be half so absorbing as Batman or Bugs Bunny?

Sex, which used to be a major enticement to marriage, has lost much of its power. For we are living in a "moral revolution," and, if a girl holds out, she runs the risk of being considered "square." If she joins the moral revolution and gives in, she runs the greater risk of losing her novelty.

Modern girls must discount sex as a means of gaining a permanent household; the existence of the Pill has destroyed the element of responsibility which used to accompany sex. It has become far too common.

If such conditions tend to discourage the pursuit of a husband, there is no reason for giving up in despair, for present-day life has provided girls with one new, major advantage in the chase. The more hazardous and confused a man's existence becomes, the more it tends to isolate him.

The frantic hustle of our world has dissipated family life. Living quarters are so cramped that children, on leaving school, are pushed out of the nest to fend for themselves. The family splits up, and its members go their separate ways. These days, when one bumps into an acquaintance, it is best to think twice before asking about "the folks." There are the hazards of recent divorces and ill-made new alliances.

At any rate, nowadays a man's kith and kin are inclined to be gauged by their nuisance value, so there are recurrent moments in the day when he feels defenseless and alone. He becomes a solitary victim of private and universal tensions. The situation leaves a man vulnerable to attack and provides a girl with one dependable aid in catching a prospective husband: that is, to be good company.

But the girl who is bad company must admit it to herself quite frankly, and, once conceded, she must rectify the fact by discipline of a high order. She must learn that no man is going to react to the way she looks after his first brief inspection.

It's all right to spend hours at a beauty parlor if it gives morale a boost, but the moment a girl steps through the doorway, she should forget all vanity and conduct herself as if she looked like the homely sister of Phyllis Diller. Nor is a man going to be impressed if a dress happens to have been made by Cardin—he's quite likely to be wearing something by Cardin himself.

Only a low-grade type of male is going to be interested in a girl's glamour. A list of men who have succumbed to history's most famous sirens contains very few who were worth pursuing. I can think only of Caesar and Marc Antony, both of whom fell for Cleopatra, and Lord Nelson, who attached himself to Emma Hamilton.

While entertaining a prospective husband, a girl should bear in mind that he doesn't actually want to hear about her troubles; she may have a headache, but he's likely to have a worse one. He isn't interested that she just lost an argument with her boss, spent a bad hour at the dentist's, or is having a running battle with her family.

Never forget, girls are up against formidable competition. A lonely man can repair to some nearby cocktail bar and mix with his own kind; he can patronize a sports arena, the theater, or the movies. And, bad though it may be, he can always look at TV.

There is a modern saying which is so true that, in time, it may become an old saw. It goes: "TV is like a wife—a man is already stuck with it, the sound is available around the clock, and it costs nothing to switch on. So why does it have to be good?"

The girls I have known who have fascinated the greatest number of real men have not necessarily done the job by their good looks. Even in the case of Elizabeth Taylor, it is not her fabulous face and extraordinary figure that have fascinated men. There are numberless cover girls as beautiful as she, whose romantic careers have been extremely dull. According to the best authority (her fourth husband, singer Eddie Fisher), Elizabeth's charm lies in the fact that she creates an atmosphere of suspense—no husband ever knows what he's coming home to. This is excitement of a type that age cannot wither nor custom stale.

A girl's best trick is, first of all, to forget herself, concentrate on her victim—and persevere. In this present age of regimentation where it takes the ego of a Cassius Clay not to feel hopelessly dwarfed, a man must be made to feel important. If a girl is worried about the quality of her small talk, she is not without assistance. Nature, which abhors a vacuum, has solved that problem today by the institution of the discothèque, where a girl can spend three or four hours with her date while the racket prohibits talk.

The mere appearance of being interested in a man can create an atmosphere of flattery which few others produce, one into which he is forced to enter simply because he can find such an ambiance nowhere except in the girl's vicinity.

Becky Sharp, the heroine of Thackeray's *Vanity Fair,* stated a fact that is as true today as it was when she first made her famous discovery: any female, provided she doesn't have a squint or a hump, can marry whomever she pleases. Success naturally requires the sacrifice of ego, but once the renunciation is made, the most hopeless spinster will find that it all pays off.

She will find that she, too, after all, can catch a husband.

Today's Youth Isn't Right About Everything

*T*HE fact that morality can take on different aspects as the fashions change might indicate that it has no basic essence, is as frivolous as the mode of the day, and inconstant as the wind or weather.

However, from the time human motives were first analyzed in the ancient classics and the Bible or used as plot material by authors all the way from Chaucer to Truman Capote, there have been no actual changes in the concept of right and wrong. If there had been, nobody today would be able to understand, much less find an identification with such characters as Ulysses, Job, the wife of Bath, or Holly Golightly. The ingredients that make up the human psyche can no more be altered than bread can be made without flour.

For some time now, a quirk that originated in the morbid brain of old Doctor Freud in Vienna has been in style: that the human spirit is devoid of nobility.

This accusation of mass guilt has so crippled our moral aims that we take sides with criminals against their victims; make no move to reject the creepy exhibitionism of such show-offs as Joan Baez and Yoko Ono or the pretenses of Marshall MacLuhan, who claimed that our identities were at the mercy of our TV sets.

And fashion in dress, which is always inclined to lay itself open to the ridiculous, has now allowed itself to be taken over by the teen-ager, possibly through the sheer nuisance value of his bad behavior. Or, largely, I would say, because the cult of Freud has enfeebled the moral stamina of grownups through its illusion of guilt.

But youth adores to be chastised; no catharsis for its turbulent emotions is half so gratifying as punishment. And the thing it most resents is having its defects ignored.

So in a spirit of revenge over the moral laziness of its elders, youth has taken advantage of several brand-new ways to be naughty; replaced its old-fashioned vogue for bubble gum and Tootsie Rolls with marijuana and LSD. The most potent of all its revenges and the most far-reaching, however, is youth's deliberate choice of ugliness as an ideal.

I am ready to grant that, in some ways, this new Cult of Ugliness shows more consideration for humanity at large than when it was thought desirable for boys to be attractive and girls to be very pretty.

It is all too true that the great majority of the human race suffers facial defects and inferior anatomy, which it is now encouraged to flaunt in a manner that used to be the rare privilege of the beautiful. Then, too, when young people combed their hair and were neat, they had a tendency to look alike and thus melt into the background.

But dirt and dishevelment can be extended into an infinite variety of eyesores. In addition, matted hair and grubby clothing can be achieved without effort; it only requires that one carefully avoid soap, water, and the hairbrush.

But far beyond the shock value of squalid clothing is the present-day vogue of wearing no clothes at all. Nudity is not only beyond compare as an attention-getter and booster for the ego, but the more one's proportions lack symmetry, the more arresting. And to cap all its other advantages, nudity is as cheap as it is invincible.

It is only normal for grownups to want to look young, with the result that, in copying the teen-ager, they, too, have embraced its Cult of Ugliness; ladies of erstwhile dignity uncover knees that are bulgy from years of too little exercise; women with well-preserved bodies assume the sleaziness of bell-bottom pants, which give them the proportions of Popeye the Sailor Man. And dress designers in Paris, London, New York, and particularly Hollywood have fol-lowed along with the trend.

Designers of taste have either held their ground against the deluge, as did Mademoiselle Chanel or, as in the case of Balenciaga, retired permanently from the fashion scene and turned their profession over to the untidy. The teen-ager has triumphed. The immature mind has hit the fashion target right on the button.

So widespread is this worship of the malformed that it has invaded every phase of modern aesthetics. In painting, it has reached its apotheosis in the pictures of Willem de Kooning, whose misshapen females could have stepped right out of the nightmares of old Doctor Freud himself after partaking of too many *kartoffel pfannkuchen*. The same disaster has happened to literature and to films, in which writers like Philip Roth have uncovered whole new areas of nausea.

In the light of this trend, it might even seem that, for present-day concepts, a new version of Cinderella may be required.

Let us suppose, then, that the time-honored fairy tale were made into a feature film which could measure up to modern standards. Its title role would be played by Barbra Streisand, who would be the victim of an insane jealousy on the part of her two stepsisters, played by Zsa Zsa Gabor and Mamie Van Doren.

To avenge their maniacal envy of Barbra's looks, Mamie and Zsa Zsa would force her to comb her hair and put on a dress of classical design, executed by Mainbocher.

But then, during a low point of Barbra's despair, there suddenly appears before her a Good Fairy, played by Phyllis Diller. Phyllis provides Barbra with a fright wig, strips her of clothing, and rolls her in cinders. After which, she takes Barbra down to a happening in the East Village pad of the hero, Dustin Hoffman, complete with a cigar and a chronic drug habit.

There, to the racket of a jazz combo, Barbra meets Dustin and love conquers all. Mamie and Zsa Zsa, hiding their symmetrical noses in chagrin, are forced to make do with a couple of rejects, played by Horst Buchholz and Gunther Gebel-Williams, while Barbra and Dustin live happily for several weeks thereafter, in sin.

I hesitate, however, before offering this rewrite of the old fairy tale to be made into a film by Andy Warhol. For I am beginning to see evidence that this youthful preference for the unsightly harbors certain signs of a retreat; that we may possibly be in for a return to the aesthetic scruples of the past.

For young people, like most exhibitionists, protest too loudly;

they make one feel that their worship of the slipshod is basically weak. I can cite the excellent Zefferelli film of *Romeo and Juliet,* in which the two young lovers are of such pure beauty and harmonious proportions that one can't imagine them being acceptable to children of an era that has embraced Barbra and Dustin as its archetypes of perfection.

And yet at every performance of this film, long lines of boys and girls, with their hair like birds' nests and garments assembled from debris, wait patiently not only to gaze on peerless beauty but to listen to the dialogue of Shakespeare. And when at the end of the film the lovers are parted by death, an audible sob shakes the theater almost to its foundations. A manifestation such as this gives one courage to hope that perhaps Tiny Tim himself, if given the choice, would like to look like Monica Vitti.

And I am also beginning to wonder about this youthful rebellion against the Establishment; is there perhaps a note of the same hypocrisy for which they themselves damn the old social order?

Students who knock down the college walls in their demonstrations against a) war, b) race discrimination, or c) the inadequacy of present-day instruction can be just as destructive as war itself. Discrimination against their own parents can be much more violent than discrimination against any race, cult, or creed.

Let youth damn our hypocrisy as it may, I have never been able to condemn it. It has always seemed to me a sort of good manners of the spirit. We are assured by the Bible that nobody is perfect; but when we put on the outer trappings of perfection and try to ape a certain purity of heart, it shows that we are not in agreement with our imperfections. In other words, we *try.*

A couple of decades ago in Hollywood, I beheld a most gratifying manifestation of hypocrisy. It was centered in the person of Aimee Semple McPherson, who was High Priestess of her own Temple of the Four Square Gospel. As glamorous as any movie star, Aimée achieved her good looks by the same means as Mae West— pancake make-up.

Aimée would, in fact, have been a star of stage and screen, except that unfortunately she was born with ankles that were thick to a degree that made it expedient for them to be camouflaged. Ergo— the best cover-up for faulty ankles is . . . what? Why, the long robes of the church!

And Aimee, standing before her altar in a gown of shimmering white, backed up by an aura of neon lights and a mass of plastic lilies; leading her choir in her own religious lyrics for a pop song of the period, "I Don't Want to Walk Without You, Baby," produced a religious exaltation I have never known to be exceeded.

A congregation of thousands who wouldn't have held still for a moment to hear Bach's Mass in B Minor, stood up and held hands clear across the auditorium in a unified manifestation of pious joy.

I think life would be more sane and certainly less guilt-ridden if present-day humanity were required to wash their mouths out with soap and practice a little good, old-fashioned, mid-Victorian hypocrisy.

Cocktail Parties of
the Twenties

*N*EW York City provides the coziest setting in the world for cocktail parties. It is not only the world's smallest big city, but the swinging New Yorker occupies that fairly limited area of it called Manhattan. Few citizens of any other borough ever find their way into a chic New York cocktail party. It is almost unthinkable to import a guest from Yonkers, the Bronx, or even Brooklyn. Whereas this might result in monotony, at the same time it makes for very fast communication.

The above statements were just as true in the twenties as they are today, but in the twenties a hostess had a more vital force of celebrities on which to draw. An average guest list might include Scott and Zelda Fitzgerald, who would always compete with each other in bloodcurdling misbehavior; if Scott was inspired to climb out on a high window ledge, Zelda could always find some excuse to take off her clothes, thus diverting attention from her husband. For in those days it was quite uncommon to be bare in public.

Then there was H. L. Mencken, whose behavior might be impeccable, but whose vocabulary exploded with scurrilous terms of his own manufacture. One subject on which Mencken held forth bitterly was the "boob mentality" of our South; he designated the state of Arkansas as "The Sahara of the Bozarts" (meaning Beaux Arts). It was at a cocktail party that Menck gave me the idea of choosing Little Rock as the proper birthplace for the idiotic blonde whose story I was writing. George Jean Nathan, the theater critic, always provided something dramatic in the way of a flapper; the fact that George was smallish required her to be smaller; she might be an Oriental. Sometimes he brought Florence Mills from Harlem. Frequently another famous George showed up and took to the piano, and we would find ourselves listening to Florence Mills sing Gershwin accompanied by Georgie himself, which was a carnival for the ears such as seldom occurs at cocktail parties anymore.

No party got into full swing until Tallulah arrived to put her particular type of zizz into it. She was always courteous to the unassuming but her gravel-voiced bitchiness would be unleashed without mercy on someone like Zelda who was foolish enough to lay herself open. One time, as an excuse for undressing, Zelda pouted, "Oh dear, my slip is showing!" "You mean your show is slipping, don't you, darling?" barked Tallulah.

Another asset to any party was Tallulah's brunette sister, Jean [Eugenia], who had a *beauté du diable* that caused even more havoc among the males than the classic features of Tallulah. Jean was as irresponsible as any hippie, but with one big difference: Her behavior resulted in action instead of apathy. Jean could bring out a man's most violent behavior patterns. On one occasion a young suitor jumped off a pier in an effort to swim after the *Ile de France,* which was bearing Jean across the sea. Jean's swain didn't get very far, but he did get sober.

Every proper guest list of the twenties included the publisher Horace Liveright. Although his catalog listed all the best-selling authors in America, Horace's most cherished asset was a little black book with the most comprehensive list of telephone numbers in New York. Horace's associate publisher, Tommy Smith, made the scene of every cocktail party, from sundown to sunup. Looking like a youthful Mr. Magoo, Tommy always seemed to be half asleep, but he never went to bed. He was on intimate terms with everyone from Texas Guinan on up to Mrs. August Belmont. Toddling about Manhattan, he wove a connecting web that made us all understand and appreciate each other. Although not involved romantically with girls, Tommy was a storehouse of comfort; other men might get us into trouble, but Tommy then took over and straightened things out. He could provide solace for any girl's indiscretions and at the same time take responsibility off the shoulders of a seducer, allowing both of them to go on, carefree, to any further misconduct.

Every cocktail party boasted oodles and oodles of flappers and equal oodles of college men down from Harvard and Yale or up from Princeton, all of them available for marriage. I can remember only one fashion designer who ever got asked around. His name was Nate Clark and he provided a definite allure to New York's indoor scenery. Nate felt a responsibility toward his clientele that no longer exists. His creations added to a girl's charm instead of taking it away, and he strove to disguise our bad points instead of showing them up.

The conversation at a twenties cocktail party was largely informative, and one departed with the inner tingle of taking away something worthwhile. The homemaker could learn new recipes for synthetic gin or the needling of near beer. Names and telephone numbers of reliable bootleggers were swapped, and one was informed of the password to use at Lüchow's in order to get the real beer that was smuggled in from Munich and served in teacups. There was information regarding the opening of any new speakeasy, such as the one run by Reine Davies, the elder sister of Marion, who held forth in an Eastside cellar that she called Reine Davies' Country Club.

The love affairs of those days were romantic instead of clinical. We hadn't yet heard of that old Viennese spoilsport Sigmund Freud. A chance encounter at any cocktail party might well develop into the love of a lifetime; it did in the case of blonde little Marion and the powerful Mr. Hearst. The Mayor of New York himself was having an idealistic relationship with a chorus cutie. She looked, talked, dressed, and deported herself exactly like thousands of other New York cuties, but Jimmy's feelings for her were strong enough to recompense for the loss of his career. A stock question at cocktail parties used to be, "What *is* it that Betty's got?" The answer to which was, "She's got His Honor!"

The fact that I can't remember the food served at those parties must mean that it was a minor part of the entertainment. Because of Prohibition, people's minds were naturally obsessed by drink, with gin occupying the place now held by vodka. However, I do remember the introduction of one sensational new libation. It had been invented in Florida, the discovery of the founding father of Palm Beach, Addison Mizner. It appeared that one day Addison, in the throes of a hangover, had an inspiration for something to replace the time-honored prairie oyster and he forthwith ordered his butler to serve him the juice of some tomatoes. The butler obeyed the barbaric order with distaste, little realizing that he was on the threshold of a discovery that would one day affect the mores of much of the civilized world.

At first tomato juice took no part in the early phases of a cocktail party, and only came into use the morning after when, spiked with Worcestershire sauce, cayenne, and any other counterirritant this side of ground glass, it would make one forget the agony of being rent asunder by bathtub gin. Then, however, some genius went to work on Addison's discovery, introduced tomato juice to gin, and gave it dignity as an integral element of the party itself. And thus was born the Bloody Mary.

One main difference between parties of the past and those of today is that the former were marked by an ambiance of great virility. As a rule this stemmed from the fact that a party inevitably ran out of liquor and the hostess had to send in a hurry for the nearest friendly bootlegger. He was welcome first of all as a lifesaver and then, being a man of important social connections, he frequently remained as a guest. Sometimes the liquor again ran low and he had to send for a confrere to bolster the supply. This situation might repeat itself over and over again until the most entrancing bevy of square-shooting male sexpots would recharge a party with enough electricity to make it go on for a week.

However, even this did not exhaust the supply of males who were brothers-under-the-skin of James Cagney and Humphrey Bogart. Complaints about the noise would eventually start up from neighborhood tenants. Then some would-be killjoy might call for the police. This brought in another body of men of a virility seldom encountered in the upper echelons of Park Avenue society. They might enter with a rather rough admonition of, "What do youse guys think you're up to anyhow?" This, however, was merely to alibi the fact that they were crashing. One look at Zelda Fitzgerald in the buff was all they needed to remain on as guests of honor. Aside from supplying the allure of sex, they contributed the warmth of a hearty comradeship between man and man. Some of the bootleggers and cops would already have met on an under-the-table business deal, so Moe, the bootlegger, and Mac, the cop, would greet each other with a gladiatorial embrace that gave their relationship the classic vigor of a Damon and Pythias.

Since no other entertainment in the twenties might conceivably vie with a cocktail party, no one was tempted to leave it; the cocktail party of today is more a place from which to escape. Seldom is an invitation to cocktails received with anything but a groan. Almost never does one hear the statement, "I just love a cocktail party!" Most of them are attended for some ignoble reason: to insinuate one's name or photo into the newspapers or to gain publicity for some venture, however devious. Then, too, the party provides an opportunity to steal a march on a competitor or wrest an asset away from its present holder. But of the impulsive cocktail party, given for good cheer and attended out of camaraderie, there scarcely remains a trace. Perhaps such events are now being held in the Bronx, Brooklyn, or Yonkers but, as a resident of Manhattan, I have no record of this fact.

When one looks at the cocktail parties of today, it is only to realize how far Cupid has scampered from Park Avenue. Most of our social relationships are no longer very sturdy; sad to report, gentlemen seem to favor their own kind. Ladies no longer dress as an incentive to romance, but only to impress fashion editors and their sort. Romance has disappeared along with vitality and the shock value of sex. Of course, a diluted form of it can be found in the East Village, where intersexual hippies exchange mates without the least twinge of jealousy. But admitting that they attain Peace, may I also hint that it could merely come from being stoned on marijuana? I always think that the gift of a flower may make a girl feel very calm but a manly clip on the jaw denotes passion.

For Heaven's Sake—
It's Christmas!

O_N a certain Christmas Eve when I was a child in San Francisco, a family friend showed up with an amazing pack of toys and goodies for us children: fireworks, Chinese dolls, lichee nuts, strips of sugar-coated coconut and a fancy jar of ginger.

That evening our friend was dressed in the long coat of a Chinese banker and I remember an apology he made to Mother. "I beg your pardon for appearing in my native dress, Minnie," said he, "but I had to preside at a ceremony in Chinatown and there was no time to change."

"Oh, that's all right, Fu Wong," said Mother. "Christmas isn't what it used to be!"

Now, as it happens, that certain Christmas with its exotic addition of fireworks still remains in my memory as sublime. So when I hear Mother's cliché repeated after all these years, I am *not* impressed.

The trouble with our rejection of the Christmas spirit today is that this tired old world refuses to realize that nothing can ever destroy the human equation.

As to the thrill of getting presents, I've seen middle-aged men of distinction strive greedily for souvenirs at a public relations banquet. So to think that the excitement of getting presents no longer exists is a gross fallacy.

And there are many more gifts available now than ever in the history of world economics. Furthermore, at Bloomingdale's basement, Lamston's and the five-and-dimes, the prices are right.

One can even find brand new items that match anything in the history of Christmas giving. For somebody totally lacking in religious fervor, an album of Duke Ellington's *Concert of Sacred Music* will elevate the hard-boiled listener as no Bach cantata ever can.

And what a Christmas present a copy of Edmund Wilson's *Upstate* can be! Even the format, designed by Edmund himself, is old-fashioned and Christmasy. And the book records emotions that will bring a thrill to anyone in his 80s who thinks that idyllic sex appeal doesn't exist anymore.

There are certain spots in New York where Christmas may even be better than it has ever been. The annual Balanchine production of *The Nutcracker* ballet packs the very highest degree of Christmas spirit for the kids and, willy-nilly, for their casehardened parents.

Tiny Tim's fine Christmas tree could have done no more for the spirit of that holiday than the tree in the foyer of the Metropolitan Museum. And those extravagant gifts of the converted old Scrooge could never stack up against Mary Lasker's gift of Christmas trees that extend the entire length of Park Avenue.

In this present awful state of our world, it is only the abnormal that should frighten us. But after all, our condition is a very normal thing. Humankind could not have unleashed the two worst wars in history without their horror and bestiality leaving a mark of Cain not only on those who were there but also on their unborn descendants.

Without the Sacred Birthday we would all be wallowing in a world that Signor Fellini showed us in his horror film *Satyricon;* an empty, hopeless smear of nastiness.

Only by holding fast to whatever good there is in life can there be hope for humanity. And one of the best things that remains is Christmas.

Hold on to it for Heaven's sake and I do mean Heaven's.

Sex Can Make a
Dunce of You

*W*HEN we children used to toddle forth to play on the cobblestones of San Francisco, we only had to dodge trolley cars, horse drawn vehicles, and bikes, since automobiles weren't yet in existence. Now we can watch a motor car as it ambles across the moon. The mores of our sex life have zoomed along just as dizzily, and whether they're forging ahead or in reverse might best be answered in terms of Hollywood.

In its heyday Hollywood reflected, if it did not actually produce, the sexual climate of our land. A screen love affair used to unfold chastely and without guile until it reached its climax in a kiss which, by a ruling of the Board of Censors, had quickly to fade out after seven seconds.

The lovers in those movies were products of the old American custom of men supporting women; so a girl's chief asset was the allure with which she disguised her normal acquisitiveness. That type reached its perfection in the gold diggers of the Twenties. Their technique might have been based on a theory that the most charming of all behaviorism lies in the canine species. Irving Thalberg used to tell me, "When you write a love scene think of your heroine as a little puppy dog, cuddling up to her master wagging an imaginary tail and gazing at him as if he were God."

It would be heartening if men no longer craved that sort of

treatment. But men are weak and constantly need reassurance, so now that they fail to find adulation in the opposite sex, they're turning to each other. And today, much as girls *look* like boys, they flunk out on the solicitude men are developing for each other. Less and less do men need women, more and more do gentlemen prefer gentlemen.

The Women's Lib movement seems unconcerned by this loss of man power, but I'm not convinced they really are. Women's Libbers look so frustrated; their expressions are grim; and the two leaders who *are* pretty are rapidly losing their looks.

I am perfectly willing to accept the sneer of being a "man-lover" with which Women's Lib brands characters like me. I could even laugh off the theft of my money by a loved one, because I'd already conceded that sex was a great big cosmic joke. I had even stated that fact in a book, the heroines of which were a blonde who got no fun out of the game and a brunette who took pleasure in giving money to a man who resented her (as mine did).

In 1925 when H. L. Mencken read the manuscript of *Gentlemen Prefer Blondes,* he told me, "I'd publish this in *The American Mercury,* but I don't dare to affront my readers. Do you realize, young woman, that you're the first American writer ever to poke fun at sex?"

We've come quite a distance since then. Not long ago, a foremost American author was asked in a TV interview, "What is your feeling about sex, Mr. Capote?" "Well," answered Truman, "it's rather like a sneeze."

I grant it can be powerful and sometimes impossible to smother, but one should still bear in mind that the aftermath of a sneeze may be nothing more than a damp Kleenex.

Not that falsified sex doesn't still have its protagonists. Norman Mailer, a less sturdy intellect than Capote, has written up his sensuous reactions to Marilyn Monroe in a book that reduces that literary "he-man" into a latter-day Ella Wheeler Wilcox. But who can deny that the sort of permissiveness that Norman finds so "sweet" can quickly be soured by unwelcome pregnancy, morning sickness, drugs, V.D., divorce, and suicide.

Bernard Shaw, a much more brilliant intellect than Mailer, was turned into a dunce when the erotic letters he wrote to sexy Stella Campbell led to a humiliating cat-and-dog fight.

Sex, on the other hand, didn't fool the sophisticated writer

Ludwig Bemelmans, who once complained to me about a shattered romance. "That affair was sheer ecstasy until sex entered in. Sex ruins everything!"

Henrik Ibsen went on record to state, "My eventual wife and I will live on separate floors, meet only at meal time and address each other formally." But then the poor dolt went on to make a marriage that landed him in a sexual morass.

Immanuel Kant stated his warning about sex by writing, "Philosophers don't marry."

To go back to an even earlier day, *The Song of Solomon* is the sexiest accolade ever written on that subject. But in his dotage Solomon collected seven hundred wives and three hundred concubines and even Our Lord got fed up with him. "Wherefore the Lord said, 'I will surely rend thy kingdom from thee!'"

Consider an incident that might have taken place between Our Lord and Satan. "Look here," the latter might have complained, "you've gone ahead and created a whole universe and left me out of everything."

"Very well, Satan, what do you want?"

"Just let me handle *sex*."

The Lord agreed; Satan promptly brought about The Fall and then inaugurated disasters of every sort: in a notable instance he only required one sexy blonde to instigate the Trojan War.

That our popular art forms have become so obsessed with sex has turned the U.S.A. into a nation of hobble-de-hoys; as if grown people don't have more vital concerns, such as taxes, inflation, dirty politics, earning a living, getting an education, or keeping out of jail.

It's true that the French have a certain obsession with sex, but it's a particularly adult obsession. France is the thriftiest of all nations; to a Frenchman sex provides the most economical way to have fun. The French are a logical race.

At this time, when pornography has become international legal tender, other countries are turning it out for profit. One worthy example was a Scandinavian movie titled *Without A Stitch,* in which the heroine happens to be a film actress. And when required to perform a sex act on camera, she hesitates in deference to her family. "Don't worry, my dear," the director tells her, "this movie will never be shown in Scandinavia; it's made strictly for the American trade."

Sex attraction, being entirely a matter of chance, has to be accepted where one finds it. Frequently its victims have nothing else in common and the whole affair dwindles into a matter of chemistry. There's nothing colder than chemistry.

The farceur Goldoni, living in Venice during one of the world's most sensuous periods, gives sex a low rating, but wrote in pure rapture about the lifetime he shared with his wife, Nicolette. "She has been my comfort in every moment. She knows just when I want her to leave me alone."

The few successful marriages I've known were between intellectuals who could regard a biological urge with fantasy: married pairs like Aldous and Maria Huxley, Edwin and Grace Hubble, Robert and Madeline Sherwood. Aside from intellectuals, I've known extremely successful marriages between joke-lovers, such as the two adorable Park Avenue clowns, Minnie and Herbie Weston.

During the Twenties we flappers patronized a beauty parlor where a lady barber used to shave certain hirsute areas into the shape of either a heart or a derby hat (the emblem of Al Smith, a political idol of the day). Knowing Minnie Weston's love for jokes, I thought she'd have selected the design of Al's brown derby. She was shocked. "Why, I couldn't be so unromantic! I chose the heart-shape in honor of my Herbie!" Theirs was that most unique of all relationships, a sexy and happy marriage. Most middle-class marriages in America are doomed, through lack of either the fantasy or sense of humor that can cope with their ever-recurrent challenges; the anxiety, discomfort, apprehension, and general messiness of sex.

After Bernard Shaw had learned the bitter truth about his liaison with Stella Campbell, he penned a resumé on the subject, stating in effect: " 'I would like to detach ecstasy from indecency. Shakespeare wrote in a sonnet about 'the expense of spirit in a waste of shame.' Lord Chesterfield made that oft-quoted declaration that 'the position is ridiculous, the pleasure momentary, and the expense damnable.'

"Ideally, sex should have no reaction of disgust; no love-turned-to-hate. But there is a pleasure in thought—creative thought—that is entirely detached from ridiculous and disgusting acts and postures. My suggestion is that the passion of the body will ultimately become a passion of the mind!"

G.B.S. optimistically went on to declare that such an advent is possible to foresee. Man knew about flight long before he could fly, why can't the power that produced him fashion a better creature than Man, just as it did eons ago when the monkey proved not up to the mark.

He proceeded to quote Browning:

> *Progress is the law of Life*
> *Man is not*
> *Man as yet.*

In *Back to Methuselah,* which Shaw considered his masterwork, he caused a learned Ancient to tell a young man, "One moment of the ecstasy of life as I live it would strike you dead. . . . The day will come when there are no people but only thought. And that will be life eternal."

The history of mankind, as we know it, has occupied no more than a split second in the Cosmic Scheme. So, give or take a few more eons, why can't human beings attain a state of weightless ecstasy?

A bumbling attempt was made to illustrate that situation in a disastrous musical, *Via Galactica,* in which a bodyless head existed for thought alone. The bumbling consisted in the dreariness of the old man's thoughts and the unfairness of giving him a young rival who was too well equipped from the waist on down.

My own experience in sex turned a strong-willed character I had adored into a sick man. If only we'd remained sympathetic co-workers without the complication of marriage, no stranger would ever have addressed Mr. E. as "Mr. Loos," which made him try to strangle me.

The deepest and most enduring thrills of my lifetime were shared with men to whom I did *not* give in. In my romance with Viscount D'Abernon, his death intervened before we ever got together on that phony excuse of chasing down the painting of Cranach.

Wilson Mizner and I were long kept apart by what I now realize to have been a heaven-sent impulse to play a practical joke. I admit that once in a while, thereafter, sex would rear its ugly head and Wilson would ask, "What are we going to do about each other, Mama Nita?" The answer, thanks to our lucky stars, was "Nothing." Wilson was rapidly ageing due to the wear and tear of dissipation; time would have been an invincible enemy, as it always has been, is now, and will forever be.

On a recent visit to Hollywood I discovered the extent to which sexuality has disappeared out there. Major studios which once harbored Mae West, Jean Harlow, and Cary Grant have become tourist traps where busloads of shoddy voyeurs gape at relics of the past, purchase hot dogs, soda pop, bubble gum, and souvenir snippets of film.

At the Beverly Hills Hotel, the Polo Room (named in honor of Darryl Zanuck's once favorite sport) still harbors a few stars, both male and female, wearing the same surplus hair and slacks. They stride in like favorites of the Caesars in Alma-Tadema's noted painting but, now that movie production is at its nadir, their attitude seems to be one of shameful boasting: "Look at me! *I've got a job!*"

The Polo Room, however, is mostly a showcase for the hopeless, because the majority of super-stars are hiding out in the Hollywood hills, racing along the freeways on their Hondas, or taking ever more hair-raising trips on LSD.

Studying film production of the present day, I come upon a mystery to which a clue has been supplied by the theories on foreign policy of Henry Kissinger. The mystery is that many of those scabrous, not to say diabolic, movies do not pay back even the small sums required to outfit actors in the nude at work in some rent-free shanty. Andy Warhol himself claims that the profits on his dirtiest film couldn't pay for a tiny diamond in the clasp of his idolized Paulette Goddard's necklace.

So now a chilling thought strikes me: are hard-core porno films secretly financed by our ideological enemies? Are they an element of psychological warfare in which innocent protagonists may not even realize that their youthful naughtiness is being used to destroy our moral fiber?

But whether this cynical thought is true or not, the forces of evil are now being challenged by a burgeoning cult among young people for old Hollywood films. Teenagers poisoned by the septic dandruff of *Hair,* or those who have copied the fashions of present-day screen idols until they look like something left over from Halloween, will sit for half the night, glued to TV screens, watching the pretty stars of those old movies on *The Late Late Show.*

Young fry haunt the film theaters that specialize in ancient films. They crowd the projection rooms of the Museum of Modern Art. These kids spend their allowances on expensive picture albums that illustrate Hollywood's past. They are familiar with silent movie stars we oldsters have long since forgotten; they speak with warm nostalgia about Louise Glaum, Fay Tincher, and Slim Summerville. I am amazed when someone little more than a child informs me about an old cornball I wrote myself and have forgotten.

Recently at a gathering of the Association of Television Arts and Sciences a young writer asked me, "Miss Loos, could I interview you on that silent film you wrote for Douglas Fairbanks called *The Mystery of the Leaping Fish?*" I could only apologize that I'd forgotten it completely. "That may be a Freudian blackout," she chuckled. "It was a terrible flop." "Then why did you ever dig it up?" I asked. "Because it's one of the few old films that hasn't yet been analyzed in the art magazines."

Later on in Rochester, N.Y., I visited Eastman House, an institution dedicated to the history and art of the camera. It has a library of early movies, which attracts students from all over the country. The auditorium, a fine example of Regency architecture, is superbly equipped. That afternoon I was ushered in to see Garbo's first American starring vehicle, *The Temptress,* filmed just before I arrived in Hollywood to do my eighteen-year stint on the MGM lot.

Students were watching *The Temptress* with reverence; several were making notes. Had I been doing likewise, I'm afraid they'd have recorded "Roll eyes heavenward to illustrate emotion," "Hand-on-the-hip indicates defiance!" In fact, I didn't find anything about that old movie worth consideration; either its super-heated plot or its technique. For my taste, *The Temptress,* Garbo, Antonio Moreno, *et al.,* belong in the trash can.

What is it that has sparked this obsession for vintage movies in a generation born long after they were released? I can only think that today's youth must subconsciously yearn for the very sentiments on which they've turned their backs. They must find a surcease for today's oafishness in the shimmering glamour of Jean Harlow, the angelic beauty of Lillian Gish, and the unchallenged masculine image of Clark Gable.

It's true that back in 1936, when Thalberg was preparing his script for *Camille,* he had progressed far beyond the crude technique of *The Temptress* and, by substituting passion with the gentle endearments of two young sweethearts, Irving attained the most profound catharsis of a love affair.

The same idyllic emotions used to be expressed in other popular art forms; today I recall a song of my youth that was imported from

France. Its title was "C'est Si Bon" meaning, of course, that love is "so good." But the ballad makers of today turn out lyrics that ask "Is That All There Is?" That hard-bitten song, recorded by Peggy Lee, was bought by millions of young people, who apparently agreed with Peggy.

It's understandable that such defeatism has resulted in impotence; that composers now write such lyrics as "We almost made it, didn't we [girl]?" *Almost!* What kind of situation is *that* to celebrate in song?

Another ballad tells of a swain who is on his way to Phoenix in order to *get away* from his sweetheart. Yet another makes no mention of love, pro or con, but glorifies an ability to disregard raindrops that keep falling on one's head.

All these ditties make me long to hear Eddie Cantor once again, jumping up and down in delight, clapping his little white-gloved hands and exclaiming "If You Knew Susie (Like I Know Susie)."

I also regret the cheek-to-cheek dancing which has been replaced by wide spaces between partners. Each one dances *alone*. I remember the camaraderie we used to achieve on bathtub gin; whereas today's kids, stoned on pot, retire inside their own personalities. They may be happy, but they seldom laugh.

*   *   *

But I have no intention of dramatizing my feelings about Hollywood. In the past, as now, it was a stamping ground for tastelessness, violence, and hyperbole, but once upon a time it turned out a product which sweetened the flavor of life all over the world.

And it would now appear that the spirit of those old films is rising from the dust to assure a new generation that the permissiveness of the Seventies is a killjoy; that those gyrations of naked bodies, which once would have made the Board of Censors reach for its scissors lead to nothing.

And if we have to tell Hollywood good-by, it may be with one of those tender, old-fashioned, seven-second kisses exchanged between two people of the *opposite* sex, with all their clothes on.

On Growing Old
Disgracefully

———◆———

*W*HILE I was writing my recent book, *Kiss Hollywood Good-by*, it began to dawn on me that the things I learned during thirty years of working on those old movie scripts prepared me better than any formal education for the wide world I was to enter on leaving Hollywood.

At MGM during the Thirties, we harbored the most distinguished tragedienne since Eleanora Duse. Yet I came to learn that America's major interest in Greta Garbo was that she wore size eleven shoes and wanted to be alone. I also found out that Clark Gable's earthshaking charisma seemed to be of less import than the unusual size of his ears.

On leaving the studios, I came to be a friend of the fabulous interior decorator Elsie de Wolfe. It was she who established interior decorating as a recognized profession and brought about an international revolution in taste. Yet the fact that really captivated Elsie's public was that she could stand on her head. Elsie's influence may still linger on. Today, isn't the whole world standing on its head?

You might feel that, at my age, I should look on life with more gravity. After all, I've been privileged to listen, firsthand, to some of the most profound thinkers of my day: Aldous and Julian Huxley, H. G. Wells, Bertrand Russell, Arnold Bennett and H. L. Mencken, who were all beset by gloom over the condition the world had gotten into. Then why can't I view it with anything but amusement?

In my own career, I've found, just like Elsie, that nothing I've accomplished nor the important people I've met have impressed anyone as much as the fact that I *like* to get up early in the morning. It has nothing to do with viewing the sunrise, breathing the fresh morning air or listening to the birds chirp as they greet the dawn.

For some reason, which must relate either to the genes or enzymes, the human race seems to be divided into night-people and day-people. Although I was born and raised in show business, I always got to bed as early as possible and woke up automatically at 4 A.M. without an alarm clock. I just happen to be a day-person.

And now, as my days accumulate, they have disclosed another unusual fact. I'm getting on in age.

Recently an earnest TV moderator asked me for a hint on how to grow old gracefully. Now what a typical TV cliché that is; when the one thing on which I am an authority is how to grow old disgracefully. I've just gone through the embarrassment of having the paperback edition of my book barred from the shelves of supermarkets in Texas . . . yet! Not on account of its text, but because the cover depicts an enticing nude who provided Texas housewives with unfair competition. So Texas husbands are deprived of seeing that last pretty blonde, driven out of the movies by the mystique of Barbra Streisand, hitchhiking away from Hollywood to escape the grim miasma of Jane Fonda and Shirley MacLaine.

Last month, on my birthday, some columnist printed that I'm 83, but I'm sure that's a lie. I'm much older. I refuse to inform myself how much, having decided that if I knew I'd begin to feel as ancient as I really am. So I wake up every morning with a childlike fascination over all things great and small.

In the first place, I can never take for granted the euphoria produced by a cup a coffee. I'm grateful every day that it isn't banned as a drug; that I don't have to buy it from a pusher; that its cost is minimal and there's no need to increase the intake. I can count on its stimulation three hundred and sixty five mornings every year. And, thanks to the magic in a cup of coffee, I'm able to plunge into a whole day's cheerful thinking.

The first thing I contemplate is my Bible. Another good habit for which I can take no credit. For nearly forty-five years, my lifestyle has been dictated by an infallible mentor, critic, and spiritual guide.

I first met Gladys Tipton Turner DeKalb in Hollywood when we were both quite young and she came to work for me as an upstairs maid. Gladys started by inspecting my bedroom, after which she reported that she couldn't find any Bible. The reason was because it was lost somewhere among the reference books. Gladys dug it out, dusted if off and then announced that she wouldn't work in any house where the lady didn't read a chapter of the Bible every morning. Well, like every other member of the film colony, I always began my day with the gossip column of Louella Parsons, but then as now, maid service was scarce. So I accepted Gladys' ultimatum as a chore. But I very soon realized there was as much lively action in the Gospel as in Louella's column. And thanks to Gladys, my first thought on waking up is still to find out what's going on in the Bible that morning.

My viewpoint on all reading matter is based on trying to be equally fair. It's quite acceptable to take delight in such scamps as Shakespeare's Richard III, Goethe's Mephistopheles, Thackeray's Becky Sharp and Dickens' Fagin. Then why shouldn't we be extra grateful for a real live Richard Nixon, not only for his astounding moral turpitude, but for a unique brand of comedy relief? Perhaps, in due time, Nixon's declaration: "I am not a crook!" will take on an epic quality, like the statement of Louis XVI who, on the date which marked the Fall of the Bastille, wrote in his diary: "Nothing happened today."

All-consuming though Watergate has been, don't let us be misled that it stands alone. I came into the world in time for my childish ears to hear about the Teapot Dome Scandal, when members of our State Department accepted bribes for government oil reserves. Then came the financial blot on France of the Stavisky case, which has only recently been made into a lurid movie. I now wait with bated breath for the film version of England's Profumo scandal, starring, let's hope, Raquel Welch.

I can appreciate all those events for having banished tedium in dismal homes all over the world and provided animated talk in what might otherwise have been some pretty dull cocktail parties.

It's true that, in our time, we can't ignore a daily roster of major crimes, but in all justice, why not follow through on those atrocities; take into account that their victims are comparatively few—while we who daily escape murder, muggers, rapists, or bombs are legion? Moreover, what human experience can match the exhilaration of a reprieve? What could be more joyful to some noteworthy blackguard who deserves a jail sentence than suddenly to be pardoned? Well, as life goes on today, the most humble citizen can enjoy the ecstasy of a reprieve just by waking up to realize he's not in jail.

The most deadening of all experience is boredom. But today one breathtaking event after another gallops by so quickly that nobody ever has to be bored. Just to read a newspaper or hear a voice of doom on TV or radio is an experience that rivals Dante at his best.

Who would want to exchange the shock value of a thief in the Vice-Presidency for a scarehead that merely stated: "Alice Roosevelt barred from smoking cigarette in public?"

One safeguard against boredom in my own case is that age has brought on semi-deafness. Attending the plays of Albee or Pinter, my ears escape the gloom of their one-dimensional content. So at the theatre, I relax, sit back and enjoy an opportunity for transcendental meditation on other matters, which may be equally one-dimensional but which also make sense: the comic strips of Al Capp and the Peanuts contingent, or that splendid single track book on Eastern philosophy, *Zen and the Art of Archery.*

There was a time when I found diversion in fashion shows. Today I can be grateful for faulty sight which views these modern garments as a mere blur. The dresses of yesteryear took cognizance of the female frame. But even a clever dress designer like Halston doesn't fool me—I know why he invented his caftan syndrome. It's because a caftan can be run up cheaply in two seams on a sewing machine, whereas the Garment Workers' Union has outpriced handtailoring until only the un-taxed rich can pay for it. But I don't mind that Halston is forced to charge more money for a caftan than Balenciaga did for hand labor, because I have two closets full of vintage dresses made of organic materials that will last as long as I do.

I can even see a ray of light in the present high cost of living. For today, when the price of so many commodities has risen sky high, sex is cheaper than at any other point in time. During the timorous Twenties, a man had to provide his girl with a hide-away in the form of an expensive love-nest, he set up charge accounts for her in the best stores and decked her out in genuine diamonds that used to be a girl's best friend.

Today any man can get the same service for the cost of a martini in any neighborhood bar. (Sometimes a girl will even pay for the martini.) And, servants being a thing of the past, any male who wants to gamble on marriage can get a wife, mother-substitute, and servant girl all thrown in for free.

We can now enjoy other benefits that have never before existed. A minor new joy is to turn on TV and with a flick of the wrist, cause "The Beverly Hillbillies" to vanish and presto-change, we have "The Ascent of Man."

One very great advantage of these days is the fact that nobody has to be faulted for running out on obligations. The cult of the praiseworthy human being has been destroyed by Freudians who supplied people with excuses to dodge responsibility by simply slumping onto a couch and being told they're sick.

So, the wide expanse of morality is confined to the narrow dimensions of a couch. Hamlets don't deride their mothers in terms of sublime poetry; they merely hate momma, except when they harbor a letch for her; and either fact provides them with complete immunity to follow any sort of snide behavior they choose.

The man of high morals, the Biblical man, the Shakespearean man, the Renaissance man has almost disappeared. The last of the Biblical type may well have been Schweitzer; the last Shakespearean, Churchill; the last Renaissance man, Kissinger. And none of them seems to have developed any spiritual progeny, although I suppose that Ralph Nader is as spiritual as one can be in an ambiance of stale motor fumes and wholesale warehouses. The area in which Ralph fails is that he doesn't exactly elevate the human soul.

In these troubled times, I take great comfort in the simple basic human equation, which is so ingrained in our very genes that it will always motivate behavior. So no matter how hopeless things appear to be the human equation will provide a clue for our survival.

Let us take the case of that terribly dangerous political affiliation, when China followed Russia into Communism. By sticking together, the two nations could easily have swallowed the entire world. But it is inherent in the human equation that Utopian allies quickly come to detest each other and the split between those two powers has made our world much safer for democracy.

I have also found that in these difficult times the best way to face up to any problem is to follow the advice of my own private guide, Gladys, who states that the Bible describes just what happens to people who behave badly and spells out, sometimes in red ink, the advantages of good behavior. So that all anybody really needs to learn are two short words: Behave yourself. And life can be as sweet as pie, if you just don't allow it to upset your stomach!

Any questions?

PART
THREE

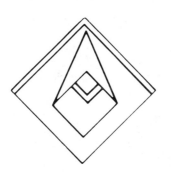

Creator of Gigi—
Gabrielle Colette

———◆———

*I*T is difficult to explain to Americans the position held by Colette in France, not only as a novelist but as a great public figure. As a novelist she might be compared to our own Willa Cather, except that Cather has never been much read or appreciated by the general public, whereas Colette is read by nearly everybody. The characters she created belong not only to French literature, they are a part of French life itself. Her *Chéri, Claudine,* and *Gigi* are the friends of every shop girl, housewife, and day laborer in France. And when it came to Colette herself, she was known, loved, and pampered as few intellectuals have ever been in any country. In her late seventies the activities of Colette supplied copy to newspapers almost every day, just as those of movie stars and sports figures do in the U.S. A documentary film was made, outlining the various phases of Colette's life and picturing the different homes where she lived. A book of photographs showing Colette from childhood to old age, with eulogies by her greatest contemporaries, became a best seller.

The basis of Colette's unique power as a novelist was that she wrote straight from the emotions; nothing mental ever got in her way, and so true was her story that never for a moment did it sink into the category of the sentimental. It was pure life itself, unencumbered by idea or purpose. In matters of sex she followed the human heart as few writers ever have done. Most novelists, when dealing with the subject, allow a moral, or at least an editorial viewpoint to creep in. But not Colette. Her description of the actual physical manifestations of a love affair makes Lady Chatterley seem one-dimensional.

An English critic once wrote of her: "About her zest for physical love she makes no bones. She accepts the fact with a readiness that amounts to complicity. Other novelists may disapprove the things they display . . . but Colette welcomes them. *Chéri* and *Gigi* would not be the marvels they are, if their author had been too squeamish to put herself into the high-heeled shoes of her Lea (in *Chéri*) or of Little Gigi's Aunt Alicia."

Colette wrote any number of great stories, but if she had never had a single story to tell, she still would have been a great poet. She employed the widest vocabulary; loved to use words with which even the French were unfamiliar, but used them so poetically that their very sounds provided their meaning.

"Nothing escapes her eye," wrote the English critic, "neither the faintest menace of dilapidation on an eyelid, nor a cat rifling the strawberry bed, nor the amenity radiating from the face of a husband who has just been unfaithful."

Every possible honor that could be won in France through literary achievement was given to Colette. The only reason she was not elected to the Académie Française was because it was then closed to women. As it was, she attained the highest position a French writer could earn through being president of the Académie Goncourt. And these honors were won by a woman who had little "education," who spent years of her youth as a touring vaudeville performer and, later on, as an actress in the legitimate theatre of Paris.

Successful and happy in her career, Colette might never have thought of changing it, but she happened to be married to a gentleman who had conjured up a rather ingenious way to earn a living. His name was Monsieur Willy and his game was to hire hack writers to pen novels of the type we call "soap operas," on which he put his own name. French literature can be endlessly grateful to M. Willy for putting his wife to work in her spare time as one of these ghost writers. It is most likely he had no appreciation at all for the exquisite prose of Mme. Willy or knew that those first books on which he put his name were masterpieces. The public appreciated them at once, however, and from the very beginning Colette's books enjoyed great success, not only with readers but with the critics as well.

When Colette finally divorced this husband and was allowed to sign her writings, she used the name "Colette Willy." But so close did she come to the lives of her readers that she soon became merely "Colette," the friend of her reader, who knew the reader just as well, or even better, than the reader knew himself. She was always surprising one into a new self-knowledge. How could one call so close a friend by any formal name?

Colette was crippled by arthritis. On the infrequent times when she left her bed it had to be in a wheelchair. She lived in an apartment overlooking the gardens of the Palais Royal and enjoyed one of the most stunning views in Paris. Always in pain, she was always gay, wryly philosophical, and always working on some new project—articles, books, film scripts, or plays.

Having myself succumbed to the cult of Colette in my youth, I was thrilled, although at the same time hesitant, when her New York agent came to me with the suggestion that I make a play from her immortal story *Gigi* but, greatly tempted, I undertook the job and worked on the play for two years. Then, one summer, I took it to Colette in Paris. She carefully went over the script, and set me right on all points where I had been "too American."

When I left Paris, Colette gave me a copy of the edition deluxe of *Gigi*. I was very proud of her inscription which read in translation:

"For Anita Loos with the hope that this immoral story will have an equivocal influence on her—and above all, with the joy of having met the most subtle and friendly of collaborators."

The word "immoral" was one of Colette's jokes. For Gigi is Cinderella, even though her story is told in terms of sex. And in it virtue triumphs through the pure heart of a young girl who has every temptation to become a glamorous figure in the demimonde of Paris.

During other summer visits I was privileged to see Paris under many aspects. First and most important was that tiny corner of Paris that belonged only to Colette, a corner in which she lay on a bed of pain that one could find no trace of in her beautiful face with its sardonic but gentle smile.

"Am I not lucky," she usually asked, "to have this exquisite view of the gardens of the Palais Royal . . . to watch and to hear the children and the birds . . . to see the day appear each morning?"

It was characteristic of Colette not to mention her agonized sleeplessness, except in terms of her pleasure at watching the dawn appear. When she began to take an interest in flying saucers, it amused her to search the sky for these fabulous visitors, which could only come from another planet and might prove to be almost as outlandish as we were.

The corner of Paris that was a second home to Colette was the restaurant in her apartment building, the historic old Grand Vefour. She would visit the Vefour on gala occasions, in the new wheelchair of which she was inordinately proud. It was made of glittering chromium and shiny black enamel and came from America. Like all things American, it boasted innumerable gadgets and mechanical marvels.

The appearance of Colette at the Vefour was always an event. The way to her table was cleared by the maître d'hôtel who was a staunch friend of many years, and Colette was ushered with ceremony and affection to her own special table, which was marked by a brass plate on the wall above it.

Luncheon was ordered in a tense collaboration with the maître d'hôtel. Food was of great interest to Colette, who was always a gourmet in the grand manner. My adherence to the regimen of Dr. Hauser appalled her to such an extent that I would not care to mention that Hauser had a substantial foothold in France and a growing number of French followers.

As an arthritic Colette was supposed to be *en régime* herself, but she enjoyed the contemplation of elaborate and complicated dishes; the final choice of a too simple entrée was made with deep disgust. The wine was equally a matter of fine consideration. The fact that I drank only water caused her a distaste that she made no effort to conceal, and an amazement that could scarcely be greater if she ever saw a flying saucer.

But who could think of food when lunching with Colette? One would overlook the great dishes to sit entranced, watching her sensitive face, listening to ideas that only Colette could evoke and to reminiscences of a life that had been more intensely lived than any other; lived in every sense, spiritually, emotionally, physically. Every visit I ever had with her was deeply engraved on my memory.

Audrey Hepburn

*A*BOUT Audrey Hepburn there always has been an aura of romance. From the day of her birth everything that has happened to her has been unusual, fabulous, exciting. She has experienced life in more of its aspects than many of us are able to trump up in our daydreams or even to suffer in our nightmares.

There was the time, for instance, during the last horrible months of the Nazi occupation of the Lowlands, when Audrey and her mother lived with her maternal grandfather, the Baron van Heemstra, in his house at Velp.

It was a time of hunger and desperation, but what made their situation even more unbearable was the requisitioning of the best rooms in the house by arrogantly well-fed and warmly clothed Nazi officials.

Then, under the very noses of the Nazi command, the dreariness of life was punctuated by a moment of melodrama. A neighbor telephoned to ask that 14-year-old Audrey be sent to fetch a rabbit that had been promised to her as a gift. A rabbit then was a rare possession. If a time came when, as a pet, it could no longer be fed, it could be eaten.

But when Audrey arrived at the neighbor's house, she learned that it was not merely to fetch the rabbit. That had been a device to get her out from under the watchful eyes of the enemy. The neighbors had sent for her because word had reached them that, during the night, an English paratrooper had dropped into the nearby woods.

The Gestapo knew of his landing and the area was rapidly being surrounded, so that it was only a question of time before he would be captured. Moreover, the woods had been stripped of leaves and shrubbery behind which he might hide. The neighbors outlined to Audrey their audacious scheme—she spoke English and, if she could penetrate the Gestapo lines and reach the young man before he was picked up, she might at least greet him in his own tongue and, best of all, get some news of what was going on in England, from which they had heard no news in weeks.

Audrey and one of the neighbor's children started for the woods on bicycles, their spirits bolstered and their energies replenished by excitement. They hid their bikes and cautiously entered the woods on foot. Luck was with them, for after a short time they found the young paratrooper.

After his initial surprise, the young man climbed down from his tree, happy to meet anyone who spoke his language. Quickly, for time was at a premium, Audrey explained to the youth that his landing had been reported to the Gestapo, that the woods were being surrounded and that there was no way to prevent his arrest. But with luck, Audrey told him, she could at least smuggle him into a friendly house where he could find comfort before being made a prisoner.

Audrey kept her promise. She led the young paratrooper to the nearest Dutch home where he had a short respite, some food, a bath and the warm ministrations of the household. When there were no possible means of hiding him any longer, he gave himself up, refreshed and prepared for his forthcoming ordeal as a prisoner of war. Before they parted, the young man gave Audrey his only possession of value, a silver locket with the Lord's Prayer engraved on it.

And, after the war was over, Audrey heard from the paratrooper and at Christmas, 1947, went across to England to visit his family and to receive his mother's thanks.

To realize the long process that went into the forming of her character it is important to understand thoroughly Audrey's background. Her mother, the Baroness van Heemstra, was of Dutch lineage. Audrey's forebears lived in the far north of Holland, in a

province the very name of which has the ring of romance—
Friesland. And the Frieslanders took great pride in being people of
a special refinement that was patterned on the culture of England.
The van Heemstra clan always had strong ties with England, and
Audrey (with the added fact of her English-Irish father) looked
toward that country as "home" even as a child.

When Audrey's mother was a young girl, she too had visions of
becoming an actress. But the accomplishments which Audrey
attained could exist only as daydreams for the youthful Ella van
Heemstra—ambitions that were invariably stamped out by her
father, the Baron van Heemstra.

So Ella followed the normal course of events and married a
proper Dutchman. The boredom of such a marriage was partially
relieved when the young couple was transferred to the exotic Dutch
colony of Indonesia. Two half-brothers to the as-yet-undreamed-of
Audrey were born there, where they continued to live and work.
They later adored their glamorous half-sister and corresponded
frequently.

A day finally came when Ella van Heemstra's first marriage went
on the rocks. The young divorcee, still avid for romance, felt she
had found it when she married the young man destined to be
Audrey's father. He was J. A. Hepburn-Ruston, a dashing English-
Irish adventurer whose family was just as good as his behavior
turned out to be bad. He considered Brussels to be home and it was
there that Audrey was born on May 4, 1929.

With her mother's large family centered in Holland and her
father's native land calling them frequently to England and his
business taking them sometimes to Paris, Audrey was never very
long in one place. These wanderings made a linguist of her. At the
age of 10 she spoke fluent Dutch, French, and English. Later, in the
dire time of German occupation, she also was to become bitterly
familiar with the language of the conquerors.

Hepburn-Ruston's venturesome spirit finally took him completely away from his family and he disappeared into the far
colonies of England. Nobody knew what became of him, or
whether he ever heard what happened to his magical child, or even
if he remained alive. He left no recollections to which either Audrey
or her mother wished to cling. Audrey's mother took back the name
of van Heemstra and that was that.

Audrey was 10 when World War II broke out. Britain's declaration of war on Germany found the family in England, but the Baroness felt that the safest place for her children would be the obscure town of Arnheim in Holland, where the van Heemstras had one of several ancestral homes. She could scarcely have made a worse move, for on May 10, 1940, six days after Audrey's eleventh birthday, they were to experience the chilling horror of the German invasion.

As time went by the Dutch resistance movement began to function and tragedy hit sharply at the van Heemstras. Audrey's uncle was one of the first patriots to be shot by the Nazi occupation force. Her handsome young cousin, attached to the royal court, also was executed. Audrey herself, even though a child, lived under constant suspicion because she spoke fluent English and French.

It is extraordinary, however, that some phases of life went on much as they did in peacetime. For instance, the Nazi occupation, in order to gain face, allowed the Sadler's Wells Ballet from London to give a series of performances in Holland. One day in 1940 Audrey was taken to Amsterdam to see the ballet. The glittering spectacle made a terrific impression on the child who was forced to live a daily life of grim despair and privation. Then and there, Audrey determined that she must be a ballet dancer.

She was 11 years old at the time and her mother knew it was almost too late to think of starting ballet lessons. But the Baroness decided that the child would have her heart's desire at any cost; she arranged for Audrey to go once a week to the conservatory of music in Amsterdam.

Audrey did what she could to help the resistance movement. She and a young pianist organized secret recitals in private homes to collect money for the cause. But, as the years dragged on, food became increasingly scarce and Audrey found herself weak from malnutrition.

Finally, on the 17th day of September, 1944, Audrey and her family went through the terrifying experience of having their own home bombed, along with every other building in Arnheim. Not a souvenir, heirloom, or photograph was left, which is the reason why there are no pictures of Audrey as a child.

After the destruction of Arnheim, the family moved to the nearby town of Velp where the van Heemstras owned another property, occupied at the time by the old Baron and a widowed daughter-in-law.

Audrey spent most of her days, as did all the others, looking for food. Nobody had enough clothing to be warm. There was no heat, no hot water, no soap, no sufficient underclothing.

In May 1945, Audrey reached 16 and received a birthday gift that could never in her life be topped. It was the unconditional surrender of the Germans to the Allies. The end of the war found the van Heemstras financially ruined. But to the Baroness this was scarcely a challenge. One day she fared forth to Amsterdam and got herself a job as housekeeper-cook for a prosperous family in the capital, a job which allowed her to send Audrey back to the conservatory for ballet lessons. They spent three years in Amsterdam, and the Baroness saved enough to take Audrey to England for an advanced course in ballet.

Red tape, the matter of a visa and strict regulations against taking money out of Holland kept the Baroness from accompanying Audrey when the time came to leave. But want had made Audrey a resourceful and competent young woman, and there were family connections and friends in England who would look after her. So, in the spring of '48, she went on alone to London. Finally, after three months, her mother secured a visa and was able to join Audrey. The Baroness found a job in a florist shop at wages which were small but at least regular.

Audrey had gained one great advantage from her war years. It was an appreciation of being *able* to work and, moreover, to work in the theatre which she loved so ardently. When not taking lessons, she spent every free moment scurrying around various offices for jobs—in movies, in revues, in night clubs and in the choruses of musicals. Even when she ultimately got a permanent place in the chorus of the London company of *High Button Shoes,* Audrey did extra work in pictures during the daytime and, after she finished her stint at the theatre, went on as mistress of ceremonies in a night club.

But in the more than two years that she was in full view of the London public not one British talent scout noticed her, not one producer asked her for an interview or made a test!

Audrey always had an arresting type of beauty. She was something special even when she was a rangy little girl with spindly legs, toothpick arms, and eyes too big for her face. Audrey's very slenderness made her unique. Her hat band measured 22 inches around, while her belt was only 20, a waist that was two inches smaller than her head. During the Gay Nineties, the great Polaire was made famous by that single fact, and Polaire was not beautiful, while Audrey was ravishing.

Director Billy Wilder's comment on Audrey's neat, boyish silhouette (while directing her picture, *Sabrina*, for Paramount) indicated an upheaval in sex values that could only be a revolution. "This girl," Wilder said, "single-handed, may make bosoms a thing of the past!"

How, then, could London have overlooked her?

The amazing fact is that it took an Italian director, Mario Zampi, who was working in England, to give Audrey her first chance in a film called *Laughter in Paradise*. And it took an American, the head of the Paramount office in London, Richard Mealand, to sign Audrey to her first real contract.

As an obscure chorus girl and movie extra she didn't get a very good contract. Although her salary might eventually be much more than she was earning in the chorus of a night club, she would be paid nothing until such time as Paramount saw fit to put her in a picture.

Then one day, Audrey was offered a job as an extra in an English movie that was to be shot in Monte Carlo. She hesitated to accept this offer because she was afraid she might miss some better job in London. But to go to France meant food—and both Audrey and her mother were suffering from malnutrition. There never had been enough to eat during the long Nazi occupation of Holland and they had moved to England during the worst days of food rationing.

Audrey's mother finally persuaded her to accept the movie job and the film company agreed to take the Baroness along.

One morning the company was shooting a scene in the lobby of the Palace Hotel in Monte Carlo. Audrey was standing obscurely among a group of extras when an old lady in an invalid's chair was wheeled through the corridor on her way to the dining room. Audrey's mother, who was watching the shooting of the scene, was fascinated by the old lady's appearance and suddenly noticed that this woman seemed equally intrigued by Audrey.

The Baroness van Heemstra saw the old woman beckon to an assistant director who pointed in her direction. When the gray-haired occupant of the invalid's chair began wheeling herself toward the Baroness, she suddenly recognized her as Colette, whose novels and stories had made her famous not only in France but all over the world. Colette introduced herself and said she would like to meet the Baroness' young daughter.

The name Colette meant nothing to Audrey. Even when Colette suggested that there might be a part in a Broadway play for Audrey, the girl was not impressed. Broadway was a long way off, and if she ever went to America she'd probably go to Hollywood to fulfill her contract with Paramount Pictures.

At the time of this casual conversation in a Monte Carlo hotel I had just finished dramatizing *Gigi,* one of Colette's finest short novels. And Gilbert Miller, who was to produce the play, was combing the English-speaking stage for a girl to play the title role.

While Mr. Miller was searching in London, George Cukor, the famous director, was hunting in Hollywood, and I was in New York looking over many would-be Gigis. None of us had been very successful and we were about to compromise on a none-too-pristine Hollywood starlet, when Colette caught her first excited glimpse of Audrey Hepburn.

Finding just the right actress for the role of Gigi was a difficult job because the part ran the entire gamut of female emotions, but the girl who played it must not look more than 15 years old. Colette was reasonably certain that she had stumbled upon the star for her story, although the girl never had spoken a word on the stage.

In New York I received a cable from Colette begging us to do nothing about signing a Gigi until we had seen her "discovery," and I then cabled Mr. Miller in London to look up a movie extra named Audrey Hepburn as soon as the English film company returned home from Monte Carlo.

A week later, I sailed for London in the company of Paulette Goddard. Mr. Miller's car was waiting for us at Victoria Station. It was driven by Glynn, the major-domo and general factotum of the Miller household. The first thing he did was hand me an enormous scrapbook with the statement, "Miss Loos, here's the star of *Gigi.*"

Glynn had driven for the Duke of Windsor when he was the Prince of Wales. Then he had gone on to Lady Mendl, who finally handed him over to Mr. Miller, who never made a move on scripts or casting without his advice.

"So Mr. Miller has already signed someone!" I exclaimed.

"Not yet," said Glynn. "He's holding out against me."

On the way to our hotel Paulette and I turned the pages of the scrapbook. We were fascinated by the pictures of a girl who had the face, the figure, the eyes and the legs—everything that is important in a female.

When Paulette closed the book she said, "There must be something radically the matter with this girl because if there weren't she would have been famous at the age of 10." I had to agree.

Next morning Audrey arrived at the Savoy Hotel to be looked over by Paulette and me. Again we had the feeling that there must be something basically wrong with this fascinating girl of 21 to keep her from being world-famous.

As soon as Audrey had departed I phoned Mr. Miller and found that he shared our qualms about her. "We'll have to hear her read before we allow ourselves to become too enthusiastic," he said.

Another meeting was arranged and Audrey read the script—with rare intelligence. When Mr. Miller escorted her to the door, he sighed and said, "I'm afraid we should have listened to Glynn in the first place."

As the world now knows, Audrey became Gigi and a star the first night she ever spoke a line on a Broadway stage.

The day after *Gigi* closed in New York she flew to Rome where, during the hottest summer on record, she began work in *Roman Holiday*, which won her an Academy Award and about every other American and English award that can be given to an actress. *Roman Holiday* became one of those movie "classics," which would be shown over and over again for years. The day she finished that picture she flew back to New York to begin the long road tour of *Gigi*. When that tour was over she flew to Hollywood to begin work in *Sabrina*, her second Paramount picture, which was a delightful story of a modern Cinderella in a Long Island environment. The day that picture was finished, she arrived in New York to begin rehearsals for the title role in *Ondine*, which earned her the 1953 award for the year's best performance behind the footlights of Broadway.

The hard work of *Ondine* and the endless demands on her time gave Audrey scarcely a moment to herself. The privations of her childhood had left her much too fragile to take such an ordeal without danger of a breakdown. Finally, her doctor demanded that all engagements be cancelled except for her stage performances.

Poor Audrey! Her head hadn't been swelled by her success, but it harbored plenty of headaches. Having to refuse interviews made enemies for her. Some of them even went so far as to attack her in print as being pompous. If she went to a restaurant with some male companion, the gossip columns said, as usual, she was "that way" about him.

With Mel Ferrer, who was her co-star in *Ondine*, Audrey had much in common, foremost being a great love for the theatre. There were rumors they would be married, as they were, eventually. But two years before, Audrey was to have married James Hansen, a handsome young English industrialist. The invitations were out for an English country wedding and her wedding gown was hanging in the closet of her hotel suite in Rome where she was working on *Roman Holiday*. But at the last moment, she called the wedding off.

"When I couldn't find time even to attend to the furnishing of our London flat," said Audrey, "I suddenly knew I'd make a pretty bad wife. I would forever have to be studying parts, fitting costumes and giving interviews. And what a humiliating spot to put a husband in . . . making him stand by, holding my coat, while I signed autographs for the bobbie soxers."

I think Audrey dreamt of a marriage that would also be a partnership in the theatre, in which both partners understood the problems of belonging to the public.

But nobody could tell what was going to happen to Audrey in the future because, for a girl so young, her life had already taken so many unpredictable twists and turns.

Tallulah

I T was my privilege to meet Tallulah when she was about sixteen and had just arrived in New York from Alabama, possessed by the idea of being an actress. She was chaperoned by her beloved Aunt Marie who was in utter accord with Tallulah's ambitions but remained so discreetly in the background that today I can't remember ever seeing her.

Tallulah's advent in New York bore a curious aura of Destiny. She and Auntie Marie knew nothing at all about the life of the big city but, when they left the station bent on finding an economical place to live, Fate unaccountably led them to West 44th Street, where they were attracted by two smallish hotels. One was the Algonquin, which was even more a hot-bed of theatrical life than it is today. Tallulah and Auntie Marie stood on the sidewalk between the Algonquin and the ultra decorous Seymour, hesitating over a choice. On the surface there seemed no difference between the two places, but finally, for a reason that could only have been mystical, they entered the Algonquin. It was as if Alice had walked smack into Wonderland without having to go down the Rabbit Hole. For, on Tallulah's first day in New York, she was under the same roof with the aristocracy of the New York theatre; among them Ethel Barrymore, her brother Jack, their uncle John Drew, Elsie Janis and numberless others. And there were always a few important film people at the Algonquin, on leave from Hollywood. At the time Constance Talmadge and Conway Tearle had come on to film a movie script of mine *(The Virtuous Vamp)* and I was with them.

Tallulah had no definite scheme to back up her overweening ambition; no letters of introduction or the least bit of schooling for the career she had chosen. Her first move was merely to take up a post in the hotel lobby where she could sit and gaze, entranced, at the comings and goings of the show folks. But Tallulah's blonde beauty was so dazzling that in no time at all, the show folks began to gaze at her. And, never known for her reticence, Tallulah was quite easy to contact. One of the first to whom she confided her acting ambitions was our director, John Emerson, who forthwith gave her a role as an extra in our movie. So my friendship with Tallulah began at the very beginning of her fantastic career.

Tallulah was so exhilarated by life in the ramshackle old studio in the East Fifties where we worked that, at first, we put her down as a run-of-the-mill movie fan. And we all considered her far too pretty to be anything but stupid. It wasn't long before we were set right on that score and alerted to the fact that our little Southern belle was to become one of the great wits of an entire era.

In those days the Algonquin dining room served as a showcase for a self-glorifying group of exhibitionists who termed their daily sessions The Round Table. Its leader was the critic Alec Woollcott, who greatly enjoyed his privileges of leadership, and one day granted the unsophisticated little blonde the special favor of attending one of those feasts of reason and flows of soul. Tallulah listened demurely as the group sat about, self-consciously cueing each other and quoting themselves, at the end of which, she turned to Alec and, in the throaty tones that were fully developed at sixteen, spoke her mind. "Mr. Woollcott," said Tallulah, "there is less here than meets the eye." From that moment on Alec pursued Tallulah but whether it was out of masochism, or through fear of comments Tallulah might make if he were *not* present, is a moot question.

With her unerring sense of values, Tallulah selected only the right people as friends from among the Algonquin set; she became a welcome satellite of Ethel Barrymore, who delighted in advising her about her career. But when that great lady of the theatre informed Tallulah that her outlandish name would work against her in show business and advised that she call herself Barbara, Tallulah refused to listen. She knew by instinct that no other name would ever express her turgid, but serio-comic, nature; Tallulah's basic essence was too strong to be diluted even by Ethel Barrymore. "Tallulah" she must always be—doubtless the most properly named character ever to tread the boards.

From the beginning of both our careers our paths were always crossing; we lived in close friendship in New York, Hollywood and London, and I saw Tallulah under every circumstance of her zooming career. For she lived at high speed, behaving as a great many of us would have done, had we ever dared.

Utterly contemptuous of phonies and anything but a self-deceiver, Tallulah never believed the middle-class theory that ambition is praiseworthy. She saw it for what it generally is, a matter of conceit mixed, more or less, with cupidity. And so Tallulah never allowed ambition to interfere with play. She lived in the grand manner of a free soul with an aristocratic disdain for caution. And although many of her impulses were unfortunate, none harmed anybody but herself; the great majority of them came straight from her enormous interest in others, her kindness and unfailing courtesy toward anyone who deserved it. Heaven help anyone who didn't; although in such cases there is evidence that Heaven generally took sides with Tallulah. Among the humble and unpretentious she behaved with the discretion and impeccable manners of a very great lady.

During the days of the silent films in Hollywood we both lived at the old Hollywood Hotel. Although it had been largely taken over by the movie contingent, there were also a number of old people from the Middle West living there in retirement. They were as truly nice as they were boring, and none of us girls who worked in films ever bothered to give them the time of day as they sat rocking their afternoons away on the front porch. But Tallulah did. And I still carry a picture in my memory of her sitting on the porch of the hotel and allowing an old lady from Iowa to teach her a crochet stitch. Tallulah, with no intention of ever crocheting anything, at any time, pretended an interest out of kindness and as a means of communication. "You can say all you want about the wickedness of film stars," the old lady said to me, "but that little Bankhead girl is as sweet and unspoiled as if she lived in Des Moines!"

Later on, when the talkies came in, I had a house in Santa Monica where Tallulah, on afternoons when she was free from work, used to come to swim in my pool. While it may be difficult today to realize there used to be a convention against taking off one's clothes in public, Tallulah like all great souls was ahead of her time; she never had any more need of a bathing suit than a dolphin. Now it so happened that next door to me there was a construction crew building a house and while Tallulah cavorted in the pool, the crew would knock off work and mount a scaffolding to watch. I happened to be busy in the studio at the time and the first I heard of Tallulah's gambols was when the owner of the new house called up the tell me that work had fallen alarmingly behind schedule and he pleaded that I ask Tallulah to put on a bathing suit and let his builders get back on the job. Heedful that their work stoppage was creating a deficit, Tallulah promptly complied.

There was a time in London when a beautiful and quite scandalous Queen of a Graustarkian Kingdom of Central Europe was causing alarm in orthodox royal circles. None of those royalties came to her rescue. But Tallulah did. She took H.R.H. in as a house guest and I remember one evening when a card game was projected that Tallulah whispered instruction to all of us to play stupidly and allow Her Highness to clean up. "She's flat broke," explained our hostess, "and trying to support the most divine young gigolo."

Living a life of high celebrity Tallulah took just as much interest in unfortunates as she did in the famous. During part of her career in New York, Tallulah was beset by insomnia and, unable to sleep, spent her nights listening to a radio broadcaster who went by the name of Big Joe. Big Joe's program consisted of interviews with down-and-outers, whose dire situations provided him with fascinating material. Listening to Big Joe, Tallulah's heart and pocketbook never failed to respond. And before very long the program became a two-way broadcast with Tallulah on the phone exchanging comments and bits of homespun philosophy with Big Joe and his assorted vagrants. But Tallulah could spot a phony, even across the airways and, as a rule, it was the most unregenerate scamps who told the truth about themselves and to whom Tallulah was the most responsive. On a cold winter night she sent for an utterly dissolute young woman and gave her one of her most expensive fur coats.

Never at a loss for the *mot juste*, Tallulah could match wits with experts such as Winston Churchill and come out even. And incidentally Tallulah could also match the Prime Minister's alcoholic capacity, drink for drink. When tight she might become outrageous but Tallulah never bored anyone and *that* I consider to be humanitarianism of a very high order indeed.

Talking About
Helen Hayes

*M*Y first connection with Helen is one she remembers well but I had almost forgotten until she nudged my memory. It occurred in 1927, at a time when I was caught up in the brouhaha of putting my book, *Gentlemen Prefer Blondes,* on stage as a play. (In later years it became a movie, a musical movie, and a musical comedy.) The play had been acquired by a Broadway producer, Edgar Selwyn, and he was having his problems trying to cast the heroine. There were any number of real-life prototypes of her on Broadway, but a high order of acting is required to play a dumb blonde without being monotonous.

Now Selwyn had been approached by two youthful stage stars who had recently been married and they brought him the news that they'd found exactly the right actress for the role . . . little Helen Hayes. She had just been raised to stardom playing a tragic young Southern belle in *Coquette,* but Mr. and Mrs. Alfred Lunt assured Selwyn that she was also a comedienne of rare talent.

As author, I wasn't consulted about the casting of my play, but Selwyn and my husband, who, following the tradition of Broadway husbands, was managing my affairs, rejected Helen hands down. I vaguely remember Selwyn saying, "Little Helen Hayes couldn't even approach that character. Why, she's a virgin!"

So Helen's connection with me began with heartbreak. And she had the chagrin of seeing a role she coveted go to a young actress who was anything but a virgin. There was a bitchy story about her current around Broadway. When she was about to be married, she had approached Tallulah Bankhead in wide-eyed innocence and asked, "When a girl marries, what can she do to prevent getting pregnant?" And Tallulah had answered, throatily, "Just what you're doing now, my dear!"

Many years later I came to realize that Helen could play anything, even the most hilarious comedy. I saw her take the stage at the Théâtre Sarah Bernhardt in Paris and deliver a comic monologue in *The Skin of Our Teeth* as well as Jack Benny, Bob Hope, or any great stand-up comedian could. And only recently she won an Academy Award for the outrageous scalawag she played in the movie *Airport*.

The girl chosen to play Lorelei Lee in *Gentlemen Prefer Blondes* was a competent actress and she got away with the part. But I now realize that had it gone to Helen, she would have given it that extra dimension which separates art from adequacy.

The early encounters Helen and I had in New York in the Twenties centered about the Algonquin Hotel, and here again our paths diverged. Helen was steered into that group of self-styled wits which called itself "The Round Table." They met at lunch every day and, from my point of view, were a boring set of exhibitionists. I avoided The Round Table as if it were a swamp, for in those days I was a devotee of H. L. Mencken, George Jean Nathan, Joe Hergesheimer, and Theodore Dreiser, from whom I took my prejudice against The Round Table. There were three people close to that clique, however, who disarmed even me. They were the Broadway wits and playboys Charlie MacArthur, Bob Benchley, and Ben Hecht, Musketeers of the Twenties who free-wheeled about town dipping into everything. And, as they were much too amiable to withstand the advances of The Round Table group, they sometimes joined it.

When Charlie fell in love with Helen, a recurrent question went the rounds of Broadway: "How could a sophisticate like Charlie MacArthur ever have been attracted to that naïve little Hayes girl?" It was a question which, in due time, I managed to answer. Helen has two qualities that have always been overshadowed by her acting talent. She was as graceful a ballroom dancer as the great Irene

Castle herself—an accomplishment that made her vastly popular with the collegiate set.

Charlie, however, was no dancing man. In the process of wooing Helen, he had even flunked a course at Arthur Murray's. But he was a very special connoisseur of a certain something that Helen had in common with Jean Harlow: an exceptional fitness to wear décolleté. On reminding Helen of this, she modestly disclaimed it as a reason for Charlie's devotion. "No, Anita, more than anything else, he needed me to listen while he talked big. That Algonquin crowd was as hard on each other as they were on everybody else. It was dangerous to expose anyone's dream to the death rays of their 'sophistication.' A fellow needed a starry-eyed listener like me."

At any rate, Charlie introduced his shy little fiancée to The Round Table, and Helen, who lacked my sour viewpoint, accepted such phony intellectuals as Alec Woollcott at their own valuation. In those days, I felt that Helen could be hypnotized by fourflushers and made to see them as they see themselves. In one word, adorable. So Helen's allegiance to The Round Table lengthened the distance between us, which was rather long in the first place.

While very few of Helen's favorite friends are friends of mine, without exception any friend I have is cherished by Helen. It is the plain, astonishing truth that in Helen's eyes most of humanity is lovable.

I admired Charlie's outrageous wit and we were good pals from our very first meeting. So after he married Helen, I became a regular visitor at their home. It was then I really came to know Helen, to realize that underneath her sentimental, homespun exterior she had a rollicking Irish sense of humor. How else could she have held on to Charlie, when even the world-renowned cleverness of Dorothy Parker had failed?

The event that really cemented our friendship took place one day in 1940. Charlie had taken the two of us to lunch at Twenty-One, during which Helen began to complain about two eminent ladies she had been portraying: Queen Victoria and Harriet Beecher Stowe. "I'm afraid of getting to be grandiose," she said and turning to me asked, "Why don't you write me a really rowdy part, where I can kick up my heels?"

As a matter of fact, I had had a play in mind for some time that concerned just such a character. I'd never before connected her with Helen, but now I did.

"How would you like to play a drunk?" I inquired.

Charlie pricked up his ears at once, but Helen looked a trace bewildered.

"Did you say a . . . drunk?" she asked.

"How about a frustrated old maid," I went on, "a teetotaler who is against anyone ever having fun? But she gets gloriously tight one evening and during a twelve-hour bender becomes an understanding and sympathetic human being?"

"That would be fine!" said Helen. "Go ahead and write it."

I was under contract at MGM at the time, writing movies, but while waiting for a conference with Irving Thalberg I had plenty of time to write *Happy Birthday*.

Before it went into rehearsal, friends warned Helen and me that doing a play together was hazardous; even Charlie felt it might end our beautiful friendship. When anyone suggested that he write a play for his bride Charlie's answer was, "Marriage is strewn with enough land mines as it is." So while Charlie desisted, I rushed in where angels fear to tread. But it turned out that Charlie was wrong; people who know their jobs seldom fight. We had both been pros since the age of seven.

What I admire most in life is an expert; *any* expert. An expert is a complete human being, at the top of his form. I believe I have as great respect for a master piano tuner as I have for a genius like Duke Ellington. Helen's rating as an expert came to full flower at a time when Rodgers and Hammerstein, who produced *Happy Birthday*, ordered changes in the script which I felt were wrong. I consulted Helen, who agreed with me, but she decided the only way to prove we were right was to go ahead and make those changes. They were disastrous and lasted for only one performance. As an expert who not only knew *her* job, but could understand mine even better than our eminent producers, Helen became pretty special in my eyes.

But even a superlative actress like Helen has her faults, the most common being a tendency to lose important and unimportant items. (When Noël Coward wrote "Don't Put Your Daughter on the Stage, Mrs. Worthington," all he needed to know about *Miss* Worthington was that she could return from posting a letter without losing her gloves.)

An actress friend of ours who is a different type of loser from Helen is Paulette Goddard. While Paulette can hold on to a vast fortune in jewels, furs, art objects, real estate, stocks and bonds, she invariably loses a pencil. This prompted one of her admirers to give her a gold one set with a ten-carat diamond. Had that pencil been Helen's, she could have lost it in quick order, but Paulette hangs on to it with a firm grip.

Helen's sense of values generally towers above material loss. Losing things distresses Helen no more than I resent helping to look for them because, during the search, we can always chatter.

I recall a day in London when Helen was scheduled to take off for Moscow the next morning. She had just finished a movie in which she played the Russian Dowager Empress who took umbrage at the Communists for murdering her family, so it would be tough enough for Helen to get into Russia even *with* a passport. A circumstance of this type gave Helen such a chance to lose something really important that she simply couldn't resist. She lost her passport.

Well, the two of us spent a long day scurrying about London in taxis until, at His Majesty's Bureau for Lost Articles, we finally tracked down her passport. But by that time, Helen figured it had caused as much inconvenience and frustration as she could get from a trip to the U.S.S.R. itself, so the two of us bounced off to Paris instead.

In addition to our work together, our fun, and the many holiday trips we've taken, Helen and I have been through some pretty rugged times. Yet even these difficult periods are, at least in recall, punctuated with unexpected humor.

During the several years when Charlie was desperately ill, Helen trusted me to watch over him when she had to be in the theatre. Shortly before he died, she was acting at the Palm Beach Playhouse and I was their house guest. One night, when I was left alone with Charlie, he suddenly lapsed into a coma and became so inert that I actually thought it was going to be the end. In a panic, I phoned for a doctor. He arrived at the house and, never having met Charlie, was tremendously in awe of his distinguished patient.

After examining Charlie, the doctor beckoned me into the adjoining room to tell me a problem. The hospital he was affiliated with was allied to a church and he didn't want to take Charlie there if his religious precepts might conflict. "What is Mr. MacArthur's faith?" the doctor asked. I was somewhat reluctant to report that

Charlie didn't have any faith at all, so I suggested that he try to rouse Charlie and ask him.

The doctor gently shook Charlie and asked, "Mr. MacArthur, what is your religious faith?"

Charlie opened one weak eyelid and answered, "I am a phallic worshiper." At which he slipped back into his coma and, for all I know, that square old doctor may still be in a state of shock.

Even the extremes of grief seem colored by a sort of black humor that no one but Charlie could have achieved. Many times during his long illness, Charlie admonished Helen to spare him the "barbaric ordeal" of a funeral. "If you do that to me," he threatened, "I'll haunt you!"

But the day after Charlie left us, Helen called me in great distress. "I may be doing something terrible to Charlie," she said, "but I just can't deny the plea of all those friends who want a chance to say good-by to him." Helen had consulted Ben Hecht, who agreed with her, so she asked if he would read a farewell message to his old friend.

Those last rites were held at Campbell's, that genteel institution on Madison Avenue and 81st Street, where tears have been shed for so many colorful New Yorkers. In deference to his pal, Ben's eulogy was anything but sad. However, in the midst of it, a large floral piece that hung on a curtain behind Ben started for some uncanny reason to sway back and forth. Helen and I watched it aghast, each of us thinking it might be Charlie expressing his disapproval.

So, in spite of Helen's ever-ready sentiment and my tough cynicism, we have been brought together at even the worst of times by the saving grace of humor.

Dear Noël

◆

WITHOUT the shimmering talent of Noël Coward, the twenties in England might have been an oafish period colored by American exportations: "Oh you kid" and "Twenty-three skidoo." But when Noël appeared, he evoked tenderly bittersweet sentiments not felt since the time of Byron. When Noël voiced "I'll see you again,/Whenever spring breaks through again," he gave Britain back its heart.

I recall a visit I made to Vienna with my husband a few years after World War I. The wartime poverty of Vienna hadn't affected its spirit. We saw one patron of the opera, eagerly standing in line to buy a ticket, who wore no shoes. His feet were wrapped in burlap.

The elegant Bristol Hotel was deserted by the Viennese, who couldn't afford the proper dress; but one evening we were greeted by a gathering of people in formal dress. My husband asked, "Where do these people come from, if they aren't Viennese?"

"Viennese they are! But their elegance is a matter of tremendous effort. You see, they're here to greet the young British maestro, Noël Coward." Noël had brought out elegance where, except for him, it had disappeared.

During the forties and fifties, critics declared the Coward plays would never endure. Their artistry was too much of a surface matter. Noël's gaiety and impudence were completely underestimated, except by one lone intellectual. Aldous Huxley proclaimed the Attic quality of Noël's wit and declared him a magician: "Coward can take situations between the most superficial human beings and whip them up into a mountain of the most delectable meringue. Only a very fine artist could have the sustaining power to accomplish such a feat."

But Noël always enjoyed a cult of devotees. There was a time in the fifties when Noël took up residence in Switzerland and auctioned off his worldly goods in London. His adherents fought like bargain hunters in Macy's basement for the quite ordinary sheets on which their idol had slept.

For Noël has never been very interested in household decor. His houses are dotted about several different countries, but their decorations might have been copied from some Hilton Hotel suite in Kansas. To Noël, the decor of a house is supplied by the personalities that frequent it, and these he selects and screens like the connoisseur of humanity he is.

Noël has never been a critics' pet. It would be much more accurate to call him a critics' pest. For he shared a disturbing quality with another genius of his period, George Bernard Shaw, an absence of that very snide attribute called humility. Noël never hesitated to advise critics of their lack of perception.

From Noël's earliest years, it had never seemed right to call him merely "Noël." Even now that he is "Sir Noël," the title doesn't quite turn the trick. In his own home, Noël is always addressed as "The Master" (with no disclaiming of the term on his part). But those who knew Noël early in his career unanimously christened him "Dear Noël." He has always been dear, in every sense of the word: precious as one-of-a-kind; expensive (who could ever rate him cheap?); not only likable, but lovable, too; cherished, charming, the epitome of witty elegance.

Through all those years when he was underestimated, Noël, knowing his critics to be wrong, held by his guns. And now come the seventies, with a reevaluation of our culture which has proved how right Noël was. Today, there is a veritable explosion of Cowardiana all over the world and in every langauge. In London, *Private Lives* is the hottest ticket on the West End, along with a concert of his songs called *Cowardy Custard*. Another such show, *Oh Coward!*, is selling out in New York. A strange phenomenon is that audiences are made up of the very young, who react with an enthusiasm that used to be evoked by the Beatles.

It is a favorite cliché to say that the present generation is "sick." But with Dear Noël as a therapist, there's no danger of hardening of the arteries of the heart. At base, we all prove to be normally safe, sane, romantic, sentimental, and sensitive once again. And we can continue to enjoy Noël's astringent talent.

Beating the Rap

WHILE reading a newspaper one morning I came upon a paragraph in a gossip column devoted to the goings-on of famous people. It was written to make its readers laugh, in which it succeeded. But this item also carried me back to a series of events so poignant and dramatic that for years they shadowed the lives of all of us who were involved.

It all began during the gloomiest days of World War II. I was then living in Santa Monica and writing scenarios at the MGM studio. My best friend, Marjorie Duchin, lived in New York and was about to have a baby. Marge belonged to the socially prominent Oelrichs clan, and she was internationally famous as a bright beauty. A tawny blonde with brown eyes, she had much more personality than is commonly allotted to blondes. Her sardonic wit and love of fun had led Marge to desert her own formal world soon after her debut, and to enter the most glamorous of all bohemias and to marry one of its great talents: Eddy Duchin, the pianist, band leader, and darling of New York's smart set.

Now that they were to have a baby, I planned to be with Marge when it was born. The studio granted me a two-week leave of absence, and I had arranged my trip to be in New York at exactly the right time. On joining Marge there I found her in great form, buoyed up for the forthcoming ordeal by a group of special friends.

They were Marie Harriman (married to Averell, who was then holding a high post in the Roosevelt Administration), Minnie Astor (then married to Vincent of the Astor hierarchy), and Minnie's two sisters: Betsy (wife of Jock Whitney, later our Ambassador to England), and Babe (New York's greatest beauty, wife of Bill Paley, head of the Columbia Broadcasting System).

Dominating that already colorful group was Marge's mother, Mrs. Charles Oelrichs, who was known to New York and Newport society as "Big Marge," in order to distinguish her from *our* Marge. Big Marge had been a reigning belle during the Gay Nineties and nothing could convince her that those glamorous and snooty days had ever come to an end. Marge was her only child, and to Big Marge she had never ceased to be "Baby." Now that Baby was to be a mother herself, Big Marge's greatest concern was that she should have the most fashionable obstetrician in New York and that Baby's baby should be born in New York's most exclusive hospital.

That hospital was called the Colony, and it occupied several floors above the Colony Restaurant, which was a favorite hangout for the elite. The hospital was terribly expensive, but its clientele was not, as a rule, suffering from very worthy ailments; a large majority were stylish alcoholics bent on sobering up, hypochondriacs pampering their egos, victims of too much rich food trying to reduce, and middle-aged beauties hiding out for a face lift. The hospital was noted for its lenient house rules; patients could order gourmet meals sent up from the restaurant below; nurses would look the other way when dipsomaniacs sent out for booze, or the overweight phoned down to the Colony Restaurant for a few crepes Suzettes. There were no restrictions against visitors, who used to drop in at all hours to enjoy cocktails or nightcaps with their pampered friends.

Just before time for Marge to enter the hospital I was suddenly called back to MGM on some emergency connected with my latest picture. I was very disappointed not to be around when the baby came. So, when Marge saw me off at the station, it was a pretty melancholy good-bye, which I put down to the war clouds that overshadowed everyone's personal affairs in those dark days. But while waiting for train time, Marge said a little uneasily, "Going into that rowdy old hospital to have a baby doesn't seem to make very good sense, does it?" "Good sense" was hardly the phrase for it; tragic would have been a better description. I boarded the train, waved to Marge through the window, and that was the last time I ever saw her.

Marge's baby arrived a couple of days after I reached home. Marie Harriman called up with the good news: it was a boy, Marge was fine, and the society doctor who delivered her had been able to leave the same day for a hunting trip into the wilds of Canada.

But two days after little Peter's birth, ominous news came over the phone that everything was not so fine with Marge. And the next day she was dead. Who can tell whether or not Marge might have died if her surroundings had been less chic and she had been under the care of a doctor who remained on his job? At any rate, the hospital went out of existence in very short order; its smart clientele had known Marge and been frightened away.

Then, as an aftermath of that tragedy a series of dramatic events ensued, and their repercussions continued for years. Marge's baby had been born with some sort of respiratory affliction which made it impossible for him to take a complete breath. He was immediately placed in an iron lung, but from one moment to the next it was uncertain whether little Peter could be kept alive. Eddy was so shattered over his young wife's death that he was scarcely able to think about his son; and Big Marge, undependable in even a small emergency, plunged into a permanent state of hysteria. But Marie Harriman stepped in and, taking charge, provided little Peter with a nurse who, luckily, turned out to be the next best thing to an angel.

Peter survived the summer, but with the approach of winter the doctors felt that, even in the iron lung, any change in the temperature might be an added danger to his precarious breathing. Other elements added to the perception that New York was no place for the baby.

But what was to be done with him? In whose care, and in which area would this motherless child have the best chance of winning his struggle to survive? Eddy was then called away to Army duty at a base near Chicago. Marie and Ave were forced to stay in Washington, where Ave's duties in the Cabinet of F.D.R. were increasingly arduous. In New York Big Marge's hysteria became almost as great a hazard as the climate. She was capable of grabbing little Peter right out of his iron lung in order to coddle him; she might actually coddle him to death.

One day, Marie called me in Santa Monica. Would I take the baby in and give it the chance of survival provided by California's mild climate? Not for a moment did it occur to me to beg off. Although I'd never had a child, and nurturing even a healthy baby would make me feel timorous, there was no question of refusing to provide my best friend's son with a home. That his mother had died giving him life and that his life hung by a thread aroused the protective instincts inherent in most of us. So, if he could be safely sent to me, I'd be there to receive him and, putting apprehension aside, do my best to look after him.

Transporting little Peter to Santa Monica was a tremendous problem from the very start, for he had to be brought out by train in a compartment provided with helium gas. It was wartime and all helium gas was requisitioned by the Army. However, as this was a matter of life and death, Ave was able to get a special permit for an adequate supply. But even with the helium there was a certain danger of the baby suffocating every time the train entered a tunnel. Ave owned the railroad, so he was able to have Peter's car routed from New York to Los Angeles without going through a single tunnel; one of the most difficult feats of transportation of those entire war years.

The baby's trip took over eleven days. I had acquired Los Angeles's foremost pediatrician, and together we met the train accompanied by an ambulance equipped with an iron lung. Peter arrived in custody of his angel-nurse who whisked him off the train and into the iron lung before there was time for him to gasp. He was taken to a hospital where the pediatrician had arranged for a couple of consultants to join him, and the three proceeded to examine Peter. They then took me aside to tell me I would have to face the fact that the baby couldn't live longer than a few weeks.

This was shocking news. Had the infant survived the rigors of that cross-country trip only to die under my care? Having had no experience with babies, sick or well, I felt obliged to believe the specialists. But from that point on the angelic nurse took over and decided she was not going to let little Peter die.

The doctors agreed that keeping him at the hospital would do no good, but they considered the dampness of my beach home a dangerous location, even though he was to remain in the iron lung. It was essential to get him to the desert as quickly as possible. So, I betook myself to the nearest desert locale, which was Palm Springs, where I rented a bungalow for Peter and his nurse. After they were safely installed, I was able to visit them every weekend by saving my entire gas ration for the trip.

Six months later, our pediatrician was utterly amazed that his patient was still alive. By this time his respect for the nurse had so augmented that he allowed her to take almost full charge of the case. One weekend she cautiously risked taking Peter out of the lung. We watched in suspense and found that he could breathe the dry desert air for nearly three minutes before he started to gasp. And, little by little, those minutes he spent outside the iron lung were extended.

Two years went by, and finally Peter was able to remain in the open air the entire day, although as a precaution he still slept in the iron lung at night. After the war, he could return to New York, where his father ultimately married a charming woman and made a home for his son. There they lived happily together until Eddy's death in the mid-fifties.

That experience of being a surrogate mother, or rather a deputy, for Peter's nurse was his real surrogate, provided an object lesson of sorts. For we have a tendency to feel, during dark periods when everything seems to go wrong, that life can never be normal again or satisfying or amusing, which, thanks to a benign providence, is not true. The frail infant, whose mother's death was so tragic, grew up to be a genius at the piano and a band leader like his father. He used to hold forth every night at the same smart rendezvous in the St. Regis Hotel where Eddy once played and directed his melodies to Peter's beautiful mama, seated at a ringside table. Like both of them, he became a favorite of New York society, and the smallest of his activities are reported in the gossip columns.

All this leads me back to the paragraph that appeared in the morning paper. It told of an altercation Peter had with a bumptious taxi starter outside a bistro in the wee small hours, during which Peter felt called on to resent an insult. And that baby, born so sick it had been given only a few weeks to live, grew up to be the hero of a headline reading: "Peter Duchin slugs doorman at a swank night-club."

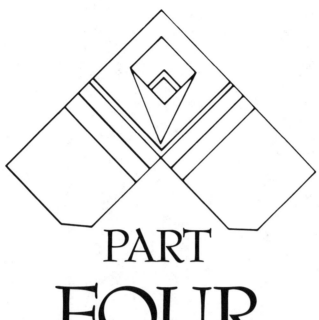

PART
FOUR

Those Were the Days

WHEN I was about twelve years old my family moved to San Diego, California, and there my father organized a stock company. We had come from my native, beloved San Francisco where, from the age of seven, I had played children's parts at the old Alcazar stock company. I had also worked for traveling companies which, in those days, didn't bother to carry children along, but picked them up locally. Now that I was twelve, my father graduated me and I became a combination child actress, ingenue, and even heavy. There was one week when I played the title role in *Little Lord Fauntleroy* and the next, by increasing my height with French heels and a tall pompadour, I became shady Lady Barbara in *East Lynne*.

In that San Diego stock company we produced plays which were pirated from metropolitan stage successes. In far off New York a shorthand expert would sit in an obscure spot of the balcony at a Broadway production and transcribe the dialogue. Then an agency, organized for the purpose of gypping authors out of their royalties, would siphon the scripts through underground channels to the vast number of stock companies that then existed in every city of the U.S. Our company would be able to play such outstanding successes as *Peg O'My Heart* for a bargain fee of fifty dollars a week, of which its author never saw a cent.

Sometimes a contretemps would develop out of this system. One week, when our troupe repaired to the local costume company to rent the furs necessary for a forthcoming production of *On The Yukon,* we found that the fur supply had been depleted by our rival stock company for *their* forthcoming production of *In Far Alaska.* Beginning to smell a mouse, spies were set to work and naturally we learned that we were both playing an Al Woods melodrama of the snow fields, the title of which I disremember. As a way out of the impasse, I suggested that we do away with furs and change our locale to the Congo by which ruse, I argued, we would be wearing a sexier type of costume. But my father felt it was too late in the week to change, and so the same play was done simultaneously at both theatres, to the bewilderment of the San Diego critics and theatre lovers.

There was one week of truce between our two rival companies. The other organization had chosen to do a certain play called *The Prince Chap,* in which the heroine had to be eight years old in the first act, after which she must segue into twelve for act two and then wind up as the eighteen-year-old bride of The Prince Chap for the finale. I was the only actress in San Diego able to encompass this entire span, so Father was approached for my services and I was loaned out (although disguised with a blond wig and billed under the name of my Vermont grandmother, Cleopatra Fairbrother). The Prince Chap was a young actor by the name of Harold Lloyd, who was later to be heard from.

But the production finished off my acting career, for by this time I was earning more important money writing scenarios for the films.

However, I never wanted to be an actress (a feeling not uncommon to children born of stage folks). Even at twelve I knew I was no good at the miming trade. Many years later I got an inkling of the reason why, from the great ballet dancer Adolf Bolm, at a time when Norma and Constance Talmadge and I thought it might be a good idea to take dancing lessons. We were all pretty bad, but I was the worst and one day Bolm blew up and shouted at me, "Mother of Heaven, will you never stop *thinking*!" Had I only been born later, I could have thought my little head off at the Actors' Studio and possibly been a success. But in that era it was the playwright who did all the thinking and the actor never interfered. Those were the good old days.

Hollywood Now
and Then

$\mathcal{S}$OON after this century was born, a random stroke of fate converted a sleepy little village in the middle of nowhere into the most famous, or notorious, town in America. Any locale in the sunny South could have been chosen by pioneer moviemakers, and surely one closer to their headquarters in New York. Instead they trekked out West, like earlier trailblazers, and alighted in a balmy burg which mushroomed into a boomtown, exported its products far and wide, and became an international legend.

Perhaps no other community in modern times has provoked so many conflicting views as Hollywood. In turn it has been admired and reviled, envied and derided, imitated and scorned, mythologized and written off as an aberration of our society.

But suppose those pioneers hadn't discovered that the ramshackle village nestling among citrus groves had a climate and setting conducive to the manufacture of movies? Or suppose, once discovered, it was swallowed by a typhoon or destroyed by an earthquake? While we're supposing let us consider what our lives would be without Hollywood.

First of all, a former movie actor probably wouldn't now occupy the White House. Only history can determine Ronald Reagan's rating as a president. Meanwhile, lacking enough perspective, we call him a great communicator. And why not? That charming presence and facility at adopting ideas and reading speeches devised by others surely were developed by acting out movie scenarios.

It is quite possible that we would have vastly different ideas about many things—physical beauty, glamour, clothing, decor, hobbies, ethics, manners, and mannerisms—without Hollywood. This proposition can be demonstrated at great length. Let us cite just a few examples.

In early days pretty girls and boys dominated the screen and set our standards of beauty. A cute girl with a headful of curls that became her trademark was a particularly potent force. If not for her, thousands of little American girls could have been spared a mass headache as their mamas yanked their hair into corkscrew curls like Mary Pickford's. My own scalp was subjected to the same indignity.

At the opposite extreme a *femme fatale* named Pola Negri had women copying her chalk-white face, kohl-rimmed eyes, slinky gowns, and ropes of pearls. Pola's paramour, Rudolph Valentino, was such a heartthrob that he set the pace for prurient males who wore wasp-waisted suits, brilliantined their hair, and danced the tango with imitation Polas swooning in their arms. Mae Murray's Merry Widow waltz had us waltzing again, and Joan Crawford's Charleston set off a national craze.

Jean Harlow's platinum hair started a run on beauty parlors and drug stores for peroxide and blond dyes. Her brief chemises, clinging satin gowns, and maribou boas became all the rage, even now revived by boutiques peddling old rags of the '30s and '40s. Gloria Swanson's clothes-horse creations, June Allyson's demure little dresses, and countless other movie styles were instantly copied on Seventh Avenue and purveyed across the country.

The rough-and-ready love-making of a Clark Gable and a Humphrey Bogart taught men how to treat women, or mistreat them and make them like it. Jimmy Cagney's gangsters showed thugs how to misbehave and gave birth to the violent clones we still watch on theatre and home screens.

To many a young couple the ideal home was an adorable little cottage with hollyhocks blooming in the front yard, until upward mobility made them long for a suburban house beautiful or a palatial penthouse, as depicted in lots of movies. We got rid of clutter and redecorated in sleek moderne, introduced by Cedric Gibbons. Now, I wonder how we'll adapt our lifestyles to the high-tech of outer-space films, except with toys and video games.

People who never cracked a book learned history from Griffith's *Birth of a Nation,* Ford's Western sagas, war movies about every conflict we ever fought, and period dramas set all over creation. If historic facts were distorted, who cared so long as visual dramas were gripping and played by our favorite stars?

Actors' private lives, blazoned forth by Hollywood's gossip mills, have had a tremendous impact on our standards of morality. Long before flower children made sex permissible, casual couplings were commonplace in the movie colony. Although studio publicists tried to hush up sleazy affairs, they often burst into headlines or led to shotgun weddings, with guns wielded by studio bosses posing as papas.

Douglas Fairbanks used to sneak away from his wife to secret rendezvous with Mary Pickford, also then married. (Doug used me as a handy alibi, when I was writing his movies, by telling his wife we had to work late.) Warned that an illicit affair would outrage their public, Doug and Mary divorced their spouses and got married. Long after their affection departed, they stayed hitched— until their careers ended.

Switching partners became so acceptable that it must have contributed to the rising national divorce rate. After all, if the sky didn't fall when stars split up, it wouldn't cave in if ordinary mortals followed suit.

Who needs marriage now? Not superstars like Barbra Streisand, Burt Reynolds, et al., who flaunt their live-in partners. Other twosomes who think they are free souls find they aren't so free when palships break up and worldly goods need to be divided. This has produced a new phenomenon, the palimony suit.

We hear that unwed motherhood, especially among young girls, has greatly increased. To blame that on Hollywood would be absurd. Yet young people follow role models. If a Vanessa Redgrave and Mia Farrow can bear babies out of wedlock, why can't other girls do so?

Not long ago there was a great brouhaha over widespread drug use in Hollywood. Why all the media excitement? In other words, what else is new? Way back, Wally Reid, Mabel Normand, and Norma Talmadge died of drug abuse. Fashions in drugs may change, from morphine and heroin to cocaine and amphetamines, but the results remain the same, everywhere.

Obviously, Hollywood can't be blamed for spreading every vice, and its influence for evil or good is exaggerated. But the folk habits of Oshkosh hardly rate notice, while those of film folk command enormous press coverage.

During a recent visit, the first since I'd kissed Hollywood good-by years ago, reminders of the past kept intruding on a lot of changes, some only superficial. This was not a nostalgic trip to recover the past, for the good old days were not all that good, or I wouldn't have departed. At least we weren't quite as earnest or stuffy as many film makers are today. To us movies were not an art or big business but just a novelty, unlikely to survive once the novelty wore off; an amusing way to earn money, and what fun we had spending it!

Back in the '20s, I recalled, the sun rose over Hollywood looking like one of its own gorgeous grapefruits. It not only nourished the many citrus groves but also provided light without cost to outdoor stages where silent movies were being filmed. No wonder such an environment turned its citizens into ardent chauvinists.

Although located on the edge of a scorching desert, the town was surrounded by a mountain range that kept gusts of desert heat at bay. Hollywood remained cool and placid in the idle air.

But the realtors were not so idle. In a short time citrus groves gave way to some industrial plants spewing forth smoke which was trapped inside the town by the very mountains that had protected it. The clear air, once redolent of orange blossoms, was invaded by smog which chilled Hollywood until about noon, when the sun finally blasted through with heat that lasted till the damp semitropical night closed in, demanding a scramble for blankets.

Thus, within twenty-four hours Hollywood experiences a full cycle of temperature, from summer heat to winter chill. There was a certain devotee of the Santa Anita Racetrack named Joe Frisco, who used to grumble, "Sometimes it's hot and sometimes it's cold. A guy never knows what to hock!"

Complaints of that sort have been kept at low key by realtors and property owners alike. So the legend of Hollywood's equable climate persists to this very day.

But the town can boast of many creature comforts found in supermarkets catering to the movie trade. Wholesale dealers in Los Angeles specialize in exotic products to meet the demands of film colonists.

Any morning a tourist can spot famous housewives like Cher and Tatum O'Neal, trundling grocery carts overflowing with passion fruit, truffles, mangos, papayas, plantains, and Mexican pinto beans. There are all sorts of novelties, such as cupcakes from Hindustan, bread from Honolulu so light you can hardly taste it and, topping all, an Oriental squash, which, when cut open, reveals a filling of organically grown spaghetti.

The cost of importing such items is astronomical, but hostesses are recompensed by their value to dinner-table conversation, of which the movie colony has always suffered a dearth.

The expansion of high-rise buildings finished off citrus crops for good, and movie studios moved into big complexes in Century City. There is still space enough, however, for enormous billboards. Those advertising a chain of bakeries caused a surprising to-do. They pictured a mother serving her child a piece of cake with hands devoid of a wedding ring. That omission so shocked the local Chamber of Commerce that it ordered a wedding ring inserted on every poster. Imagine, in a town where so many couples are unwed!

Time was when, for a season, the state of California became a sea of wind-swept wild poppies in bright shades of orange and yellow. (I was handed a single blossom as a curio, but it soon wilted, maybe through chagrin over being outclassed by masses of bougainvillaeas, trumpet flowers, and cabbage roses.) Blossoms as modest as the poppy end up in the maws of a grass cutter.

The motion picture industry has gone almost the way of the wild poppy and dwindled markedly, curtailed by million-dollar stars, overpaid executives, and demanding labor unions. So, they've outpriced the making of movies locally and caused them to retreat to such locations as Yugoslavia and Spain.

Yet so strongly ingrained is the mystique of old Hollywood that movie-struck youth still flocks there from all over America. Whether they come from Texas, Alaska, or the Bronx, the males bear a strong resemblance to each other, with narrow torsos that widen to massive shoulders above and very long legs below. These boys adorn the beaches like magnificent clones and seem to pay less attention to girls than to one another.

This brings to mind the observation of an ancient seer that if the human male ever becomes prettier than his counterpart, boys will prefer boys and bring about the end of the race.

The girls are also lookalikes, fresh-faced, long-limbed, and athletic; like the boys they have roller skates attached to their feet, if they don't happen to own an automobile or motorbike. A talent scout on the lookout for an exceptional specimen of either sex would find it hard to distinguish one.

In any case, the talent scout is a member of a vanishing breed. His service isn't required because the old studio system of acquiring and grooming a stable of young hopefuls no longer operates. Major studios that used to churn out hundreds of movies every year now confine their output, due to staggering costs, to a handful of blockbusters. A few massive failures can wipe them out, so they hedge their bets by distributing films made by independent producers and grind out cheaper TV movies. But as TV mini-series become more spectacular, they require financing by bankers and foreign consortiums, as do theatre movies.

The dwindling of total production has left a great many experienced actors, directors, writers, and members of craft unions unemployed. Large talent agencies that guide the destiny of superstars now scramble to find them jobs on television, which they once scorned, or export their clients to foreign outposts.

Sometimes a neophyte (let's call him Donald) ventures into an office that once handled the flamboyant spectacles of Cecil B. DeMille. Its decor has now been updated to conform to the subjects of recent movies. Lithographs of Claudette Colbert in *Cleopatra* have been replaced by lurid posters for such features as *Invasion of the Body Snatchers*.

Donald announces himself to a cool young woman in command of the reception desk. She looks like a double for Liv Ullmann, but Liv happened to get inside the industry first.

Donald's appointment with a latter-day VIP is arranged by intercom. To his surprise a voice of authority booms out the announcement of an immediate interview, whereupon his knees start to quiver like Jell-O and his spinal column seems to shrivel.

Presently a door is flung open by a nattily dressed gentlemen who enters breezily, opens his arms, and greets the newcomer like the answer to a prayer. "Donald, *baby!*" he exclaims exuberantly.

Exalted and dazzled, Donald takes a stance that enhances his magnificent torso and utters a modest plea: "Is there an opening in your new Caligula spectacular?"

Now the super agent is forced to play the flip side of his

phonograph record. It seems that the Italians have already supplied his needs and he requires no more bodies in the buff. Despite disappointment, Donald can sustain hope because this great agent called him *baby*.

Then too, the lack of a job can always be blamed on studio politics. For crooked politics have been steadily on the rise both in and out of the film industry. Zealous reformers trying to change conditions are accused by skeptics of making a lot of noise to attract public notice to themselves, not their ideals.

Once a concentration of great power, Hollywood had its share of tragedies as well as triumphs, and sometimes the two came hand in hand. A case in point was Marilyn Monroe, whose self-destruction seemed ordained by her success because she couldn't cope with it.

It was surprising that a girl so intensely shy would want to be an actress, but perhaps that was a form of compensation. None of us ever got to know her, for she spoke so seldom and in such muted tones that conversation languished. But she radiated a childlike sweetness that was disarming.

Marilyn knew how to communicate without language. Evidently she felt no shyness when she approached Twentieth Century boss Joe Schenck for a job. While he concentrated on her fabulous face, Marilyn shook her torso free of a flimsy shirtwaist and, bare to the waistline, asked in her girlish whisper, "Do you think you could use me in a picture, Mr. Schenck?" Joe took a long look at her delectable torso. "Not unless we got a board of censors to come up from Mozambique," said Joe. Marilyn squealed a dainty giggle and got the job.

Few normal men could have coped with the extravagant daydreams that obsessed Marilyn. She was always convinced that any affair, no matter how casual, would end in marriage. When it failed, she was well into her next romance with the same unreal expectations.

Long before Marilyn's pursuit of playwright Arthur Miller, her affairs had ceased to be taken seriously. The combination of the highbrow and the sexpot was regarded as a joke. Perhaps Miller was overcome with guilt for leading the poor girl on; besides, her beauty was a magnet. And so, the pair was trapped into the most unfortunate of her several marriages.

Beset by illness and victimized by the drugs and alcohol that kept her going, Marilyn became grossly overweight. But her value at the box office was still so strong that the studio used every possible trick to make her acceptable to the camera.

She was at MGM in the midst of filming a picture called *Let's Fall In Love,* at a time when President Kennedy was due to have a birthday. Marilyn concocted the idea of flying to Washington and making a surprise appearance at his birthday celebration.

"Have you been invited?" asked her skeptical agent.

"Oh no," Marilyn replied. "But we're engaged to be married."

Her agent reminded her that the President was already married and, as an ardent Catholic, would never divorce his wife Jackie. Evidently this made no difference to Marilyn whose answer was an evasion: "I was born to be Mrs. Jack Kennedy."

At the studio word of her "engagement" provoked laughter and also the sad remark that poor Marilyn had "gone round the bend." With a secrecy typical of the obsessed, she arranged a flight to Washington, where she checked into a hotel and proceeded to cram her swollen body into a tight satin evening gown. Then, she made her way to the White House and through the amazed throng that surrounded Kennedy. And with the uncertainty of an untrained singer, she managed to get through "Happy Birthday To You."

A group of MGM public relations people took Marilyn in charge and got her back to Hollywood. But *Let's Fall In Love* was never finished. Before long Marilyn was gone, a victim of sleeping pills that couldn't quell her own lethal daydreams.

There was only one real male who could have met her outrageous requirements. He was Joe di Maggio, who occupied the same exalted position in American baseball as Marilyn held in films. Being an Italian, Joe could enjoy a woman as a toy and excuse a lack of wifely qualities. But as an Italian he was torn by jealousy of any man who even looked at his wife. And on an occasion when Mrs. di Maggio was filming a scene where she had to walk in front of a wind tunnel, Joe reacted explosively. A marriage that might have been made in heaven went through hell. Joe and Marilyn really loved each other, and Joe still places red roses at her gravesite.

With all its problems Hollywood still remains a universal mainspring of American hope. In all fairness one cannot agree with the journalist Kenneth Lamott, who once wrote: "All the statistical evidence makes one thing clear: Southern Californians in the main are the unhappiest people in the United States."

I cannot quote statistics but common sense precludes such a sweeping generalization. Ordinary citizens, no matter where they live, are apt to have similar joys and sorrows, and they escape from humdrum workaday lives with the same sort of entertainment. Television fare is pretty much alike across the country.

In Hollywood, as elsewhere, when dinnertime draws near one hears the clatter of TV dinner trays, which minimize kitchen labor and introduce the evening's diversion. When time comes for the late late movies, middle-aged and elderly viewers are brought face to face with their own particular heydays.

Although recent films depict excessive violence and sex, one can make excuses even for them. There will always be a certain public that demands the scabrous and will seek it out willy-nilly, even if it means reading the Old Testament. And history supplies such episodes as that in which a certain courtier begged Henry VIII, "An' it please Your Majesty, may I be full dead when you cut out my bowels."

Even more blood-curdling was a nineteenth century German philosopher, Jean Paul Richter, who penned a hideous fantasy, "What would life be like if there were no God?" The passages he wrote are far more horrifying than any present-day horror story or film.

If there were no Hollywood, no doubt we'd have to invent it, a place to project our fantasies and reflect our dreams, no matter how outlandish. In a sense perhaps the town is our escape hatch, letting off steam that might otherwise be trapped and explode elsewhere.

A Poet in Love

*T*HE first reputable author ever to defend the movies was certainly the poet Vachel Lindsay. In the early days of silent films they were viewed with such disdain that even the theatrical trade papers, such as *Variety,* relegated them to an obscure department at the back of the paper. Beyond a doubt we who made movies were cultural outcasts. But back in 1915, when I was a scenario writer for the D.W. Griffith organization, Vachel Lindsay began to eulogize the films in such high-class magazines as the *Atlantic Monthly* and the *New Republic.*

When, in the course of time, Vachel's words of praise reached our notice, we were somewhat staggered at being treated so politely. And then, in addition to these tributes, our defender began to write fan letters. Now, most of the fan mail of those days, scrawled on grubby pages torn from copybooks or even on scraps of wrapping paper from the grocery store, was so humbly inarticulate that nobody paid it much attention. But one day my chum at the studio, who was Mae Marsh, came to me with an extraordinary fan letter from this knight errant of the movies. It concerned a film entitled *The Wild Girl of the Sierras,* which I had written, and Vachel's praise of Mae was so eloquent that she felt she must, out of common politeness, write an answer. "But," said Mae to me, "I wouldn't know what to say to such an intellectual gink."

The upshot was that I, being an "authoress," took on the job. A lively correspondence developed of which Mae's part was composed by me, and thus I became a small female Cyrano de Bergerac. I haven't the faintest memory of what I wrote to Vachel or of his replies, except that they were increasingly ardent. As the romance unfolded, we tried to conjure up an image of our hero and, having no clue, except for the beauty of his prose, we settled for one that was a cross between Lord Byron and Percy Bysshe Shelley.

There was no chance of the lovers meeting, for Mae was anchored in the Hollywood studio, while Vachel seemed always to be traveling through the Middle West. But finally came a time when the two of them were to be in New York at the same time. Vachel was due there for a poetry reading and, as it was summer, the Griffith organization was to take advantage of a season mild enough for outdoor filming in the East. Vachel had informed Mae that he would be at the Brevoort Hotel, which was a locale romantic enough to harbor any poet. He was immediately to phone Mae on arrival and arrange their tête-à-tête.

But Mae was in a panic at the idea of that first encounter. Would her ad-lib dialogue match up to the literary content of my letters? Would she be as delectable in the flesh as she was in those superb camera effects which caused her freckles to disappear? More important than anything else, what setting could possibly be romantic enough for their first rendezvous?

Mae and her family lived in a flat on Riverside Drive which, at best, could only be called commonplace. Worse than that, it was overrun with innumerable small, noisy and nosy Marshes, who couldn't be trusted to behave in company. "What," asked Mae, "could be done about the matter?" Again, was I able to come to the rescue? I had arrived in New York unchaperoned and rich, for I was getting all of $250 a week in the days when every dollar was worth ten. So, I had splurged on an expensive apartment, the parlor of which was decorated in red and gold and seductively lighted by *seven* floor lamps with fancy red shades. I later realized that my landlady must have been in a wanton line of business and that the parlor was not designed for permanent romance; but Mae and I considered it to be the ideal setting for a love affair that would go down in history.

This, then, was to be our plot. When Vachel telephoned, Mae was to invite him first to take tea at her girl friend's apartment.

Under this arrangement I would come in handy during lulls in the conversation and, once the ice was broken, Mae could arrange for subsequent tête-à-têtes with her poet.

Before tea time arrived, we spent hours on our decor which featured a number of heavy cut glass vases with American Beauty roses; pink bulbs in the light sockets to dim out the freckles of which Mae was painfully self-conscious; and the air was perfumed with incense specially imported from Chinatown. As a gown worthy of the occasion Mae had chosen a green-and-gold Fortuny robe which clung to her graceful figure and even trailed a little bit. With her beautiful red-gold hair hanging in waves to her shoulders, Mae looked like Melisande.

The stage was set long before Vachel was due, and the waiting period was a sort of delicate agony. But when our poet arrived on the scene, he broke every rule laid down by dramatic unity. He clashed violently with the background. He resembled neither Byron nor Shelley. From head to toe he failed to conform. His hair was full of cowlicks without any attempt at control. His shoes were made for his favorite form of travel: viz, tramping. The most accurate image I can conjure up of poor, darling Vachel, is that of the red-headed ventriloquist dummy called Mortimer Snerd.

He was a hurricane of activity; he seldom sat, he paced. He never spoke normally; he shouted, he bellowed, he roared. It was poetry, but nevertheless, he roared it. Even the ambience we created put no damper on Vachel. I doubt he noticed the pink lighting and I'm sure that no whiff of the incense permeated the pure breath of his nostrils. For in no matter what surroundings Vachel found himself, he could always drag the spirit of the cornfields with him.

Disappointed as Mae was in our poet, she was even more embarrassed. Without any resources to meet the situation, she hadn't a word to say and, in her panic, she made an excuse to withdraw and left Vachel on my hands.

I now feel that Vachel Lindsay's roaring bumptiousness was the camouflage of a sad and lonely man. Certainly he was avid for friendship, and he clutched at mine. The transfer from Mae to me took place very quickly and our Cyrano de Bergerac relationship might have had a happy ending, except that I was unable to live up to his ideals. When, after about two weeks of seeing each other daily, Vachel spoke of carrying me off to a cottage in Springfield,

Illinois, there to live the classic American life within the confines of a white picket fence, I could only hedge and change the subject.

After Vachel left New York, our correspondence was resumed and I could then sign the letters with my own name. I never confessed to the literary ruse with which our friendship began and Vachel himself never suspected it. He also continued writing to Mae and, once she had lost her awe of the poet during their first meeting, she was able freely to answer his letters in her own Irish whimsy which was a lot more poetic than the souped-up prose I concocted for her.

When Vachel had news of my marriage, he wrote me, "Be sure I send you my most fraternal Godspeed in your thrilling adventure. I feel very communicative indeed, for no one, not even me, knows what I may say. Look out! May Santa Claus come to see you every Christmas and George Washington every Fourth of July. May St. Valentine appear ever and anon through the whole year, and may all the other Saints bless you and keep you. I do not know the exact stage of Mae Marsh's adventure, but hope her garden has blossomed by this time. By her account to me, a month back, we are to look for Castor and Pollux, Damon and Pythias, or something else in pairs. I am thinking I will suggest Vachel and Rachel, if it is that kind of a pair. I wish I was married."

Poor Vachel! He was always falling in love, as a poet should, but he was always searching for the pioneer maiden with whom he could live out his own version of the American dream. Mae failed him; so did I and many of the others. But I feel that the great tragedy of Vachel's life lay in the failure of the American dream to live up to the rugged promise of its past. And, when he sensed that our native spirit was losing vitality, he lost his joy in living. I had a hint of this as early as August 1920, when he wrote me, "I know I am a poor thing, but take me as I am and do it at once before it is too late." Before it is too late: how prophetic those words became in the face of Vachel Lindsay's suicide.

MGM Makes Room
for a Genius

*I*N the summer of 1926 my husband and I were living in New York, where my existence was hectic in the extreme. The previous year *Gentlemen Prefer Blondes* had been published and was giving rise to stirring incidents almost every day. I was getting countless letters from people I'd never met; the most exciting of them all came from Aldous Huxley, written at a time when he must have been on a lecture tour:

Congress Hotel
Chicago

14–May–1926
Dear Miss Anita Loos,

I have no excuse for writing to you—no excuse, except that I was enraptured by the book, have just hugely enjoyed the play, and am to be in America so short a time that I have no leisure to do things in the polite and tortuous way. My wife and I are to be in New York for about a fortnight from Monday 17th onwards and it would be a very great pleasure—for us at any rate—if we could arrange a meeting with you during that time. Please forgive my impatience and accept the sincere admiration which is its cause and justification.

Yours very sincerely,
Aldous Huxley

Soon after Aldous and Maria arrived in New York they came to tea at our apartment. On first meeting Aldous, I was immediately struck by his physical beauty; he was a giant in height, with a figure that was a harmonious column for his magnificent head; the head of an angel drawn by William Blake. His faulty sight even intensi- fied Aldous' majesty, for he appeared to be looking at things above and beyond what other people saw. But his chief trait was an intense curiosity and, while he was the greatest of all talkers, he was equally the greatest of all listeners.

Maria, a lovely brunette no taller than five feet, with wavy hair, pointed oval face, and big blue-green eyes, was as unusual in her way as Aldous was in his. It was after I came to know her well that I learned the real meaning of the word "fey," for Maria lived a life of pure fantasy. She studied palmistry, believed in the stars, and even in the crystal gazers of Hollywood Boulevard. At the same time, she had practical virtues that made her the truest helpmeet I ever knew. As well as being Aldous' best-loved companion, she was his house- keeper, secretary, typist, and she drove his car in California. She protected him from the swarms of bores, pests, and ridiculous disciples who try to attach themselves to a great man, and all the while her unconventional reactions amused Aldous as well as amazed him.

Following that tea party in New York, our correspondence was resumed and later the same year we all met in Paris, then in London, by which time a friendship with Aldous and Maria had become a constant factor in my life. After my husband and I moved to Santa Monica, the Huxleys came to settle in nearby Los Angeles, bringing their son Matthew, whom I met for the first time. Many complex reasons have been offered as to why Aldous left London— but the explanation is really quite simple. The dry air of Southern California was most soothing to his lungs, which were never robust, and his faulty vision was at its best in the California sunlight, which was still of a pristine clarity. Later on, when smoke and grime polluted the air, the Huxleys used to go for breathers to nearby desert areas or Aldous remained in town and suffered, for his American roots were too firmly implanted for him to pull free.

From the time they arrived in Los Angeles the Huxleys were in daily contact with us; if we did not meet, at least we spoke on the phone. They soon collected a group of friends; among the regulars were Edwin Hubble, the distinguished astronomer and theorist of the expanding universe, his wife Grace, Gerald Heard, Christopher Isherwood, Charlie Chaplin, Paulette Goddard, and Greta Garbo.

For years our lives ran along the most pleasant lines. No place in the world provides as much food for laughter as Los Angeles and its environs: its extraordinary assortment of kooks and goons; its fantastic religious cults; the Four Square Gospel of Aimee Semple McPherson, the Holy Rollers, and the Great I Am were a constant source of amazement and delight to Aldous. He took as much pleasure in speculating about these cults as their devotees did in practicing them.

Every Sunday our group came to my house on the oceanfront at Santa Monica for lunch, after which we usually took long walks on the beach, entertained by Aldous' infinite variety of comment on botany, sea shells, birds, and what have you. Walking was his favorite entertainment and, like the Pied Piper, Aldous led us all after him. When work was over, we went for almost daily excursions either on the beach or through the firebreaks plowed across the crackling, dry hills that surround Hollywood. Those walks, by the way, set us apart from the majority of Southern Californians, who are so dependent on wheels that they've lost the use of their legs except for crossing sidewalks from their cars to front doorways. Any citizen caught by the police using his feet for transportation is suspect. On one occasion, Aldous, out for an evening stroll in Beverly Hills, was stopped by two officers of the law who wanted to know what he was up to. Aldous' reply that he was merely taking the air didn't at all convince the patrolmen, who ordered him to get off the sidewalk at once or they'd haul him to the station. That near-arrest greatly amused Aldous as a measure of the Southland's Kultur.

Both Aldous and Maria loved picnics; the thought of one made them happy as little children. I recall one particular outing with *dramatis personae* so fantastic that they might have come out of *Alice in Wonderland*. There were several Theosophists from India, the most prominent being Krishnamurti. The Indian ladies were dressed in saris which were elegant enough, but the rest of us wore the most casual old sports outfits. Aldous might have been the giant from some circus sideshow; Maria and I could have served as dwarves, but with our tacky clothes the circus would have been pretty second-rate. Nobody would ever have recognized the glamour of Greta Garbo and Paulette Goddard in that tatterdemalion group. To protect themselves from fans who might crop up out of nowhere, Greta was disguised in a pair of men's trousers and a battered hat with a floppy brim that almost covered her face; Paulette wore a native Mexican outfit with colored yarn braided into her hair. Bertrand Russell, visiting Hollywood at the time, Charlie Chaplin, and Christopher Isherwood all looked like naughty pixies out on a spree. Matthew Huxley was the only one of the group who was a mere normally disheveled teenager.

The picnic gear was as unusual as the cast of characters. Krishnamurti and his Indian friends, forbidden to cook their food or eat from vessels that had been contaminated by animal food, were weighed down with crockery and an assortment of clattering pots and pans. Greta, then strictly a vegetarian, was on a special diet of raw carrots which hung at her side in bunches. The others could and did eat ordinary picnic fare, but Paulette, to whom no occasion is festive without champagne and caviar, had augmented the equipment with a wine cooler and Thermos cases.

We had started out in several motor cars, with no definite objective except to find a spot where a fire could safely be built and the Theosophists could put their uncontaminated pots and pans to use. It wasn't easy to find a location; we dared not venture into the dry brush because of the devastating fires that plague Southern California when it isn't being devastated by flood. Finally we found a place which, in the matter of safety, was ideal. The scenery, however, left quite a lot to be desired, for we had chosen the sandy bottom of the Los Angeles River, which is a raging torrent for about two weeks during the rainy season and drier than a desert the remaining fifty weeks of the year. As we trooped down into the hot river bottom, we failed to notice a sign that read, "No Trespassing."

Krishnamurti and the Indian delegation set about cooking their rice. And while the remainder of us were unpacking sandwiches, Greta's raw carrots, and Paulette's caviar, we were shocked by a gruff male voice ringing out with, "What the hell's going on here?"

Stunned into silence, we turned around to face a Sheriff, or some reasonable facsimile, with a gun in his hand.

"Don't anybody in this gang know how to read?" he demanded of Aldous.

Aldous meekly allowed that he could read, but still no one got the man's implication until he pointed out the sign. Then Aldous, feeling that we were not going to desecrate the bed of the Los Angeles River (already strewn with rusty cans and assorted rubbish), politely asked if we might be permitted to stay. The Theosophists' rice was on the fire, our food on the tablecloth, and Aldous promised that as soon as lunch was over we would clean up and leave the river bottom neat and tidy. It was apparent that his plea was getting us nowhere; the Sheriff merely glowered and fingered his gun. Then Aldous played his trump card. He indicated the presence of Miss Garbo, Miss Goddard, and Mr. Chaplin. The Sheriff's measly little eyes squinted only briefly at the group.

"Is that so?" he asked. "Well, I've seen every movie they ever made," said he, "and none of them stars belong in this outfit. So you get out of here, you tramps, or I'll arrest the whole slew of you."

We folded our tents like the Arabs, and guiltily stole away. It was not until we were in the garden at the Huxley house where the picnic was resumed that we began to think about the titillating headlines our adventure might have produced and how they would have added to the long list of Hollywood scandals. "Mass Arrest in Hollywood. Greta Garbo, Paulette Goddard, Charlie Chaplin, Aldous Huxley, Lord Bertrand Russell, Krishnamurti, and Christopher Isherwood Taken into Custody." That Sheriff might have had his picture in newspapers all over the world and realized every humble Californian's dream of sharing billing with the greats. But, alas, he missed his chance by letting our batch of scofflaws go free. I hope he reads this now and is properly regretful over losing his one opportunity for fame.

When the expanding industries of Los Angeles began to darken the air with smog, the Huxleys retreated to Santa Monica, and their home on a hilltop overlooking the Pacific became a source of fun for all of us. The house had been furnished by a somewhat eccentric previous owner, and it gloried in a swarm of conversation pieces, which could have been assembled in no other culture in the world. The first thing to greet one on entering the hall was an *objet d'art* that had once been used to advertise some movie—a larger than life-size facsimile of King Kong, the Ape Man, in whose hairy arms a sparsely dressed cutie was struggling, while Kong looked around for a convenient spot to commit rape. The remainder of the decor did Kong full credit; there was a bar that was an Arabian night's dream of dowdy grandeur; red lights revolved and blinked down on a large, stuffed crocodile, and there were layer upon layer of tortured motifs cut out of wood with a fret saw.

Of course, Aldous could have thrust that eyesore of a bar together with King Kong and his sexpot victim into the cellar, but he didn't. He seemed to feel it would be a shame to dispense with a unique source of amusement in a world filled to the brim with sadness.

During World War II, Aldous' proud sensitivity made him look on its grim course as a matter so personal that it shouldn't be discussed. I remember the night when Paris fell and a number of our group came to dine at our house. When Aldous arrived his face was dead white, he bore the expression of someone who was peering into hell; but the talk was mostly some sort of scientific discussion between Aldous and Edwin Hubble. Nobody mentioned Paris.

Incredible as it may appear, there were times in our relationship when I was able to feel a little superior to Aldous. He once came to me to say that, staunchly as he had remained apart from the movie industry, he now felt tempted to try for a job in it. The Battle of Britain was on in full force, his income was curtailed by it, and his obligations increased. Did I think he might possibly make good in one of the studios? I laughed at his ridiculous humility and told Aldous that nothing could be easier than to find him a job.

I was working at MGM at the time and, on investigating the new projects coming up, found one that seemed ideal—a movie version of *Pride and Prejudice,* which was ready for dialogue. When I informed the producer that the great writer was available, he set up an appointment with Aldous for the very next day.

Very soon after their interview my phone rang; Aldous was calling, with Maria listening on the extension, and their mood was that of gloomy resignation.

"I'm sorry," Aldous said, "but I can't take that movie job."

I wanted to know why not.

"Because it pays twenty-five hundred dollars a week," he answered in deep distress. "I simply cannot accept all that money to work in a pleasant studio while my family and friends are starving and being bombed in England."

"But Aldous," I asked, "why can't you accept that twenty-five hundred and send the larger part of it to England?"

There was a long moment of silence at the other end of the line, and then Maria spoke up.

"Anita," she said, "what would we ever do without you?"

"The trouble with Aldous," I told her, "is that he's a genius who just once in a while isn't very smart."

Aldous did take the job, of course; his family and many friends in England benefited thereby. So did the movie, for Aldous' dialogue was fine, as television viewers of the Late, Late Show can now attest.

Among our diversions in those days were any number of experiences among the mystics of that world center of mumbo jumbo; the more ridiculous our adventures, the more they helped Aldous to measure the outer boundaries of human idiocy. But occasionally an incident turned out to be thought-provoking in the extreme.

We all came to believe in the powers of a handwriting expert who worked in a shoddy booth at Santa Monica, for our very first encounter with that lady instituted a healthy respect for her. A group of us had gone to the pier to have dinner at a little fish restaurant, and while waiting to be served, Charlie Chaplin noticed a sign across the way that read, "Scientific Handwriting Analysis. Ten Cents." Charlie decided, as a joke, to try the expert out. Aldous stopped him. It would be too simple for a swami to "read" for Charlie because his appearance was familiar to practically everyone in the world. On the other hand, no one would recognize Aldous. So Charlie wrote a few words on a scrap of paper and Aldous took them to the lady. He returned from his interview in a mood of deep contemplation and reported what had happened. The lady had studied the writing a moment and then looked up at Aldous suspiciously. "Are you trying to make fun of me, sir?" she asked. Aldous assured her he was not and wanted to know why she asked. She paused and studied Charlie's writing more closely. Then, still suspicious, she asked, "Did you write this while you were in an unnatural or cramped position?" Aldous then admitted that the writing was not his own but he assured the lady that it had been done quite normally. "Then," said the expert, "I don't know what to say, because if what you tell me is true, the man who wrote this is a God-given genius." We were all duly impressed. Later Aldous came to know the handwriting lady personally; she turned out to be well-versed in her trade and we consulted her frequently.

* * *

In my own particular view, Aldous' sense of humor outshone all the other facets of his tremendously complex nature. It even came into play at the time when one of those hellish Southern California brush fires had destroyed the home where Aldous lived with Laura, whom he had married the year following Maria's death. He and Laura had scarcely escaped with their lives, but Aldous' manuscripts, Maria's diaries with their record of the happy, eventful years they had spent together, Aldous' priceless letters from most of the great people of his time, and a library that had been collected during the major part of his life, had been reduced to ashes. On reading about the catastrophe, I phoned Aldous from New York for a firsthand account. I could sense that he was smiling when he said, "It was quite an experience, but it did make one feel extraordinarily *clean.*"

I shall always think of Aldous as smiling. One of my most cherished mementos of him is a delicious bottle of Schiaparelli perfume in a fancy pink box made in the shape of a book. On the flyleaf Aldous wrote, "For Anita, one of the few books that doesn't stink."

About *San Francisco*

T is revealing to look back on work written years ago; generally it discloses why some material stands the test of time better than others. And it becomes obvious that any story that's rooted in strong *personal* feelings outlasts a contrived plot, no matter how clever.

The idea of writing *San Francisco* came to Robert Hopkins, my collaborator, and me out of our mutual love for the exciting city where we had spent our childhood.

The two of us never met in San Francisco, but early in the thirties I went to Hollywood to join the writing staff at MGM, and there formed a lasting friendship with Bob Hopkins (or Hoppy as everyone at the studio called him).

Hoppy's position in the scenario department was unique. It had nothing to do with writing. He had been hired by our studio boss, Irving Thalberg, to inject jokes, ad lib, into any scripts that tended to be dull. Hoppy was the studio's one and only "gag man."

Now Hoppy and I happened to share a particular distaste for Southern California; one which is the heritage of all natives of San Francisco. We delighted in memories of the city of our youth; its brisk Northern climate which generates energy, just as the tepid air of Southern California dissipates it. We had a deep love for ancient San Francisco landmarks, of which the entire Los Angeles area had none; we cherished the free-and-easy spirit of forebears who had risked their lives crossing the plains in covered wagons, suffered tremendous hardships and fallen afoul of attacks by Indians in order to reach their El Dorado. We shared an equal contempt for those citizens of Southern California who had none of the imagination and braggadocio that motivated our own colorful pioneers.

One day when the two of us were pacing the broad main Alley of the MGM studio, voicing our nostalgia for San Francisco, it crossed our minds to make its romantic charm the subject of a movie. It wasn't necessary to search for a character who might symbolize the spirit of our city. We had both known him for years. His name was Wilson Mizner, and he had begun his adventurous career as a gambler on the Barbary Coast of San Francisco.

Now Hoppy, as a boy, had been a Western Union messenger on the Barbary Coast. He had run errands for the clientele of a glamorous gambling casino where Wilson hung out, and where the handsome young adventurer had become Hoppy's idol.

I had met Wilson at a later period in various capitals of the world, where his life was as full of adventure as it had ever been in San Francisco. Wilson and I became close friends. And it later came about that Wilson was drawn to Hollywood as the world's newest frontier for adventure. Thus Hoppy and I were able to enjoy our friend's matchless companionship and wit for the last few years of his life.

Inspired by memories of Wilson, Hoppy and I began to improvise a story—partly out of love for our now departed pal; partly for nostalgia for our home town and, during the process, to contrast its romantic spirit with the grubbiness of Southern California.

We finally took our idea to Irving Thalberg. Now Hoppy, as a gag man, had never worked on a full-length story, but Irving was impressed. Furthermore, he himself had known and greatly appreciated Wilson Mizner. "Go ahead," said he. "Put something down on paper. We'll see if it's worth filming."

Our collaboration proceeded, with Hoppy talking out his ideas while I did the paper work. And from time to time we went to Irving to report progress. Steadily his interest mounted. "It's beginning to look like a natural for Clark Gable," said Irving.

But just as Hoppy and I were finishing our final script, Irving died.

For years he had been warned by doctors to slow his pace, but Irving felt it better to die of overwork than be bored to death by inactivity. His death, while still in his thirties, plunged us into deep despair. In addition to heartfelt personal grief was the realization that, without Irving's help, our script of *San Francisco* faced grave danger. Who among that group of hobbledehoy MGM producers could understand the subtleties of a character like Wilson Mizner?

From that point on *San Francisco* became the most important issue in the lives of both Hoppy and me. To him it meant a graduation from "gag-man" to "author." And, most of all, our film would be the means of waving a last good-by to both Wilson and Irving Thalberg.

But then followed a series of almost unsurmountable disasters. Our movie was assigned to Irving's greatest disciple among the staff of MGM producers, Bernard Hyman. But poor Bernie had been raised in the Bronx, and it became clear during our early conferences that Bernie could never understand our hero, who was as ruthless as he was fascinating.

We were soon staggered by another blow. MGM was trying to build up the career of an unknown contract player, and the front office ordered Bernie to put that colorless neophyte into a part which could only be played by Gable.

Difficulties kept on mounting; the next setback turned out to be a serious brush with the board of censors. It protested a sequence in which our antihero, bent on exploiting an innocent girl in a notorious dive on the Barbary Coast, met with the violent opposition of a young Catholic priest. And, in a rousing battle between those forces of Good and Evil, our antihero hauled off and knocked the good priest out cold.

The administrator for the censor board, Joe Breen, sent for Hoppy and me and said grimly, "Look here, folks, we can't allow that so-called hero of yours to humiliate a Catholic priest."

We argued that our story told of the regeneration of an evil man. Unless he were violently wicked, his regeneration wouldn't be very dramatic. But it appeared that a censor's idea of regeneration was to establish that a character is rather naughty and then allow him to improve.

"Your hero's regeneration takes place toward the end of the script," protested Breen. "In the meantime a priest has been degraded in a way that will bring the entire Catholic Church down on us."

Hoppy and I felt that the Catholic Church had an understanding of artistic values, but Breen wouldn't agree. We had to delete the sequence.

The next day we were cursing the idiotic shortsightedness of those censors who were emasculating our story, when Hoppy suddenly thought of asking for help from the priest of the small Catholic chapel across the boulevard from the studio.

Father Benedict was very movie-wise. He was often sent for to advise on religious scenes; his confessional was frequently visited by show-biz sinners; all of which made him tremendously understanding and sympathetic to movies. Father Ben heard our problem out and racked his brains. Then presently his face lit up. "I've thought of something that may save your precious scene," said he.

Following Father Ben's suggestion, we went to work and invented the scene he suggested. The next day we took it to Joe Breen, and Hoppy proceeded to defend our sequence as if he were Shakespeare fighting to keep the soliloquy from being tossed out of *Hamlet*.

The episode we had devised took place in a gymnasium where we showed a friendly boxing match between our antihero and our priest, in the course of which we established that the husky young priest could easily outbox, outslug, and outsmart our antihero. Then, when the two men faced their moment of truth, the priest would *purposely* allow himself to be knocked out, thus "presenting the other cheek" and making our priest the hero of the encounter.

I knew our solution was weak but Hoppy's fast-talk finally won out over the censors. *San Francisco* was granted the go-ahead.

Now Bernie had managed to secure the great Woody Van Dyke to direct our film. This was a triumph, for Woody was the hero of MGM's latest smash hit, *White Shadows in the South Seas*. And having snared that ace-director gave Bernie the crunch to demand Gable. We got him, with Clark's full cooperation . . . he too had known Wilson Mizner.

But no sooner did the filming start than Hoppy and I realized we faced a new disaster. Van Dyke, who was capable of understanding the mentality of South Sea savages, was an oaf when it came to the subtleties of the San Francisco tenderloin.

We were horrified watching a scene in the projection room where our hero reproved an underworld sweetheart for wearing a gaudy necklace and, indicating it, said, "I told you not to wear that. It looks cheap." That dialogue should have been spoken casually in the manner of a gentleman. But Van Dyke caused our character to bark the speech out like a hooligan and to jerk the necklace from the girl's throat with a brutality that might have cut into her skin. All of Clark Gable's native charm could never have overcome the loutish behavior in which he'd been directed by Van Dyke.

We hurried to Bernie's office to demand a retake. Bernie was surprised. "Why, I thought the way Woody directed that scene was swell!"

For over an hour Hoppy and I conjured up the spirit of Irving Thalberg, explaining that one crass move on the part of any character in any film can cause it to flounder beyond recall.

Bernie, bless his simple heart, finally got our viewpoint. He ordered the sequence reshot with Hoppy on the set in the future to guide Van Dyke. And from that point on things went relatively well.

San Francisco has become a permanent survivor on the late, late TV programs, and I believe it is due to the fact that its authors had such deep feelings for their subject. We were homesick for San Francisco; we adored our pal who epitomized its lusty spirit, and thus were our sentiments strong enough to keep that movie alive and well in television through all these years.

Only recently *The New York Times* scheduled our film in its weekly TV program guide:

THURSDAY, 1:30 A.M. *San Francisco* (made in 1936) Clark Gable, Jeanette MacDonald, Spencer Tracy.
The works: love, opera and that super-duper earthquake. Grand show.

Postscript

It might be interesting to paraphrase here some key scenes of our script in order to explain how Hoppy and I established our major themes.

The following episode occurs early in the movie and shows our feelings about the difference between the natives of San Francisco and Los Angeles.

A drunken lout is seated in the Paradise saloon with one of its girl "entertainers."

DRUNK

(Calling off to singer on stage) Your singing stinks!

GIRL

Sh! You mustn't hurt the artist's feelings.

(In protest the Drunk throws a handful of confetti into the girl's glass of beer. By this time a waiter enters scene to relieve the girl of annoyance.)

WAITER

(To Drunk, quite genially) Come on out, pal.

(He starts to steer the Drunk toward the door.)

DRUNK

(Again calling to singer) Aw shut up!

WAITER

(Suddenly getting an idea, stops) . . . Say!—Where are you from?

DRUNK

(Proudly) Los Angeles!

WAITER

I thought so!

(Saying which, he looks around to be sure he's unobserved. Then, still holding the Drunk with one hand, gives him a short, quick sock on the button and knocks him cold.)

The following scene is the one that saved our film from being destroyed by the board of censors.

Fade In On: A gymnasium.

In background can be seen street types exercising, swinging clubs, etc., etc.

Close shot of Gable in role of Blackie Norton. He is boxing with a husky young man, Tim Mullin, played by Spencer Tracy.

One of Blackie's minions, Mat, comes up to watch them box a moment—then—

MAT

Blackie, I came over to tell you that the girl singer you hired last night didn't show up.

BLACKIE

(None too interested) . . . That so? Well, forget her.

TIM

She wasn't any good, eh?

BLACKIE

. . . *Good?*

(*Chuckling sarcastically*) Why, her father is a preacher!

MAT

Gee—that's an old gag!

TIM

Well—maybe her father *is* a preacher!

BLACKIE

(*To Mat*) Tim still believes in Santy Claus!

TIM

The trouble with Blackie is he doesn't believe in anything!

BLACKIE

That's where I'm smart!

(*He lands a pretty good sock on Tim*)

TIM

Did you say *smart?*

BLACKIE

That's what I said!

(*At which Tim lands a sharp quick sock that flattens Blackie to the floor*)

MAT

Gee! That guy sure packs a wallop!

BLACKIE

(*Trying to get his breath*) Yeah. For twenty years the big mug has mauled me around and made a chump out of me and I always come back for more!

The following scene shows our priest turning the other cheek.

(*Mary, wearing the scanty garb of a cafe entertainer, is in Blackie's arms. They kiss, after which she speaks diffidently*)

MARY

Blackie—let's set the date for our wedding, so we can tell Father Tim, eh?

• 180 •

BLACKIE

(Evasively) Well sure—the first chance I get I'll let you slip that halter on me.

(Kisses her lightly on the forehead)

Never thought I'd be so nuts about *anyone!*

(O.S. a knock on door)

BLACKIE

Come in.

(Tim enters and reacts in shock at Mary's semi-nudity)

BLACKIE

(Glibly) Hello, Tim.

MARY

(Abashed, tries to cover her deep decollatage) Good evening, Father.

BLACKIE

What's wrong?

TIM

Are you getting ready to show Mary—like this—to that mob out there!

BLACKIE

Look, Tim! I'm going to make Mary the Queen of the Coast! See that poster! Five thousand of 'em will be plastered all over Frisco tomorrow! And ten thousand little ones—for ash cans and the front of trolley cars.

TIM

I'm not going to let you do this, Blackie.

BLACKIE

Come here, Mary!

(Mary joins Blackie. He puts his arm about her)

Will you tell his "holiness" you made up your own mind to sing in my joint?

MARY

. . . I love him, Father.

TIM

It isn't "love" to let him drag you down to his level!

BLACKIE

Wait a minute, Tim! *Why, I'm going to marry the kid!*

TIM

Not if I can stop it! You can't take a woman in marriage and then sell her immortal soul!

BLACKIE

(In fury) I've stood for this psalm-singing blather of yours for years and never squawked. But you can't drag it in here! This is *my* joint!

(O.S. Music starts up introduction. Another knock on door)

STAGE MANAGER'S VOICE

Mary! Mary Blake!

TIM

(Taking his stand in front of door, blocks Mary's way) She's not going out there!

(Blackie looks at him one brief moment—then hauls off and socks Tim squarely on the jaw. Tim stands there—taking it and making no move to defend himself. Blood starts to trickle from his mouth)

BLACKIE

(To Mary) Get on out there, Babe!

MARY

. . . I'm not going, Blackie!

(Taking off her head dress)

I'm going with Father Tim.

BLACKIE

(Livid) If you leave now, you're never coming back!

(As answer she takes cape from Tim and puts it on. Tim leads her out. The scene ends with Blackie looking after them in fury)

Then comes the final scene in which we more than made good with the board of censors. It takes place in Golden Gate Park. The earthquake is over, the fire has diminished, and a troupe of survivors is streaming into the scene; among them Blackie and Tim.

Presently O.S. we begin to hear the strains of "Nearer My God To Thee" interspersed with infrequent distant dynamiting. As the survivors approach the foreground one voice rises above all the others—it is Mary's.

Blackie and Tim react with joyous relief. They hurry on, reaching a vantage point where they stop and look off.

ANGLE SCENE SHOT THROUGH FOG

Mary is singing to the refugees, her evening dress hanging in rags, her hair falling about her shoulders.

BLACKIE

(Tears of emotion welling into his eyes) . . . I want to thank God, Tim. What do I say?

TIM

Say what's in your heart, Blackie.

BLACKIE

Thanks, God! Thanks . . . I really mean it.

And there it all is—to quote *The New York Times,* "the works."

Lillian Gish—A Tribute to a Trouper

*N*OW that Lillian Gish is to be honored with a formal tribute by the Museum of Modern Art in New York, it might be well to update the account of her extraordinary career in motion pictures.

Lillian's entrance into films was through a stage door. The family base was Massillon, a small city in Ohio, but Lillian and her sister, Dorothy (younger by two years), had spent much of their childhood touring with theatrical troupes through the Eastern states and the Middle West.

At that time, motion pictures were shown in converted store buildings called nickelodeons. They lacked the dignity of show business, but when the girls received an offer to work in movies, their mother welcomed it. They would have to give up their native Massillon to live in New York, but it meant an end of touring and the advantage of a permanent home.

Mamma Gish, an attractive young widow, could easily have had a life of her own. But her main concern was the children: to bring them up in that strange new environment to have the ideals, integrity and common sense that were a heritage from their Midwestern forebears.

Keeping pace with an industry that was gradually becoming an art, Lillian's progress never faltered. She has given unforgettable performances in films that are landmarks in the history of motion pictures. In D.W. Griffith's *Birth of a Nation,* Lillian plays the Southern belle who reveals the gallantry of the South during our Civil War; she is the Mother who endlessly rocks the cradle in *Intolerance*, a performance that took only a half hour to film but will remain forever in the memories of its audience. Lillian played the pathetic adulteress of *The Scarlet Letter*; the wayward Mimi of *La Bohéme*; the helpless waif of *Broken Blossoms*; and she co-starred with her sister, Dorothy, in "Orphans of the Storm." These films are occasionally shown today, and largely due to Lillian's performances they still retain their freshness and vitality.

The list of Lillian's films goes on and on. Her latest major release, and incidentally her 100th movie, was Robert Altman's *A Wedding,* filmed in the late 1970's. And today, as the most elegant and youthful of grande dames, she is at work on a television feature being filmed in California.

Lillian and I have been friends for almost 50 years. Our first encounter was by remote control. I had just mailed my first scenario to the Biograph Company in New York from my home in San Diego. With beginner's luck, it was directed by D.W. Griffith himself, with Mary Pickford and Lionel Barrymore playing the leads. In those days, D.W. used his entire troupe when extras were required, and in a crowd entering a church are Lillian and Dorothy Gish.

Later on, the Biograph Company moved to Hollywood and D.W. asked me to join them as permanent scenarist. When I first arrived at the studio, Lillian was away on location, but I met Dorothy. She was a bit of a clown, both on screen and off, and we became cronies, but it was some time before I really got to know Lillian. I never worked on her pictures. My stories were largely satires in which Lillian would have been out of place. Satire requires a touch of malice and of this Lillian has none. Dorothy and I loved to tease her by pretending she was "stuffy," which wasn't true. But she has a delightful sense of the ridiculous. There was no lack of fun in Lillian's whereabouts; we became good friends.

Lillian's beauty; the benevolence in her smile; the wide blue eyes and golden hair, have always suggested an angel that belongs at the top of the Christmas tree. But of late, listening to Lillian on the trends that films have taken is to invite an Angel of Wrath into your parlor. Her viewpoint on films has been unique; she considers them as *Power;* a power that generates energy as great as that of Arab oil or the nuclear stations. "There's no question," she says, "that films influence the entire world as nothing has since the invention of the printing press. But the impact of the printed word is nowhere near as strong as a visual experience. And the 'entertainment' foisted on our young people today is terribly disturbing.

"It is hard to understand the prevalence of degrading movies in view of the fact that they are far outgrossed at the box office by such legitimate entertainment as *The Turning Point* or *Kramer vs. Kramer.* It seems that they must be the product of some evil intention."

One day Lillian and I sat in my New York living room, discussing the changing viewpoints since we were teenagers at the old Biograph Company in Hollywood. She recalled with a sense of pride that her sister, Dorothy, had once turned down a contract from Paramount of a million dollars to make eight comedy films. It was an offer that would have forever banished the ghost of poverty that haunts every actor, but Dorothy turned Paramount down.

"Oh, no," said she, "to have a million dollars *at my age* might ruin my character."

Mother Gish's training in common sense had taken root.

Looking back on those early days I remembered that Lillian had a premonition about the importance of films that few of us shared. It was Lillian alone who took those silent flickers seriously. We others looked on them as a fad that would soon lose public interest, as did those projectors of snapshots that were gathering dust on every parlor table. Even the fact that we were working with D.W. Griffith, who would one day be acclaimed a genius, failed to impress us; as it did Griffith himself for a time.

As a young actor he had dreamed of becoming a playwright; a modern Shakespeare who would bring poetry to the Broadway stage. His first play was so dismal a failure that D.W. realized the theater was not for him. He returned to picture making with a resigned bitterness that seemed to mark the end of his career.

But Lillian had a remarkable vision of a future toward which D.W. might be heading. Watching him direct, she began to sense that D.W. was viewing his effects with the eyes of a poet.

It took Lillian a long time and thousands of feet of film to build up D.W.'s satisfaction in his work or to recognize his own unmatched talent. It was Lillian's delight in watching rushes in their projection room and her appreciation of certain subtleties of direction that raised D.W.'s opinion of films and, little by little, released his inspiration.

Lillian grew to be sort of an all-purpose collaborator to D.W.; she acted roles of every type and even coached other actresses when D.W. felt a need of female intuition. Which brings to mind an episode in which a certain star playing "Judith of Bethulia" had a torrid love scene. To D.W. it was a touchy situation, for Judith's costume was scant and D.W. didn't want to flaunt verity by adding to it. So he ordered a placard to be propped against the Babylonian setting which stated, viz, "During Judith's love scenes the actress was chaperoned, off-screen, by her mother." I may have had some part in the removal of that placard, but as I remember both Lillian and I giggled over D.W. 's prudery. Such was the "porno" of that innocent day.

But on reflection, it now appears that much of the sensitivity in D.W.'s work may have been rooted in what was to my irreverent view a lack of sophistication.

D.W. grew to consult with Lillian more and more, even on lighting and the cutting and editing of scenes. He told her, "You know more about films than I do." And once when D.W. was forced to go on a trip to raise money, he turned over an entire production to Lillian.

Her experience served to increase her awe of the medium and her respect for its infinite capabilities, "which," says Lillian, "we haven't yet even begun to realize."

Absorption in work kept D.W. and Lillian as close as if they were sweethearts, which the public, always ready to jump to wrong conclusions, decided they were. But D.W., in spite of his sensitivity to all human emotions, gave little thought to his personal affairs. Early in his career he had married an actress from whom he was divorced several years before he even met Lillian; she never even met D.W.'s wife. At any rate, she had no time for romance, unless it was taking place on screen.

Lillian's devotion to her mother required much of her time and energy. Mother Gish had suffered from a stroke that confined her to a life of inactivity. And, with disarming pride, she seemed to think that nobody but the girls could manipulate a wheelchair.

Meanwhile Dorothy had married the film actor James Rennie,

and her husband required most of her attention. So for years it was Lillian's chore (and her delight) to take Mother Gish window-shopping whenever duties at the studio permitted.

While other film stars were indulging in a succession of husbands, fiancés, and love affairs, Lillian has kept aloof from all such involvements. And this is not due to any lack of opportunity. Suitors have pursued Lillian all her life, and in her fan mail, the love letters outnumber all the rest.

I recall a comment on Lillian's sex appeal made by Cedric Gibbons, our set designer at MGM. One day he happened to overhear a group of girls discussing sex appeal, of which MGM had a corner on the market, viz. Garbo, Crawford, Del Rio, Shearer, Loy, et al. Cedric interrupted the discussion. "What does any girl know about the things that excite men?" he chided. "There's more sex appeal in Lillian Gish's fingertips than in all you flamboyant sexpots rolled together."

They subsided and gave Cedric the decision. After all, he was married to Dolores Del Rio and knew whereof he spoke.

A time finally came in the association of Lillian and Griffith when her box-office value reached astronomical proportions. And D.W., all of whose earnings were poured back into his films, persuaded Lillian to accept one of her many offers. To be separated after their three years of idyllic collaboration was heartbreaking.

After their parting, when Lillian's career was at that high plateau from which it has never descended, D.W. made a confession to a writer, which she later quoted in a memoir.

"I never had a day's luck after Lillian left me," said D.W.

"But D.W.," gasped the writer, "Lillian didn't leave *you* . . . you chucked her out!"

"I 'chucked her out' because I was cheating her of the fortune she could earn with another producer. I allowed money to come between us."

"But you were only thinking of *her*."

"I was thinking of my own ego. Lillian never thought of money. I did!"

The friendship between D.W. and Lillian remained as strong as ever. And when D.W. in his later years married a childish little bride, Lillian assumed a sort of guardianship that included both bride and groom. D.W. needed Lillian in yet another capacity. He had become an alcoholic.

Foremost among the heritage of Lillian's pioneer ancestry is her pride and devotion to her country. "The time was," she explains, "when I used to visit Europe every year to see my foreign friends and study their work. Those days are over. Now all my friends visit America because they know it to be the best and freest place on earth. I need go no further than the Algonquin to visit them.

"As to the future of films, I take heart that the theme of D.W.'s *Birth of a Nation* is just as vital today as when it was filmed. Only recently there was an active demonstration in a San Francisco theater where the *Birth* was shown. And there are other issues of American life just as dramatic as our Civil War. Hollywood has never filmed the dramatic story of Thomas Jefferson, which culminated in our Constitution.

"If Americans must be materialistic, we possess resources, opportunities, luxuries, comforts and gadgetry of which our pioneers never dreamed. But we've lost our self-esteem. Let's strive to get it back.

"We don't need to be 'born again' with infantile thinking that has brought about the sorry state we're in today. We need to regain the pioneer spirit of our beginnings . . . a respect of our ideals that will bring a measure of hope, appreciation and joy to our moving picture screens once more."

Lulu Baby

---◆---

*W*HILE I was strolling through the park one day, in the merry, merry month of May (1980), just as in the old vaudeville refrain, a polite young stranger approached me to ask, "I beg your pardon, but aren't you *Louise Brooks?*"

Now Louise Brooks and I had met many years ago when we were working as novices at the old MGM Studio in Culver City. At that time the two of us had several points in common that might have given that movie fan some basis for his confusion.

But to be mistaken for Louise Brooks, at any age, was a double compliment. She was by far the prettiest girl in Hollywood, a fact which was only the beginning of her incredible career. For today's film critics all agree that Louise Brooks became the greatest actress in the history of moving pictures.

During a span of about twenty years, most of which were spent in idleness, she made only two movies of major importance, but they established a cult for Louise Brooks that is mounting steadily as time goes on.

The resemblance between Louise and me started with our measurements; at a height of four feet eleven inches, we each weighed a meager ninety-two pounds; and, in a world where it was almost an obligation to be blond, we never tampered with the blue-black color of our hair. We wore it at shoulder length and were the first of the trend-setters to venture into bangs.

Our jobs at the studio varied; Louise took the easy way and settled for playing extras, bit roles and posing as "cheesecake" for the publicity department. I earned my keep by concocting movie plots.

But there was a magnet in the guise of snobbery that drew us together. Among the mishmash that made up the personnel at MGM, we avoided the actors as bores who took themselves too seriously.

I used to be put to all kinds of trouble by one superstar who was finicky about the close-ups I planned for him. He accused me of introducing embraces into his scenes with a leading lady who suffered from halitosis. He would drag me from the set to complain, "Look here, young lady, if I've told you once, I've told you scribblers a dozen times to keep that dame and me at arm's length."

I tantalized him by promising to write him into a double exposure against Louise Brooks. It was a feeble joke, but the very idea brought forth a grin that lit up almost all his teeth. "Well," said Mr. Gable, "*now* you're talking like Shakespeare!"

There was no question that Louise was looked on by the younger directors as their own special property. They were as yet too inexperienced to be handling anything but slapstick comedy; so Louise's contribution had little to do with acting, but it provided endless excuses for "cheesecake."

We girls considered it chic to rebel against custom, so we refused to dine at the studio commissary. At lunchtime our boss, Louis B. Mayer, used to make the rounds, stopping at every table to describe the merits of his chicken soup, the recipe of which had been handed down through generations of Yiddish grandmothers.

As an escape from such boredom, the younger producers organized a Dining Club where the elite gathered at the lunch hour. It was restricted to movie intellectuals such as Walter Wanger, A. Edward Sutherland, and Willis Goldbeck; all of whom boasted college backgrounds. There were always a few men-about-town from Los Angeles and the polo teams joined us from Santa Barbara.

Le Club occupied a tacky bungalow in Culver City, complete with bootlegger and a black "fry cook," who provided comedy relief. The Club garden was so cramped that a neighborhood apartment dweller once complained, "Every time I go to my window for a breath of air, your cook grabs his skillet and bastes my bald head." We laughed off such repartee, drank our martinis out of tea cups, and looked down our noses on such earnest "drips" as Greta Garbo and Kate Hepburn, who still paid homage to Daddy Mayer's chicken soup, a single helping of which would have made a potful of the brew they served us at le Club.

Louise and I earned plenty of money, most of which we spent on hats and frequently borrowed them from each other. I remember a favorite straw sailor with a single flower sprouting on a long wire stem. Its gyrations increased our impertinence as we lolled around the Club bar.

I, being hooked on a career, occupied myself writing movie plots. Louise became a sort of magnificent floater who took no interest in where she was headed. Ultimately, she outgrew her more-or-less unconcluded affairs at le Club and became a girl-about-town, under the protection of the young director Eddie Sutherland, the Beau Brummel of that era.

Louise's connection with Hollywood was finally broken by a gentleman from the East on a business trip to California. He had invented a process of washing dirty linen "en gross," and then turning it over to housewives to do their own ironing. George Marshall made millions by such simple means as smoothing wrinkles out of unpressed laundry. As a reward for Marshall's devotion to Louise, she peacefully gave him the nickname of "Wet Wash," with which George Marshall was forced to live thereafter. But by his purchase of the Washington Redskins football team, he provided himself with the glamour of a sporting career.

George Marshall might well be called the love of Louise's life, had she ever found a single love sufficient. But George burned with a desire to show the entire world the treasure he had acquired. He spent fortunes on trying to further a career in the movies which Louise didn't want. It interfered with her social life as Queen of the Washington football team. In addition to being lazy, she refused to cooperate in the business contracts George arranged; she liked money well enough, but didn't want to be bothered with it.

I remained at MGM for eighteen years but kept track of Louise through the movie grapevine. It appeared that during her extensive pleasure trips, some of them abroad, Louise's spectacular beauty caught the interest of studios wherever she went. But her favorite form of exercise was walking off a movie set, which she did with the insouciance of a little girl playing hopscotch; thus upsetting

George's ambitions to be a Pygmalion.

During her years of misbehavior, Louise's movie offers dwindled to a paltry few. When she found herself at odds with Marshall, there were numberless others waiting to take his place. Louise became a full-term "kept lady." But sometimes when pressured by George, she went back to him for a while.

Then on one fateful day, a Berlin movie producer named G. W. Pabst, who was a friend of George Marshall's, was preparing to make a film of two of Wedekind's famous sex-ridden plays called *Pandora's Box,* and in describing his project to George he explained a major difficulty: that the leading lady must be "the most beautiful girl in the world." George Marshall felt his destiny as Pygmalion had arrived. "That girl has *got* to be Louise Brooks!"

When approached to consider yet another unwelcome job, Louise's first question might well have been, "What time would I have to report on the set?"

But when she read the Wedekind plays, Louise's attitude began to change. As an ardent lover of life she found little "life" in those film scripts that came her way. Activity perhaps—but that was not enough.

Her exceptional beauty had brought Louise offers of such innocuous roles as Goethe's Marguerite, or the even more pallid Charlotte of *The Sorrows of Werther.* English movie companies had tried to tempt Louise with such lollipops as *Dorothy Vernon of Haddon Hall* or *Sweet Nell of Old Drury.* But as Lulu in Wedekind's *Pandora's Box* Louise found a heroine that she could get her teeth into.

Lulu was a creature of flesh and blood, especially blood. A sequence in Wedekind's play that particularly fascinated Louise was one in which its heroine confesses that her most cherished daydream was to be ravished and murdered by an insane rapist.

Louise accepted the role of that gore-soaked victim with an eagerness very foreign to her supine and fun-loving nature. Her performance as Lulu turned out to be a showstopper even to the dissolute Berliners. Louise's boyish "patent-leather hair," which had caused her to look like a healthy young Lochinvar-out-of-the-West, turned her into a creature of Oriental decadence.

There are not many actresses who will allow an audience to know what they're thinking. At any rate, most of those thoughts are too self-centered to have any relation to life outside an actress's looking glass. But Louise was no dissembler; she had faced her own life with a gaze of peerless clarity. She was too honest to "play it coy," to delve in self-pity, to hide behind the mask of her fabulous face, or to smear the ugly scars of human nature with "Covermark."

As she played Lulu, the venal thoughts of that prostitute reach out and grip the audience as in a vise. And after the vise is released, it leaves a scar on one's mind that will never disappear.

Movie critics have tried to explain what it is that turned Louise Brooks's erotic ecstasy into a masterpiece. One is tempted to quote a few international film writers on the subject, viz:

"Louise Brooks is much more than a myth, she is a magical presence."

"Louise Brooks by merely walking across a stage creates a work of Art!"

And from Henri Langlois, the late director of the Cinémathèque Française: "The camera seems to have caught her by surprise, without her knowledge. Her art is so pure that it becomes invisible."

And the most hard-boiled of British critics, the late Kenneth Tynan, had to resort to poetry to express his feelings about Louise. "For I have sworn thee fair and thought thee bright, Who art as black as hell, as dark as night!"

With the release of *Pandora's Box,* not even Louise realized what she had done with Wedekind's monstrous study of an adulteress.

That *Pandora's Box* was more than an accident was proved when Louise was enticed into one more film, *Prix de Beauté,* which turned out to be as great a work of art as *Pandora.* A few years later, possibly because of boredom, Louise quit acting forever and never made another picture.

She had given a full account of all the lessons her own life had taught her. She had asked all those questions for which humanity will never find an answer; and she had the smile of the Mona Lisa with its wit, guile, and cruelty.

"I don't think I ever loved anyone," Louise once told me, although, for a short two years, she had married Eddie Sutherland. But when in need of funds, she intermittently went back to Marshall until the day he died. (She confessed to having lived with three men of wealth at one time without their being aware of the deceit.)

But finally crippled by arthritis, she had found a new diversion. She enjoyed talking. She and I had a mutual friend in Tom Curtiss, the drama editor on the *International Herald Tribune,* and his latest report on Louise is of a series of addresses she made to Parisian film aficionados. But they were so full of German technicalities that the French couldn't understand them.

"You'd never recognize the Louise of today if you saw her," Tom Curtiss wrote me. "Her hair is almost white. She looks and even talks like a New England schoolmarm. And for the first time in her life she has become bitter."

Like a homing pigeon who never had a home, Louise fluttered to a nest at the Rochester Academy of Motion Picture Arts, of which she was its brightest and most revered adjunct.

Everybody who loves the movies has got to adore Louise Brooks because of what she has put into our lives through them.

In order to see these miracles, one is forced to hie to the International Museum of Photography at George Eastman House in Rochester, New York, where only seven films of Louise exist. But you had best be warned, that *Pandora's Box* may sear your eyesight.

On that day in the park when I said goodbye to that stranger who had so poignantly brought back the past, I expressed regret at not having been Louise. "Don't apologize," said he, and added with a sigh, "but I sure am sorry never to have met Lulu!"

Fashions in Faces

*I*N the early 1900s the Hollywood film industry began to take cognizance of the vast assortment of raw movie material created for it by Nature. Certain faces started to emerge from the mishmash of humanity and to earn colossal profits for the film industry back in New York.

But Nature, which could create an arrangement of atoms, cells, and DNA to produce the shimmering features of Marlene Dietrich could, by using the same biological ingredients, come up with a total blank. So, film makers cannot escape the whims of Nature in this respect.

There are two basic elements in movies as crucial as any techniques. The first is personality, which its possessor can control to some degree; it can be faked, if done cleverly. The second, even more important, requirement can only be achieved at birth. It is the unfathomable cinematic mystery of being photogenic. This quality doesn't stem from the emotions or the mind, but is a miraculous alchemy of both which comes to the surface in the light of the eyes, the charm of the smile, the poise of the chin; it is a certain radiation emanating from a face that reaches you and fills you with excitement.

Almost impossible to identify precisely, it is well worth consideration, for its profits can endure forever. The first noteworthy example of *photogenesis,* to coin a term, belonged to a little blonde teenager who began to dominate movie screens and flood the Wall Street backers with dollars. As a result every studio in Hollywood was ordered to undertake a search for a duplicate of little Mary Pickford. Hollywood Boulevard became a showcase for footloose blondes, most of whom were synthetic.

At length the Paramount studio brought forth a young blonde named Mary Miles Minter, whose childish figure, pink cheeks, and golden curls were fairly close ringers of the original. Paramount placed Miss Minter in the hands of drama coaches who spent enormous effort on training her to imitate the Pickford giggle, the childish stance with arms akimbo, and a certain coy expression called, in French, a *moue.*

But the camera was not to be fooled. Not only was the imitation Sweetheart a dud but she became responsible for Hollywood's first major scandal. In a jealous rage Mrs. Minter was supposed to have shot the man who directed her daughter's films. For all her careful grooming and expertise the poor child turned out to be the most repugnant type of femme fatale, the baby vamp, the ghost of which still haunts movies today.

Of course, I've known rare cases of unrelated beings who did look alike, but in Hollywood the resemblances never carried very far. Some element usually was missing from those fake superstars.

One actress who combined genuine beauty with talent was Billie Burke, a reigning comedienne of British musical comedy before she went into movies. Billie was photogenic to a high degree. The very camera fell in love with her and registered every nuance of her charisma. She was always chosen to play such historic charmers as Sweet Nell of Old Drury or Dorothy Vernon of Haddon Hall.

Now, among the group of players on the lot at that time was Mae Marsh, who could have been Billie's identical twin. Both were of Irish descent, with the same red-gold hair, green eyes, turned-up nose, and freckles. But Mae generally was called on to play the homespun girl-next-door. There was something in Mae's biological amalgam that indicated a preference to play softball with the kids on the back lot rather than to flutter a fan. So film companies never realized what a beauty Mae was, or gave her the chance to portray the glamorous women played by Billie Burke.

It isn't often that the star herself is to blame for being overlooked.

Some movie people are nicer and more sensitive than any nonprofessionals. Indeed I found among beautiful girl friends a much deeper sense of humility than of conceit. They nursed a strange feeling that their looks set them apart as "freaks" or, at least, as not quite normal. Showgirls of unusual height or other uncommon proportions are apt to think they have something to hide or to apologize for. This creates a disadvantage, which is almost impossible to overcome. Their superb figures seem to embarrass them, and they generate a feeling of rivalry that seldom leads to very happy friendships.

But there is also the narcissistic type who falls in love with herself. An outstanding example was Mildred Harris, whose looks won her the role of Mrs. Charlie Chaplin. Mildred's beauty had the purity of an advertisement for bottled spring water, and she produced thoughts that were like bubbles. She went about with a small looking glass, and stood it beside her place at the dining table. It made her a mirrored witness to the meals she shared with Charlie.

By the way, almost the entire female population of the American South was similarly self-intoxicated. The girls were so pampered by Southern gentlemen that they believed in the myth of the Southern belle, whose charms often were more fanciful than real.

In the beginning the MGM studio was a sea of loveliness that seemed almost to engulf us. Strolling down the main alley of the studio, beauty was so common we scarcely bothered to look at it. In addition to the star material, many unsung beauties were engaged merely for the gloss they provided to still pictures.

Of course fashions in beauty kept changing, like styles in dress, on and off the screen. But films were the acknowledged pacesetters, influencing the way women looked almost everywhere.

The Twenties fixed on a type copied after Clara Bow, who was small, dark, and pert. The novelist Eleanor Glyn (the Jackie Susann of her day) dubbed Clara the "It" Girl. The word s-e-x had not yet come into audible use. "It" meant sex, and was accompanied by rolled sox, long cigarette holders, bangs, and Ha-Cha-Cha.

Clara was the idol of the illiterate, and from her dainty lips came nothing more seductive than bubble gum. Fans of Western films adored her, so did cowboys, but her fascinations were decidedly limited.

In a later era Marilyn Monroe assumed the mantle of the sex goddess. Although the delectable Marilyn was an arrant egotist about her beauty, she possessed a degree of shyness that made communication almost impossible. Her lack of worldliness was staggering. She never learned anything about taste, even in the matter of food. In a world where caviar formed an island in a sea of champagne, she once told me that her favorite food was mashed potatoes and gravy. (Marilyn used to bicycle about the studio with a volume of Euclid under her arm, in a pathetic attempt to make Arthur Miller think she was studious.)

Two bright lights of my early life in Hollywood were of a different breed. The sister stars, Norma and Constance Talmadge, were the prettiest girls at any gathering, but preferred jokes to compliments, an attitude that never earned a film star great success. But they made up for a lack of interest in careers by a devotion to rich New York clubmen. And more than all the other film luminaries I've known, they did have fun.

The spinning wheel of fashion carried one young actress to stardom, even though she wasn't photogenic—or maybe because of that. She found a form of compensation. Her looks were the ordinary type of a rather spare department store clerk. Her one asset was a head of natural blond hair. She wore it loose and flowing, and combed a long strand into a lock covering one-third of her face. What lay behind that hair was a well-guarded secret. But with most of her face in hiding, Veronica Lake became not only a beauty but a mystery too. Veronica enjoyed a fairly long career, and proved that sometimes a girl's features matter less than the mystique she is able to generate around them.

It is the fashion nowadays to make lists, so let us tabulate a set of features which have created entire cults, dominated fashion, influenced history, earned fame and, at the same time, broken all the accepted rules of beauty. We might begin with the nose of Barbra Streisand and end with the feet of Greta Garbo. In between one could include other seemingly esthetic mistakes: For instance, the porcine features of a new star of TV and films, the adorable Miss Piggy. That girl must have flirted with a camera that found her irresistibly *photogenique*.

No doubt the best judge of beauty is Time. To pass that severe test and remain unforgotten for years is surely a mark of distinction. Few of the beauties in today's films seem slated for this roster. But there are stars of the past who are eternal symbols of desirability. Such names as Marilyn, Brigitte, or Sophia might head a list of memorable actresses. But at the top of my list, shining like the lady on the Columbia Pictures logo, stands Louise Brooks, long forgotten until Kenneth Tynan, the British critic, called her one of the most mysterious and potent figures in the history of the cinema.

Louise Brooks was one of the first performers to penetrate to the heart of screen acting. Although she made only a few films, she has run through my life like a magnetic needle. Because I knew her well I could never be surprised by what she was (and still is), or by the quality of her art and beauty. Those who have seen her, said Tynan, can never forget her.

Having quit films years ago because she hated work and disliked Hollywood, she can now be seen in a small flat near the University of Rochester, where she lies abed reading Milton. To me this elderly arthritic woman remains memorable as an actress combining a rare photogenic beauty and talent.

Anatomy of a Siren

$\mathcal{T}$HE pure-bred siren is as extinct these days as the great white auk. That female breed has vanished for obvious reasons: most women today are more intent on pursuing their own lives than on being pursued by men. Any girl who has an overwhelming urge to make conquests is afraid to acknowledge it lest she be booted derisively out of the sisterhood.

On the other hand, in Hollywood's heyday many women aspired to join what might be called the sirenhood. Beauty was not the only requirement, or even the most essential one, for membership. It took a certain flair, wit and acuity to acquire a union card.

There were ravishing girls from whom men ran like wolfhounds; sirens whose sex appeal was synthetic or manufactured by publicity departments for fan magazines. Most stars worked harder on their public images than they did in films. In private life that phony image was apt to freeze the ardor of any man expected to kneel in homage.

A rare actress indifferent to this demeaning game was my friend Paulette Goddard. The British emigrée Constance Collier used to call her "a natural born honey-pot" to whom adulation was as persistent as breathing. Paulette's reaction was to underplay rather than to dramatize this faculty.

One summer, when I sailed on the ship *Raffaelo* to meet Paulette in Italy, it amused me to recall our past adventures. The liner was, as always, full of mystery passengers; the mystery being how they ever got the mental urge to travel. But never mind. I would soon catch up with Paulette in Rome, and conversation would take a turn for the better.

Often in the past we had joined one another in our travels. At first, the distance between us was very short, from Santa Monica where I then lived to Beverly Hills where Paulette presided over the household of her husband, Charlie Chaplin.

Before Paulette entered his milieu, Charlie had led a very meager social life. His first wife, blond vacuous little Mildred Harris, resembled most film stars by being her own best fan. At mealtimes she used to set up a rather large mirror beside her plate so that she could look at herself while at table. Mildred's admiration of what she saw left her quite speechless.

Charlie's second helpmeet was a somewhat pretty starlet, a piece of Mexicana named Lita Gray. But both those early unions had been induced by unplanned pregnancies; Mildred's was never completed, which simplified divorce. To do credit to Lita, she remained Mrs. Chaplin long enough to produce two sons.

By that time important visitors from all over the world had begun to descend on Hollywood. But its social gatherings were beset by lethargy because the movie contingent was forced willy-nilly to talk, a hazard only to be relieved by steering guests to the rumpus room and running a movie.

It was frustrating to an outstanding dinner guest, such as H. G. Wells, to sit next to a dazzling movie queen who said, for openers, "Mr. Wells, don't you think that Louis B. Mayer ought to take a trip to Russia and stop Communism?"

No such crack would ever come from the third Mrs. Chaplin. Paulette would have realized that Louis B. could only have been an argument *for* Communism.

True, Charlie Chaplin could extemporize a very good show on his own, and much of his after-dinner entertainment was as funny as the gags he did on film. In one comic turn Charlie would imitate an art critic studying pictures in a gallery. He would commence by examining a miniature that hung about three feet from the floor, then proceed along the wall, studying paintings that hung higher and higher until he reached one at the end which required the stature of a giant to appraise. To watch Charlie's contortions as he seemed to grow from three feet to well over six left everyone in stitches.

In Charlie's entourage there was one shining woman-of-the-world, a companion of his days of poverty in London. By now Constance Collier was a famous Shakespearean actress, but as a showgirl in London she'd been the inspiration of Max Beerbohm's heroine in *Zuleika Dobson,* a siren who caused the entire student body of Oxford to commit mass suicide for love of Zuleika, after which she moved on to Cambridge.

Both Paulette and I, closing the generation gap that separated us from Constance Collier, latched onto her for being as bored as we were with the petty gossip and never-ending shoptalk about films. Mrs. Chaplin, in particular, was getting restless.

As the author of his own movie scripts, Charlie was given to reading them aloud to guests after dinner. Excellent as these scenarios were, they failed to hold attention after several readings. So, Paulette used to sit on the floor behind Charlie's big armchair, under which she stashed a bottle of Dom Perignon to help keep her alert. Even so, those recitals were frequently interrupted by the snores of Mrs. Chaplin.

On marrying Charlie, Paulette became the step-mama of his two little sons, who happened to be equally unimpressed by the importance of their papa. When she moved in, she adopted the boys, not as a mama but as someone much more fun; the French term *copain* defines her relationship with them more exactly than the cold sexless word *pal.*

Many years after Paulette moved beyond Charlie's orbit into more rarefied circles, Charlie Junior dedicated to her the book he wrote about his father. And after Sidney had become a popular sex symbol on Broadway, he still brought his touchier problems as a Casanova to her for advice.

During her tenure as Mrs. Chaplin she gave no encouragement to suitors, which kept Charlie from being jealous. And so it was that falling in love with the wife of the divine clown took on the proportions of a cult.

She had a particularly violent effect on a prominent international playboy, Count Bosdari, who dropped into my house one day for advice on a serious problem. "I want to send some flowers to Paulette that will have a special meaning for her," Maurice declared.

"What flower is her favorite?" Offhand I'd have suggested orchids, the costliest. But the Count insisted that I find out from Paulette herself.

When I happened to mention Maurice's query, I learned that I'd underestimated my girl friend's acumen. "Tell the idiot I adore white violets," said Paulette with a grin. "He'll never find any, so I won't have to bother to thank him."

But she underestimated her besotted admirer. He tracked down a florist in San Francisco who undertook to force some white violets in a hothouse. It took weeks before his token was delivered to Paulette. Then Maurice waited for a response, and waited. I doubt it ever came. Maurice would have done better to send white diamonds.

Early in their marriage Charlie began to detect signs of boredom in his bride. To overcome her ennui he set about casting her as the leading lady in his movies. She played her first major role in *Modern Times,* which still evokes critical acclaim, and continued with a long successful movie career of her own. But success in films never fulfilled Paulette's roving mentality.

As Charlie Chaplin learned along with many others before and after him, it took a man of remarkable brain and wit to hold Paulette's interest. An aura of intelligent raillery surrounded her, which put some men on the defensive. It even posed a hazard to the intellect of H. G. Wells, who paid court to her while she was Mrs. Chaplin.

Recently, a fellow movie star asked Paulette to join a foursome; her date was to be someone comparable to chairman of the board of IBM. Paulette bridled at the invitation. "I never never in my life dated a businessman," she maintained.

It was toward the end of the Chaplin marriage that George Gershwin's tragic romance with Paulette transpired. At the peak of his fame George had been brought to Hollywood by Sam Goldwyn to compose music for films.

I had first known him in New York where a group of us, including Norma and Constance Talmadge, Marilyn Miller, and Marion Davies used to trail George to Harlem to listen to jazz-in-the-raw. His indifference to all those charmers used to puzzle us. George did not prefer boys; that was for sure. But his emotional needs remained a mystery.

Now, at a time when he was so near the end of his short life,

George fell in love. He used to follow Paulette everywhere; he came to life in her presence as he never had before. George expressed his feelings for Paulette in one of the last ballads he ever composed, "They Can't Take That Away From Me," with lyrics, as usual, by his brother Ira.

But George was not at all well. He was beset by headaches of alarming intensity. At that time Freud's psychoanalysis had come into vogue, bruited about by people who understood it least. Among the first to be enticed by Freudian theories were George's kin. So, they sent him to a Hollywood analyst who theorized that George's headaches were caused by his guilty love for the wife of a friend, Charlie Chaplin. George was spending hours on the couch of that analyst who was attempting to cure a brain tumor with psychiatric double-talk.

One day, at a gathering around the Gershwin swimming pool in Beverly Hills, George had a sudden excruciating headache that made him scream in agony. Paralyzed with fright, none of the family was capable of action. Up to that time Paulette had never meddled in their personal affairs, but now she took over. She phoned Charlie and asked what should be done. "I'll get hold of Dr. Reynolds right away," said Charlie.

Dr. Reynolds, a leading brain specialist, came at once. He examined George, summoned an ambulance, and took him straight into the operating room of the Cedars of Lebanon Hospital. Operating on George's brain, Reynolds uncovered a tumor the size of a fist. Had he been called in when George was first stricken, George's life might have been saved. Now it was too late, and alas, George died.

Had he lived beyond the age of thirty-eight, we could have enjoyed many more Gershwin melodies. And perhaps he would have won Paulette after she and Charlie split up. But that is idle speculation. Too often a spellbound romance ends in disenchantment. As it was, George remained a sad, haunting memory.

The fact is that any man yearning to settle down in a sedate, tranquil marriage was better off choosing a cozy little wife. The first of the four brave men who chose Paulette was the scion of a wealthy family of the Old South. They met when she was a teenage beauty in the Ziegfeld Follies, and she was enticed by the young man's love for sports. (Even then her tennis was of championship caliber, as was her skiing on both snow and water.)

She rode to hounds with her husband's pack, and found that sport in the deep South was unaccompanied by thought and thought, both outdoors and in, was replaced by bourbon. When boredom set in Paulette walked out and headed for Hollywood where, she supposed, life might be less tedious. Already an inveterate student, she learned a lesson from that first experience: the inadequacy of a scion of the rich.

Her second matrimonial venture leaped over the wide distance between a dunce and a born genius. (It was unforgivable of Charlie to slough off his life with Paulette in a few short paragraphs of his autobiography. True, he wrote from the vantage point of his ideal union with Oona O'Neill. But in Paulette he'd found a sparkling wife with innate glamour, unlike the synthetic dazzle promoted by Hollywood. And she had turned his haphazard home into a kind of salon.)

The third incumbent was stage and screen actor Burgess Meredith. Burgess was then young, good-looking, and talented. He had the wit of his Irish heritage; and he earned a movie star's salary. But Paulette's scheme of life had always been "onward and upward." To supplant the great Chaplin even with a charmer like Burgess seemed puzzling.

After their divorce, Burgess cooked up the explanation that Paulette had married him to gain some sort of tax deduction. She never dignified that cockamamie alibi with a denial, having adopted the credo, "never complain, never explain." But in a moment of truth she once told me the bona fide reason for that marriage.

One night during World War II she was in New York, drinking champagne at the bar in El Morocco, when a man she had met in Washington stepped up and asked, "How would you like to go to China and entertain the troops?" Having left Charlie, she was free, at loose ends, and also a bit tipsy. So she agreed.

She always accepted an invitation, knowing that when she bowed out she could express urgent regrets. This time she was trapped. American troops under General Chenault were on the move, fighting the Japanese invaders. Before realizing what she'd done, Paulette found herself in war-torn China; the first and only female among acres of men in khaki. Night after night she danced with soldiers on makeshift platforms while the campaign surged around them.

Now, it was only to be expected that those partners took every possible advantage of dancing with Paulette. And she endured their lack of restraint as best she could. "Those poor boys were on their way through hell," she said, "so how could a girl blame them for being pushy."

Those six weeks of being mauled in China seemed like six years of hard labor on the waterfront of Marseilles. Every bead had been rubbed off her ballgown. And she was left with one desire: to spend the rest of her life as a wallflower.

Paulette staggered off a plane in California and found Burgess waiting for her. "Gee, but you look awful!" he said, a remark that canceled out the creepy double entendres that had assailed her for weeks. When Burgess added, "Let's get married," it seemed to put a limit on sex for once and all. "So I let him lead me straight to the license bureau," Paulette acknowledged.

Her six years as Mrs. Meredith became a series of letdowns. A climax came when she heard from Burgess' own lips of his love for a rival. At that time the Merediths were living at a lovely little farm in New Jersey.

One week Paulette invited Salvador Dali to Sunday lunch, and boasted that he'd be served fresh produce from their own farm. In planning the menu she figured it ought to be somewhat exotic, to match the eccentricity of the outrageous Salvador. Then came a sudden inspiration: the main dish could be a suckling pig.

On Saturday night Burgess went to the icebox to get a can of beer and suddenly froze motionless at a sight that met his gaze: the piglet, all ready for the oven, stuffed, garnished, and with a little apple in its mouth.

Addressing it, Burgess gasped, "Leonora! What have they done to you, Leonora?" And he looked absolutely stricken.

Paulette was flabbergasted. "It was the first time I'd ever heard a word about those feelings of his. I could have sworn that I was the only one he loved."

The humiliation of sharing Burgess' love with a piglet was too much. One frustration followed another until the Merediths faced each other across the breakfast table one morning and decided to call it quits. After their divorce they remained the best of enemies.

But at long last came a marriage that made up for the perils of the preceding ones. Erich Maria Remarque fulfilled every one of

Paulette's tough requirements. More than handsome, he was elegant; more than elegant, he was a wit; more than witty, he was a famous writer; his anti-war novel, *All Quiet on the Western Front,* had won him worldwide renown. And Erich's brilliant career had made him a millionaire. He had become a connoisseur of every amenity: art, women, jewels, food, and wine. His appreciation of Dom Perignon champagne and Persian caviar matched that of Paulette herself.

Several of the most celebrated beauties in the world had been Erich's mistresses. In fact, he first met Paulette by chance in a Park Avenue florist's shop where he had gone to order flowers for her predecessor. He sent the flowers but he asked Paulette to dine, which they did every night until Erich died fourteen years later.

Erich had a gallantry toward women that has now gone out of fashion. As a European and German-born at that, he was not quite as bewildered as most men are by the enigmas his bride presented; he merely put them down as "shenanigans" and they amused him. But Erich also considered Paulette seriously as the greatest specimen in all his collections, more fascinating than his Egyptian bronzes or his Monet water lilies.

In 1971 when Erich finally departed from the special world he created around Paulette, romance must have disappeared from her life forever. In Erich she had more than met her match, and I doubt there's another of his caliber around anywhere.

To accompany Paulette into her own world, as I did for many years, was as unusual a trip as entering Wonderland along with Alice. Looking as freshly seductive as when she was Erich Remarque's bride, she still changed the human metabolism around her. Women couldn't believe she was not the hard-working sexpot her jewels and vast worldly goods indicated. They took a cue from men who never behaved in her presence as they did elsewhere.

To cite a single instance, one day in Paris a taxi driver not only refused Paulette's tip but wouldn't even let her pay for our ride. A *Paris* taxi driver!

During the spring of 1973, in the first shocking week of the Watergate investigation, some journalist wrote, "The only scandalous element lacking in the Watergate affair is *sex*." Well, thanks to Paulette, it could even have had a whiff of that. Now, with Watergate behind us, the incident can be revealed.

It began in New York one afternoon, when Paulette went to a Seventh Avenue wholesale showroom to pick up a bargain dress or two. While she was studying the collection she became aware of a distinguishd elderly gentleman studying *her*. Presently, he wangled an introduction through the owner of the firm, in which he happened to be an investor.

It turned out he was a gentleman of great wealth, who also held a post in the nation's capital, ostensibly because of his contributions to the fund for reelecting President Nixon. (Otherwise how could someone in a chronic state of intemperance be appointed, as he had been, to the President's Council on Physical Fitness?)

To disguise his identity let us call him Mr. Miller. But the old boy had acquired a nickname in his native Texas where he was called "Whoopsie."

Paulette had scarcely returned to her apartment from the dress showing when a telegram arrived, saying:

To the elegant Paulette Goddard:

Paulette, I've been waiting around all my life to be disarmed and struck by a beautiful girl. Paulette, your dancing eyes, your neat figure wrapped up in that gray plaid suit somehow kind of got to me. Paulette, I can hardly wait to appoint you as a special advisor to the President's Council on Physical Fitness. Paulette, please call Whoopsie Miller at PL 34500, Suite 501 anytime this afternoon.

> Paulette, you're neat nifty and nice.
> Affectionately yours, Whoops

Endless phone calls followed with proposals of marriage which, of course, Paulette declined. Men want to marry her on the same impulse that makes a rabbit charge the headlights of a Rolls-Royce.

Now, at the very time that Whoopsie was hellbent on supplying a sexy angle to Washington news, some of the President's men were singing a requiem for their leader at the Watergate hearings. This fact ought to have made Whoopsie wary of supplying news media with a possible headline such as: "Whoopsie Miller offered post on President's Council on Physical Fitness to—guess who? Paulette Goddard!"

"Whoopsie shouldn't have sent that telegram," Paulette observed, "until he made sure I'd toss it into a shredding machine." And then she mused, "But it goes to show that a shredding machine is the last item a girl should own!"

Some years later, when we resumed our travels in Europe we were required, as usual, to flash passports. In the space allotted to one's profession Paulette had stated "actress." This is inaccurate. Paulette's profession should read "siren." In her case I think it is an honorable calling, for it involves no pretense but comes so naturally.

Sound

*T*HE sounds that used to reach our ears in the course of normal living have swelled greatly during the existence of the movies. Even so, the lifespan of motion pictures has been so short that some of those who were in on their beginning are still around. By the time the first sound cameras started grinding out footage, I had already become a professional in that new brand of show business.

When my father was manager of a stock company that produced plays in downtown Los Angeles, I was put to work on stage in such plays as *Little Lord Fauntleroy* or *Way Down East,* both of which required a child actress. An enterprising showman, Pop took to screening short motion pictures during the entre-actes of our plays. Those flickering images enthralled me, and I managed to see as much of them as I could from my vantage point backstage.

Because film rentals were in short supply, Pop was forced to run the same picture week after week. A favorite was *The Fall of Rome,* a spectacle in which a group of Hollywood extras draped in sheets straggled wearily down a dirt road in a suburb of Los Angeles called Azuza. The film was so scratched that Azuza looked like a tropical rain forest, but clouds of dust rose from the sizzling roadbed.

Audiences never seemed to tire of that historic event, and waited eagerly for the sudden appearance of a local farmhand in overalls, who unwittingly swung into view on a bicycle. Then in pride at finding himself a movie actor, he made funny faces at the camera. Later on he entered the profession and became famous as Ben Turpin.

Although most films were strictly episodic, there were others that followed a vague story line, and it presently crossed my childish mind to take a chance on writing a movie. In fact, ink must have filtered into my bloodstream from my Pop, who used to publish a weekly newspaper and write most of it himself. I proceeded to scribble a plot, and mailed it to the Biograph Company whose New York address was printed on a film can.

When my first script was accepted, I was hooked for good. After writing a good many silent films, I felt rich beyond the dreams of Thespis. I have never considered an acting career as anything but a self-indulgent ego trip, so it was a relief to quit acting altogether.

Those of us involved in the new industry thought that as soon as movies lost their novelty, they'd be as dated as the kinetoscopes that still gathered dust on parlor tables.

Writing scripts was easy and gave me plenty of time and money for shopping on Wilshire Boulevard, which was quickly acquiring luxuries imported from New York. On one occasion a suspicious shopkeeper sent for the police because I wanted to pay for a baby grand piano with a pocketful of greenbacks.

It was a mixed bag of inhabitants that occupied the Hollywood of those salubrious days, when the landscape was still dotted with orange groves and movies were screened in open-faced sheds; when the air was not yet polluted by industrial smog or the even more heady fumes of pot.

Not only did the film industry take advantage of that clear, clean air but a more distinguished colony followed suit for reasons unrelated to making movies; they were mostly seekers of health, drawn by California sunshine. Aldous Huxley, a semi-invalid, moved from London to Los Angeles, with his wife Maria and their young son Matthew. Other intellectuals soon followed, such as the Igor Stravinskys, together with Igor's biographer Robert Craft. The three comrades settled on a hilltop just above the wobbly high-rise sign reading "Hollywood," which Craft claimed was required because otherwise people wouldn't believe such a place existed.

The great pianist Artur Rubinstein became a resident of Beverly Hills, and what a treat it was on moonlit nights to linger on Artur's lawn and listen to him practicing Chopin. Christopher Isherwood, heartsick over his beloved war-torn Berlin, purchased a house in Santa Monica, as did the noted German novelist Thomas Mann, and the famed French director René Clair, with his chic Parisian wife Bronya.

Visitors often came for a "breather" from the war, among them H. G. Wells, who used to dash over from England on business or pleasure, the latter concerning Paulette Goddard. She presided over Charlie Chaplin's household, but her husband was so preoccupied trying out new gags on their guests that he failed to notice every man in the room was in love with his wife.

Two leading British poets, W. H. Auden and Stephen Spender, and the philosopher Lord Bertrand Russell, sometimes joined the group, as did King Alfonso of Spain. A philosopher of sorts, Alfonso alibied Fatty Arbuckle's accidental murder of a party girl by remarking, "What a catastrophe! It could have happened to a girl at any party." There was a sad inevitability about Fatty's romance, but other high-voltage affairs intrigued gossips.

Leopold Stokowski came ostensibly to bring his orchestra into movies, but actually to pursue his idyll with Greta Garbo which, in his mind, rivaled the passion of Richard and Cosima Wagner, or even of Tristan and Isolde. Their greatest bond was a vegetarianism so ardent that Stoki insisted on edibles that grew only underground, thus preserving direct contact with Mother Earth.

At Stoki's lunch parties we used to sit in lotus position on the ground, at a table made of a California redwood stump. We ate from earthen bowls full of chopped raw carrots, radishes, beets and yams, and imbibed Stoki's pronouncements about their cosmic effects on the psyche.

None too impressed, Greta finally fled to Europe, with Stoki in pursuit. He inveigled her into a villa on the Côte d'Azur. But again she ran away, back to Hollywood, where Cecil Beaton fell crazily in love with her.

Silent film stars were sort of homespun types. They didn't take acting lessons and never heard of Stanislavsky, so they never became self-conscious. Their off-screen behavior was not yet contrived by studio policy. Without the benefit of press agentry, they lived in a paradise of free will.

Hollywood carried on as if there were no such thing as a world war. Our dresses were still crossing the combat zones from the Paris houses of Patou, Mainbocher, and Balenciaga. The war seemed very far away, while close to home something totally new began to happen. Movies were invaded by a sort of silent genius more subtle than the old-fashioned art of mime. Artists of the caliber of Griffith or Garbo could break one's heart with a silent image, or Chaplin bring forth gales of laughter by flicking a tattered derby.

A scene in *Intolerance* where a love-sick Union soldier, guarding Lillian Gish, gazes at her blond beauty with a mixture of lust and longing, couldn't be enhanced by the poetry of a Shakespeare. And who could dismiss the anguish in another episode, showing Mae Marsh waving a hesitant farewell to a lover being led off to execution?

With such a roster of talents to draw on, Hollywood looked like a coming center of culture. It could have become a modern Athens.

But then, in 1931, a black-faced comedian named Al Jolson took his stance in a closeup, opened his big mouth, and shouted *"Mammy!"* into the ears of the world.

The curtain had closed on silent films forever.

Up to that time the motion picture cathedrals of the Twenties were so awesome in their grandeur that it didn't seem they could ever crumble into dust, or be transformed into today's cinema-chain boxes, without atmosphere, and usually located in the basement of a high-rise structure.

One regrets those old film palaces, where we occupied armchairs upholstered in brocade, and any ordinary girl and guy cuddling to the strains of Brahms or Schubert could feel exalted by an experience almost like religion.

Sound seemed, at first, merely a new gimmick. Actors who had had stage experience could handle dialogue. But film-bred thespians ran into trouble. There was the much-cited case of Jack Gilbert whose high Irish voice had overtones of falsetto. Despite his many romances, he was rumored to prefer boys to girls, a completely false rumor fed by Garbo's having walked out on him. The demise of his career might have contributed to his early death, such being the ego of an actor. Garbo herself survived, thanks to a throaty voice that suggested a low-keyed Swedish foghorn.

A certain period of chaos remained, but only for a short time. The sound technicians gained control, and reproduced any noises known to mankind, the louder the better. Moviegoers became inured to this assault on their eardrums, as they did to radio and TV noises, and as today's disco fans can listen all night to caterwauling that could be better done by cats.

Silent films have largely disappeared. They had to be printed on nitrate stock, which was so inflammable that the slightest jolt could ignite a spark that might send a whole theatre up in flames. So, as soon as a film had run its course, it was destroyed. Very few movie-goers ever gave silent pictures a thought until October 1978, when *The New York Times* ran a big headline saying, "Treasure Trove of 500 Lost Silent Films Found In Yukon." The *Times* article explained how a bulldozer operating in Dawson City had just unearthed a goldmine of these films in their original tin cans. They had been used as landfill for an old construction site, dumped into an excavation, covered with earth and forgotten. In a normally mild climate the movies would have melted into goo, but in the frigid arctic they were literally frozen in time.

The job of restoring them would be colossal. In Canada it is against the law to transport nitrate on common carriers. So, a tractor-trailer had to be padded with asbestos and guarded all the way on a 4,000-mile journey to a laboratory in Ottawa, where the treasures could be treated and, with luck, restored.

Perhaps in time this will be done, and moviegoers can again see Mae Marsh as *Polly of the Circus* execute a curtsy in her tutu. Or an ancient number called *For Her Father's Sins,* filmed by Mutual in 1917, and devised by this writer, might be laughed at by sophisticated viewers.

In the early days of sound, I had a talk with Aldous Huxley, which showed how vulnerable even a fine brain could be. Aldous was then desperately anxious to send money to victims of the bombing of Britain. So, he accepted a large fee to speak on a broadcast sponsored by a well-known brand of gelatin.

Now, in England Aldous was not quite respectable, for he monkeyed around with psychedelic mushrooms of antic habits and other drugs beyond the pale of scientific propriety. The gelatin firm knew this, but being a bit snobbish, felt a Huxley was a Huxley. So, they assured him he could talk on any subject he liked. Aldous chose the Quakers, who were in high esteem in England. (They ran the entire candy industry of the Empire, and there was a theory that no Quaker was ever known to be poor.)

Pacing Sunset Boulevard en route to that broadcast, Aldous, in a state of euphoria, became almost lyrical. "Just to think that sound has made it possible to reach listeners who never heard of Quaker philosophy and their manner of living!" Aldous declared. "And people can hear words spoken in pure English. We are approaching a new Utopia!"

But on our way home, Aldous became rather distrait. It had transpired that his broadcast was frequently interrupted by commercials touting the sponsor's gelatin as a cure-all for any disease known to mankind.

"I hope the British critics won't think I set myself up as a swami or some sort of faith healer," he fretted.

As I tried to assure him that no intelligent person took commercials seriously, we passed a supermarket. Suddenly, Aldous halted. "D'you mind stopping in here a moment?" he asked. "I think I'll buy a box of that gelatin and give it a try."

Such was the hypnotic force of a commercial on this thinking man. But I have since wondered whatever became of the soul-stirring sounds of Aldous Huxley's new Utopia.

Harlow's Hollywood

I'D been working on the script for a picture called *Red-Headed Woman,* and one day Irving Thalberg, MGM's head of production, told me that the most likely contender for the lead in the picture was a young actress he'd just seen in the Howard Hughes movie *Hell's Angels* playing a femme fatale who smoked cigarettes in long holders and drove men wild, just as Theda Bara had done for the previous generation.

Irving was undeterred by some seething criticisms of the girl's talent. Robert Sherwood, later to become one of America's foremost playwrights, was then movie critic on the old version of *Life* magazine and he wrote Jean up as "an obstreperously alluring young lady named Jean Harlow of whom not much is likely to be heard."

The only doubt Irving had about the sinister young actress was whether she could be funny. On the day of Miss Harlow's first meeting with Irving, he asked me to his office to help make an appraisal of her. Jean's own tawny hair had been bleached to a "platinum" blonde, but she'd been ordered to the makeup department to be fitted with a red wig. She might have been sixteen and her baby face looked utterly incongruous against the flaming wig.

Jean didn't seem at all nervous in the presence of the man who could skyrocket her into fame; she had that sort of gently sardonic attitude that comes from having gone through the many ups and downs of any budding career in the studios.

Irving, being self-removed from life, dearly loved gossip. "How did you make out with Howard Hughes?" he asked Jean. "Well, one day when he was eating a cookie he offered me a bite." When we laughed, Jean interrupted. "Don't underestimate that," she said. "The poor guy's so afraid of germs, it could darn near have been a proposal!"

"Do you think you can make an audience laugh?" asked Irving.

"*With* me or *at* me?"

"...*At* you!"

"Why not? People have been laughing at me all my life."

As Jean breezed out of the office, she stopped at the door to give us a quick, bright little nod; a gesture I wrote into the script and look for every time I see that old movie. "I don't think we need worry about Miss Harlow's sense of humor," said Irving.

Jan. 22—9:30—Report to set.

Sitting with Jean while a technical crew adjusted the lighting, I began to learn something about her street-urchin personality. "I love people to think I came up from the gutter," she remarked. "Wouldn't it be dull to know that my grandpa's present on my *fifth* birthday was an ermine bedspread?"

Jean had been an only child. Her real name was Harlean Carpenter, and the family lived in Kansas City where any wealthy grandpa might think of a five-year-old in terms of ermine bedspreads. At sixteen she had married one of the town's rich playboys. They had drifted to Los Angeles where Harlean, incapable of being a housewife, took a new name and started to work as an extra in the movies.

Underlying Jean's raffish sense of humor was a resignation unusual for one so young. Nothing would ever surprise Jean. She knew exactly how people were going to react to her; if men were stupid, they'd fall for her; if they had good sense, they'd laugh her off.

Now, there is a certain type of sexpot who is not resented by women; Constance Talmadge and Marilyn Monroe were like that. But women were invariably catty toward Jean; largely through a noblesse oblige on her part. Jean agreeably supplied them with the shocks they expected. I recall an occasion on the set where the camera was to cease grinding abruptly at a moment when Jean started to remove her jacket. But for some reason the boy in charge of the clapboard failed to give the signal to cut, so Jean "innocently" continued to take off her jacket, under which she was nude to the waist. Nudity was rarely seen in those days, and Jean's had the startling quality of an alabaster statue. Visitors on the set scarcely believed their eyes. The lighting crew almost fell out of the flies in shock. Wide-eyed in her "apology," Jean addressed the director. "I'm sorry, but nobody gave the order to cut."

Jean and I were together a lot during the filming of *Red-Headed Woman*. One sequence took place on the merry-go-round at the Santa Monica pier. And, as Jack Conway was busy filming another segment of the script, I went out with Jean and directed the scene— my first and last attempt at directing.

When *Red-Headed Woman* was released, it instantly catapulted Jean Harlow into stardom. The picture enjoyed all sorts of fringe successes. It won the award of *Vanity Fair* magazine as the best film of the year, and the London office of MGM reported that the royal family kept a copy at the palace for entertaining guests after dinner. Among its many distinctions, *Red-Headed Woman* made film history because it brought censorship to the movies and caused massive difficulties to the industry for years to come. The film outraged ladies' clubs throughout the land, but not because of any episode which might be termed salacious. It was because our heroine, the bad girl of whom all good husbands dream, ended her career as many such scalawags do: rich, happy and respected, without ever having paid for her sins.

Now, one of the adventures of our heroine was a scene in which she was driven home from a shopping tour by a handsome young chauffeur who, laden with packages, respectfully followed her upstairs to her bedroom. But after dropping the packages onto a chaise longue, the chauffeur took his red-headed employer in his arms and kissed her in a long, slow fade-out. The role of that chauffeur, although short, was important, and one morning Irving sent for me to discuss the casting of the part. "We've got a French actor here on a six months' option," said Irving, "but I'm letting him go because nobody can understand the guy's English. His option is up in two weeks, which would be just long enough for him to do the part of that chauffeur. So take a look at his test and tell me if you think the role is worth rewriting for a Frenchman."

When I looked at the tests in the projection room, I recognized the young actor as a friend of Yvonne Chevalier's whom I had met on the Santa Fe. So! Now he was to be sent back home to Paris . . . one more heart broken by Hollywood. But I figured the young man's accent wouldn't be too big a problem since his actions were a lot more understandable than words. So he was put into that bit part, in which he finished out his contract and left for Paris, thinking he had shaken the stardust of Hollywood from his feet forever.

Sometime later, when Irving and I were going through the postcards from our previews, we found a startling unanimity. Not since the days of Rudolph Valentino had any actor made such an impact on the female audience as had that chauffeur. None of us involved in the picture was aware of the young actor's power to enchant. It took those suburban housewives to advise Irving that even his French accent was an asset. Irving immediately cabled the Paris office to send the actor back to Hollywood. His salary while under option had been $350 a week. His new contract called for ten times that figure on a two-year guarantee. And for Charles Boyer, that was merely the beginning.

One afternoon while Hoppy (screenwriter Robert Hopkins) and I were having coffee in our local hangout, the Trap, he thought of a colorful character on which to base a movie for Jean Harlow. She would play the daughter of a horse trader, born and raised in an environment of racetracks. The locale would be Saratoga, which would also be the title of the film. We told our idea to our producer, Bernie Hyman, who said, "That sounds like a possibility. Go ahead!"

When our story was ready to be put into script form, Bernie hired a jockey from Santa Anita Track to supply a proper vernacular for the dialogue. (Our pal Bernie was a stickler for authenticity. When he produced *The Great Waltz,* he rented a Stradivarius violin at a thousand dollars a day for an actor who couldn't have played a harmonica.) Our jockey was a wizened little man of about forty who bore out my contention that jockeys are among the most civilized men in the world. Sitting over coffee in the Trap, he gave me a lesson I couldn't have gotten in a Yale drama course. "Look, honey," he said, "if you use jockey terms in your dialogue, you'll be writing a movie for jockeys, and just between the two of us, folks who spend their time with horses don't care very much about films. Write your dialogue in your own words and it'll sound O.K. even to a jockey."

The filming of *Saratoga* had been completed except for its final scene when Jean was suddenly taken with a mild sort of ailment that kept her home. Jack Conway started "shooting around her," as they say in films. One afternoon, a group of us were sitting in Bernie's outer office; there were Clark Gable, Bernie's secretary Goldie, and the switchboard operator who happened to be a boy. We began to talk of Jean and to wonder what her ailment was. No use asking her Ma because Ma didn't believe in the existence of disease. "Probably drunk again," said Clark, making a pretty stupid joke because Jean was not given to drinking when on the job. "Let's call up and ask her when she's coming back," I suggested. The boy at the switchboard got through to Jean's house, talked briefly to a servant and then hung up. "They've taken Jean to Cedars of Lebanon!" he said with apprehension. We all began to be disturbed, because for Ma to allow her precious baby to be hospitalized was a pretty radical move. Clark suggested we call the hospital. The call went through. Presently, the boy's face went deathly white and the receiver clattered onto the desk. We knew what had happened before he told us. "Jean's dead!"

Then was the studio thrown into dismay; Jean had earned millions for MGM and stood to make millions more. L.B. (Louis B. Mayer, head of MGM) took the tragedy as a personal affront, but just the same he issued a humanitarian edict. "The next time one of our valuable properties gets sick, the studio's got to find out what's the matter."

Jean's funeral at Forest Lawn was an orgy of grief, with mobs of weeping fans, monitored by the police. L.B. sent a heart of red roses five feet tall pierced by a golden arrow. But those of us who were close to the bier were more impressed when one of Jean's co-stars, Bill Powell, strode up to place a single white rose on her breast.

After it was too late, the studio tried to find some reason for Jean's death. She'd always enjoyed the best of health. When stricken, her symptoms seemed to be merely those of fatigue. One theory was that overexposure to the sun might have poisoned her. The strangely iridescent skin, which was the reason Jean's platinum hair looked so natural, was as sensitive as an albino's. But then, she never went into the sunlight unless protected by long sleeves, a high neckline, a big floppy hat and a parasol. Ma *could* be relied on for that! Another notion was that excessive use of bleach might have brought on a fatal uremia. Whether there was any truth to that or not, the doctors and nurses who had hovered over Jean at the hospital agreed on one thing: she had refused to put up a fight. And this fact bolstered a theory of my own on what caused Jean to die.

Unlike Marilyn Monroe, Jean was no Narcissus. To her, sex had come to be an incessant matter-of-talk that would have bored Messalina. She recognized her looks as an accident of birth. The platinum hair which brought her to fame was a nuisance because she had to spend an hour in the makeup department every second day for its roots to be touched up. Jean's attitude toward clothes was that of a small boy who balks at being dressed up. I never knew her to go shopping. Jean's mother bought everything for her. Jean would slip into a new dress without bothering to glance in the mirror. Why bother? She always looked the same . . . terrific.

So all right! She *was* terrific. But to whom? To her distant public, to a trio of husbands which included a Kansas City playboy, a German psycho, and a mild little MGM cameraman, all of them the dull type of gentlemen who prefer blondes. Between those three disastrous episodes, which Jean philosophically called "marriages of *in*convenience," she lived with her mother, who was her replica in looks, platinum hair and all, except in a more opulent form. Ma was married to a florid gentleman of Italian descent named Marino Bello, who was equipped with all the gigolo tricks to make a female happy. But Marino was given to writing Jean unwelcome love notes which had to be kept secret from her mother.

Jean was always lonely; she longed to find companionship in a lover, one with wit enough to respond to her compulsive wise-cracks. But very early in life she realized she was doomed to failure. Irving, for instance, found her nothing more than a booby trap for male stupidity.

Because Jean granted so little importance to sex, she could be thoughtlessly cruel at times, especially with Paul Bern, the plump, mixed-up MGM producer who was her second husband. Soon after she married Paul, he took Jean and me to a football match. That day Paul made a great issue of his wife's comfort, supplying her with a cushion, a lap robe, a hot dog, a bottle of soda. Finally, he asked if he could get her anything more. Jean indicated a husky fullback down on the field and said, "Yes, Daddy. Get me that one!" Jean and I laughed, having no inkling how the joke must have tortured her impotent and psychopathic bridegroom.

But the selfsame sex that could so easily be a joke ultimately caught Jean up in the most horrifying experience a girl in Hollywood ever had to go through. Bern adored Jean as abjectly as only a German psycho might. But expecting no return of his ardor, he had had to woo her with arguments unrelated to sex. He maintained that, as a producer, he'd devote all his talent to her career. He was good and kind and gentle, and Jean had had too many experiences with men who were weak, selfish or evil. At that very moment she was living under the same roof with one of the worst, her own mother's husband. "It'll be a relief to get away from the rat before Mom finds him out," Jean told me. In short, for Jean to marry someone as respectful as Paul Bern seemed a very bright thing to do. "Paul's so sweet," Jean said to me. "He'd cut out his own heart before he'd ever do me in." And then, even *Bern* did Jean in.

He may have counted on his marriage producing a miracle and that, with an inspiration like Jean, he could conquer his impotence. Well—he couldn't. As time went on, the poor man tried to assuage his guilt by practices that Jean was too normal to accept. But she understood; didn't blame her husband, assured him how little sex meant to her.

Jean's tolerance went even further; "Just do anything you like, sweetheart," she said, "but count me out of those sessions. Find yourself someone else. I won't object. I'll understand."

Still putting up a bluff at manhood, Bern agreed. And then one evening, to bolster his pretenses, he told Jean of a rendezvous he'd made. When he left for his date, Jean kissed him tolerantly and wished him good night. Next morning she found a note under her bedroom door. It said, in essence, "I hope you'll understand that last night was a farce. Now I'm yours forever. Paul."

Puzzled, Jean went to ask for an explanation. Bern lay sprawled on his bedroom floor in a pool of blood. There was a bullet hole in his head and his squat, fat body, so ill-equipped for marriage, was shamefully naked. Paul Bern's suicide was the very apotheosis of masochism, for he had killed himself while looking in a full-length mirror.

Jean's role in that tragedy of Beauty and the Beast must have destroyed the last small vestige of faith she may have had in men.

But then, just prior to filming *Saratoga,* she had co-starred in a picture with William Powell. Bill had all the qualities that Jean despaired of ever finding in a sweetheart. He was a gentleman, urbane, witty and charming. It began to flash on her consciousness that sex need not be snide and degrading. She turned her full battery of feminine charms on Bill.

But Bill happened to have been the victim of another blonde. He had been married to Carole Lombard, whose incredible glamour made him feel inferior: reduced his ego practically to the situation of a Paul Bern. Bill needed some Little Miss Nobody in order to regain his polarity. So he walked out on Jean and about three years after her death he finally discovered just what he'd been looking for—a blonde as cute and pretty as Jean but with the one virtue Jean lacked, anonymity. Bill married the charmer and they lived happily ever after.

After Bill's rejection, Jean seemed to lose interest in everything and, when stricken, she refused to put up a fight. It was as if she took advantage of a minor ailment to escape from life. Her mother's reason was saved by her faith; she never admitted that Jean was gone.

The filming of *Saratoga* was completed with an actress in a platinum wig substituting for Jean. All the camera angles featured Clark full face, with the substitute's back to the camera, *Saratoga* confounded all the experts who claimed that Jean's tragedy would keep people out of the theaters. The movie stacked up a fortune which, to Louis B. at least, made for a happy ending.

To become a star an actress must be sensitive. A letter Jean wrote me after the Bern tragedy could only have been written by a woman of warmth and sensitivity.

ANITA DEAR,

Could I but make you know the depths of gratitude I have for your most wonderful letter with its expressions of loyalty, friendship and understanding. Without friends, I could not have gone on. Please know I shall always treasure your wonderful faith in me and will never disappoint you.

Devotedly and gratefully,
Jean

Jean had all the sensitivity required to be a star. But to remain one, an actress also has to be an egomaniac. Jean didn't have enough ego to survive, and so the movies' greatest femme fatale simply died of sex starvation.

Orgy at MGM

The "orgy" was the annual Christmas party, given to cement morale, break down class distinctions and keep workers happy throughout the coming year.

Although I had been at the studio less than a week, I'd already found two new cronies; members of the writing staff, Howard Emmett Rogers and John Lee Mahin. As a rule writers are a bore and never talk about anything but their work; Rogers and Johnny never mentioned it. (Those friendships worked out to be delight-fully uncomplicated; Rogers was married to a flaming redhead, an ex-Follies beauty, so attractive she had no urge to be jealous of me. Red was a philosopher. One day, discussing the sexes, she re-marked, "Men know more than we do, honey, but you see we're smarter!" If I have always been partial to men, it's because there are so few girls like Red Rogers. Johnny Mahin, tall, brown-haired and agreeable, was in a constant state of romantic flux. So many fiendish starlets were battling over him, marrying him, divorcing or suing him that I became a sort of Platonic haven.)

The day of the orgy turned out sunny, clear and hot. Rogers, Johnny and I first went to the Beverly Hills Derby for lunch with my "friend" Wilson Mizner. We were trying to talk him into going to the party when W. C. Fields toddled in like a rowdy old Santa, tugging a suitcase which gave out the seductive clank of bottles. Wilson preferred to remain with W. C., so we left them to make merry on the contents of W. C.'s suitcase.

Arriving at MGM, we proceeded toward Mayer's office and ran smack into the orgy. The entrance to his suite was blocked by a bawdy mob voicing a lot of innuendo. We heard a messenger boy declare libidinous aspirations to Joan Crawford, who fended him off with an arch slap on the wrist.

The situation inside L.B.'s office was a switch on the old *Droit de Seigneur* in which a VIP was licensed to make a pass at any humble maid. In this case the privilege belonged to secretaries, manicurists, hairdressers, wardrobe girls and whatnots, who were taking over the boss's lap as if they were starlets. Presently Irving wandered through to pay his respects to pleasure for once in the year. At sight of Irving, the girls attacked him en masse. While he was being smeared with lipstick, we moved on toward Arlie's office. There the mob was smaller but no less impetuous. Arlie (Albert Lewin, Thalberg's executive assistant), as a gourmet, had supplied it with champagne and caviar and, his face frozen into a grin, sat fondling a starlet on each knee—had Arlie been granted a third knee he'd have taken on another. I was willing to be a benign spectator to all this, but Rogers and Johnny had enjoyed too many real adventures to bother with such meager license, so they suggested we move on to the music department.

Musicians, sensuous by nature, also tend to be uncontrolled, so L.B. had located them out of sight where they couldn't be spotted by the daily guided tours. They occupied a row of sheds at the far end of the back lot, and there we ran into license that was for real. Music was pouring from every sort of sound equipment; office doors were wide open and a number of ladies of the street had been sneaked in through a back entrance. A certain amount of clothing had been discarded and a disheveled Jack Barrymore was offering stardom to a young thing in whose talent he was shamelessly disinterested.

Once in a while I hear a bawdy joke that is as sound as if it had been worked out by Euclid. That orgy reminded me of this one. It seems a traveling salesman from Cincinnati made a trip to Iran where a certain beautiful princess picked him up as a curiosity. When our hero got back home he described the adventure to a friend. He told of the princess's exotic beauty; the palace to which she took him; the vintage wine; the perfumed bath; the hidden violins; the priceless jewels and garments she discarded; and, at last, her shimmering nudity. "And then what?" our hero's listener gasped. "Oh, then it was just the same as it is in Cincinnati."

So much for that Hollywood orgy. But it was possible for those festivities which we found so innocuous to be accompanied by grim violence. On Christmas Day the obituary columns were lengthened by drunk drivers who left the studio in droves. That celebration in '31 was followed by a number of motor crack-ups, some serious but none fatal. However, a carpenter had fallen down a narrow iron staircase on the outside of a sound stage just as he was calling out the last "Merry Christmas" of his life.

When I reported the orgy to Mr. E. (my husband, John Emerson) by phone, his psychology, based on clichés, always made him suspicious of the wrong things. My idea of festivity was to be with Wilson, so Mr. E. asked, "Did you see Gable at the party?" I explained that L.B. had ordered Clark to keep away for fear the girls would tear him limb from limb. At any rate, he was then firmly in the grip of his second wife, Ria Langham, who was rich, refined, ten years older than Clark and by appearance could have been mistaken for his mother.

It would have been pointless to tell a husband that Clark had no more allure for me than a chatty young man who delivered my groceries. Clark was happiest when on camping trips, but, like most "overly male" Americans, he felt required to have a large quota of affairs. Without any thought of being disloyal to a wife or sweetheart, he'd take on every pretty girl who ran after him. Their name, of course, was Legion. As a rule they were not outdoor types. Clark's third and fourth wives, Carole Lombard and Sylvia Fairbanks (widow of Douglas), were indoor girls, from both of whom I heard complaints about what occurred in that canvas sleeping bag of Clark's.

I mostly admired Clark for his lack of vanity. He was equipped with a premature set of false teeth about which he felt no embarrassment. One day I happened on him at an outdoor faucet in the Alley where he'd stopped to wash off his denture. Clark grinned, pointed to his caved-in mouth and said with an exaggerated lisp, "Look! America's thweetheart!"

Clark had great luck in his fifth and last marriage to Kathleen Spreckels, a full-blown American blonde. Clark left a son, born after he died, who from all accounts is already affecting female hearts in the tradition of his daddy. (Contrary to press releases, the boy is not Clark's only child. A short but hectic affair Clark went through with a co-star when they were far from Hollywood on location had resulted in the birth of a baby girl. She is now a Park Avenue matron, a dream of a beauty like her mamma and married to an important young business executive. I don't know whether she suspects who her father was, but I'm not going to tip her name off now.)

Carole Lombard was Clark's third wife and the wish fulfillment of every man in and out of Hollywood; a natural blonde who, both a lady and a hoyden, had a sense of humor and lack of pretense that seldom go with beauty as glittering as hers. I recall one day when she was strolling down a road and a passing truck driver offered her a lift. Carole accepted and, because the driver had charisma, she drove with him all the way to Bakersfield. But before very long the young man began to sense he'd picked up an angel unawares. "Know something, baby?" he ventured. "You remind me of Carole Lombard." "If you compare me with that cheap floozy, I'll get right off your truck!" Carole flared up. So the driver apologized.

Carole was a truly understanding mate, in a sense that few wives could ever be. Having first been married to William Powell, she understood film stars thoroughly; knew that their status as sex symbols existed largely in the minds of the public. Which I'm told is often the case with athletes, prize fighters and baseball and football idols.

It can now be told that Clark needed assistance in order to live up to his virile appearance and Carole was just the wife to supply it. One day at a "cat" party Carole explained an incident to us girls which came about like this. Carole had made an acquaintance among the ladies who hung out around the musicians' quarters, who tipped her off to a trade secret which went by the mystifying name of "Peppermint French." It required a dime's worth of essence of peppermint which a girl would then use, undiluted, as a mouthwash before a rendezvous with her loved one. Carole carried out instructions and, on entering the boudoir a certain night, found Clark sound asleep. This gave her an idea. Why not add an element of surprise to the innovation of that peppermint? Without waking Clark, she proceeded in a very gentle approach which caused her hero, startled by the sudden sting of peppermint, to jump off the bed and sprain his ankle.

Carole always had an antic slant on sex. It never ceased to amuse her. I recall a day when we happened to be on her front porch as one of our higher-class gigolos strode down the street, exercising his ladyfriend's Pekingese. "Hi," called Carole in friendly greeting. "Hard at work, eh?"

Carole was killed in a plane crash while on a patriotic tour concerning the war effort. The tragic news was phoned to Clark in the middle of the night when he was with another charmer, merely following the normal course of an American male when the little wife is on a trip. It took Carole's death to remind Clark that he'd been unfaithful. He loved her devotedly and must have suffered unbearable guilt. We all felt his enlistment in the Army was an effort to assuage it.

Lunch at George Cukor's

The luncheon was in honor of Lady Mendl, who had sold her tiny palace in Versailles to set up an equally chic household in Benedict Canyon. Her Ladyship, having invented the profession of interior decoration, was the most extravagant of that breed. She employed knickknacks galore, snubbed real works of art or paintings that would pass muster at the Met. Much of her bric-a-brac, however, was authentic, as was Elsie herself, a sort of 18th century cockatoo with a voice to match.

Among George's luncheon guests was Tallulah Bankhead, who was then making movies for Darryl Zanuck. Tallu was rated as America's Number One Naughty Girl. In those days "naughty" meant piquant, but values have so changed that now in the Seventies it generally means nauseating. How can one match Tallu against that young female in *Last Tango in Paris*?

Several of us were sitting about George's pool when Lady Mendl could be heard approaching. Quick as a wink Tallulah slithered out of her dress and by the time Elsie reached us, she was lying on a marble bench, starkers except for a bunch of violets which Tallulah held in the pose of Goya's "Maja." George was furious; Her Ladyship gasped, "Cover yourself at once, you shameless child!" And Tallulah obediently did.

But Tallu's misdemeanor had had an implication over and above nudity. For violets had recently been given a bad name by a notorious Broadway play *The Captive*, in which a bunch of them was used as a secret message between two young women who were in love with each other. The play had been raided and closed by New York police, on hearing which Lady Mendl pretended ignorance of the reason why. Slapping her tea tray with a characteristic gesture she demanded in her cockatoo voice, "What is a lesbian? Tell me what they do!"

Now for years Elsie had had a close relationship with a Broadway play agent, Elizabeth Marbury, a lady of width and heft who wore her hair in a crew cut, sported ground-gripper shoes and was given to shooting her cuffs in a manly gesture.

And when Tallu heard of Lady Mendl's question, she asked, "If Elsie doesn't know what lesbians do, who *does*?"

One of the real attention-getters of the MGM lot was Judy Garland. Already a star at the age of twelve, Judy was a compulsive weeper. There are some characters who simply cannot endure success. Judy was one of them. She loved to pace the Alley, stopping all and sundry to whimper over some imagined affront. "Nobody loves me!" Judy would lament. She was "persecuted" by L.B.; her family "neglected" her; even the servants overlooked Judy. "When I come home from work exhausted and call for a cup of tea, the maid forgets all about it and I have to make it myself." Judy was such a good actress that listeners were frequently impressed. Not her screenwriter friend Hoppy. He called Judy's tears "a Hollywood bath."

Judy's mental attitude may have been pathetic, but it turned her into a great bore. And if my memories of her are few, it comes from lack of interest in a character who allowed her destiny to be ruled by petulance. Judy's disregard for her obligations as a star was appalling. I recall a day at the studio when mild little Vincente Minnelli (Judy's husband of the moment and the father of Liza) was waiting to direct Judy in a scene for *The Pirate*. She was late for work, as usual, and everybody, including a hundred or more extras, had been marking time since nine that morning. Finally, at noon, Vincente was summoned to the phone to learn that Judy required him to get home at once and escort her to an ice cream parlor for a soda.

I tried to avoid Scott Fitzgerald, although I'd known him and Zelda intimately in New York, Paris and on the Riviera. I liked them well enough when they were sober which, alas, was all too seldom. When drunk, their behavior could be downright hazardous or, at best, pretty tiresome. Zelda had a habit of stripping in public, which might be described today as "chutzpah," of which the rule is, "If you've got it, flaunt it." But to flaunt something you haven't got can be a mistake. Zelda's face could have landed her in the front line of the Ziegfeld Follies, but she should have kept her bosom under wraps. Zelda's striptease could be compared with Tallulah's, whose figure suffered the same identical drawback. But Tallulah flaunted her nudity through an impish desire to shock, whereas Zelda felt that hers was delectable.

Another disturbing memory of Scott and Zelda concerns a night in Paris when Mr. E. and I were on our way to a party at Gertrude Stein's and dropped by their hotel to take them with us. When we arrived, Scott and Zelda were tight and the baby was in its crib bawling her poor little head off. Zelda was afraid Scotty's screams might get them evicted, so she filled a nursing bottle with warm water, sugar and gin and then, looking as lovely as a Botticelli Madonna, she fed the mixture to Scotty. As we went into the night, the baby was already in a stupor, untroubled over being left alone and drunk in a strange apartment.

During a time when we were all staying at the Hotel du Cap in Antibes, Zelda went through an appendix operation. She'd been released from the hospital on condition that she remain sober and keep to her bed until the surgeon removed her stitches. Late one night Scott stumbled into their room and found that Zelda had disappeared, leaving an empty gin bottle at her bedside. We went looking for her and, on reaching the veranda, finally spotted Zelda through the darkness. She'd gone for a swim and her head was barely visible, bobbing far out in the icy, rough Mediterranean.

Scott dashed through the lobby calling for help and waking everybody up. Finally a lifeguard was alerted and sent off to the rescue. We all gathered on the veranda, too intent on Zelda's fate to notice that Scott was busily dashing the porch furniture down into the sea, perhaps as something to which Zelda might cling, but possibly just for the fun of breaking up furniture.

When the lifeguard pulled Zelda ashore limp, pale and shivering, she'd sobered up enough to explain her escapade: "I had a fever of 104 and thought a swim might cool me off." That the stitches in Zelda's wound held fast and that she didn't drown or get pneumonia could only have been due to the special Providence that looks after fools and alcoholics.

My *most* horrendous experience with the Fitzgeralds took place one night in Great Neck. Scott had picked me up in New York to take me to their place for dinner. I didn't notice he'd been drinking but we'd gone a little way when I realized my error. By a miracle we arrived at their country house without an accident and, once there, I found to my relief that Zelda was cold sober. Scott soon disappeared and when a very informal butler shuffled in and announced dinner, Zelda and I took our places at the table. Presently Scott came in, silent and glowering, and proceeded to turn the latch on the dining room door. Then, facing Zelda and me, he announced, *"Now I'm going to kill you two!"*

We hadn't had time to get up from the table before Scott started pitching things at us from very close range, heavy things—a water carafe, a metal wine cooler, its contents and a silver platter with a leg of lamb which the lackadaisical butler had left on the table. Any of those items, properly aimed, could actually have killed one of us. Screaming for help, Zelda and I took cover under the heavy oak table.

Then came a hero to our rescue; that tall, spindly black butler behaved with more courage than any proper servant might have done. He broke a glass pane in the door, reached through, switched off the latch, entered and grappled with Scott. He managed to hold onto him until Zelda and I could scramble out into the night. We ran across the road to the Ring Lardner house and alerted Ring. He got us safely inside and went to look for Scott. It took Ring nearly an hour to find him. When he did, Scott was kneeling on an unpaved road scooping up dust and cramming it into his mouth. "What are you doing?" asked Ring. And Scott, his throat clogged with mud, gasped, "I'm eating dirt to pay for trying to kill those two lovely girls! Those darling girls who never harmed anyone in their lives! And a swine like me tried to kill them!"

It was all very pleasant to be called "lovely" and "darling" and for Scott to admit swinishness, but Zelda and I had put in a very rugged evening.

Well—a lot of time had now swept by: Scott and I were safely at work in Culver City; Zelda was in a Midwest asylum for the insane, where she had been placed for her own safety. (It was there she ultimately met a horrible death in the fire that destroyed the place.) Poor Scott had quit drinking and, from being a nuisance when tight, had taken on that apologetic humility which is often characteristic of reformed drunks. I would hear a tap on my door in the Thalberg Building and knew it was Scott because nobody else ever bothered to knock before entering my office. I'd ask Scott to join whoever happened to be there; he'd enter a couple of steps, then stop. "You people don't really want to see me!" he'd say with an embarrassing meekness. We were sorry for Scott because he seemed so alone. He never mentioned a girlfriend who popped up after his death.

After a spell of uninspired conversation, Scott would conclude, "I know you want to get rid of me so I'll go now." Between being dangerous when drunk and eating humble pie when sober, I preferred Scott dangerous. An alcoholic is much more bearable when he's like Brendan Behan, roistering his way through to a tragic end, than for his life to fade out, as Scott's did, in one long, dull apologia.

One afternoon a few months before Scott died, he came to our house and wrote a last apology in an autograph book that's arranged according to birth dates. Scott's was September 24 and he composed the following:

> This book tells that Anita Loos
> Is a friend of Caesar, a friend of Zeus
> Of Samuel Goldwyn and Mother Goose
> Of Balanchine of the Ballet Russe
> Of Tillie the Viennese papoose (Tillie Losch)
> Of Charlie MacArthur on the loose
> Of Shanks, chiropodists—what's the use?
> Of actors who have escaped the noose
> Lots of Hollywood beach refuse
> Comics covered with charlotte russe
> Wretched victims of self-abuse
> Big producers all obtuse
> This is my birthday, but what the deuce
> Is that sad fact to Anita Loos

> F. Scott Fitzgerald

PART

FIVE

The Italians Have a
Word for It

*T*he Italian word *pace* (pronounced "pa-chay") means peace. And there is a hotel by that name in Montecatini which combines peace and the pursuit of health with a very unusual degree of opulence.

The Hotel Pace makes a fitting crown for one of those Tuscan hills that rise as a dramatic background for the city of Florence. The town of Montecatini, as a world-famous spa, supports more than two hundred hotels and countless pensions. They cling to hillside streets that rise like steps; most of the hotels are modest withal, but their façades provide a colorful show of trellises, greenery, flowers and awnings and, as a rule, their dining quarters are gaily open to the streets. A number of large hotels boast their own private grounds and are quite grand. But the grandest of all is the Pace.

The history of the spa goes way back to the days of Imperial Rome, when it was merely a collection of rolling hills covered with dry grass, from which there burbled numberless springs of hot mineral water. And nestling in a hollow among them was a vast sea of bubbling volcanic mud.

It may well be that some Caesarian generalissimo who suffered from gout inadvertently happened to stick his toe into that hot mud puddle. As if by magic the pain decreased, and a few repetitions of the action brought about a cure.

It would be several centuries before scientists stumbled onto the theory of radioactivity. But in the meantime, those mineral springs and that sea of mud kept on bubbling with such gusto that early Tuscan physicians began to experiment with transferring that vitality to their patients. The rustic mud puddle became a rendezvous for the arthritic and overweight.

By the seventeenth century, the Tuscans had built an ornate stone bath establishment where the elite could take their mud. (I have an engraving of that establishment, which was discovered by Kate Hepburn in a collection of old prints and sent to me by her, since she knows of my dedication to Montecatini.) The establishment still functions, with modern improvements, but outwardly it looks much as it did when it was first opened.

In time, a luxury hotel was built, and with Italy's admiration for British chic, they named it in honor of that worldwide peace they thought had been established for all time by the Battle of Waterloo. The "world peace" has never transpired, but the Hotel Pace still flourishes today: a rendezvous for the ailing of every category.

The Hotel was first given a grandiose title, "Le Grand Hotel et la Pace," which is still used on its letterheads. But there are thousands of Grand Hotels about the world and only a single Hotel Pace. And that is how it came to be known—as the one and only Hotel Pace.

One reaches the Hotel in rather a roundabout manner. Montecatini is so close to Florence that one could get there by plane in less than fifteen minutes, but Florence has always refused to tolerate an airport; so the most convenient way for a traveler to reach Montecatini is to board a plane either in London or Paris and fly south to Pisa. The two-hour flight is as dramatic as it is short. The plane skims the Alps and threatens to scrape the top off Mont Blanc. The journey is climaxed by a sharp dip toward Pisa's Leaning Tower, which looks as if it could topple right before one's eyes.

But the grandeur that is Italy is not yet apparent; on leaving the airport, a shady Pisan enterprise greets the traveler. The market place is bristling with *objets d'art,* alabaster miniatures of the Leaning Tower and, far more appealing to the tourist from the U.S., hundreds of alabaster bird baths: shallow bowls of various sizes with adorable carved doves billing and cooing on their brims, all guaranteed to be hand-carved by Pisan sculptors. They aren't! They are mass-manufactured of alabaster dust, pressed into molds like Jell-O. American tourists ship these artworks home by the thousands. But the first time there is a rainfall, the glue that holds them together dissolves, and doves, basins and pedestals drool into a gooey alabaster stew on Milady's front lawn.

Forget Pisa! Pack your luggage into a taxi which will skim onto the Autostrada, and you're on your way southward to Montecatini and the Pace.

One waits with bated breath for the sign that marks the detour into Montecatini. But first the Autostrada skirts the mountain of Carrara, with the big white gash still visible from which, centuries ago, Michelangelo released the marble for his gigantic nude of David.

That colossal nude, which now graces the Piazza della Signoria in Florence, more than makes up for the con game practiced by those Pisan "sculptors." No tourist from Des Moines will ever forget the example of macho in the raw produced by that nude.

The Autostrada passes numerous villages, which appear less ancient than simply run-down, but are brought up to date by vivid advertisements for motor oil, gasoline and Campari liqueur. But finally there appears a majestic archway of wrought iron, spanning the Autostrada and indicating the detour into Montecatini. We are nearing the threshold of the Hotel Pace.

At first glimpse, the Pace is rather a letdown. Its gardens, arbors and swimming pools are at the back and out of view, and the façade of the hotel melts into a maze of city shops. It is further obscured by its color, which is that unobtrusive terra cotta so prevalent in Italy. In design, the building belongs to the period when Italy copied the spare and square forms of ancient Egypt, with flat roofs and restrained terraces. But don't be misled by its outward austerity because once the weighty plate glass doors swing open, one enters a vast foyer glittering with marble, brass and crystal objects, so ornate that they may have been installed when England's Edward VII set the fashion. Looking about the lobby, one finds that its floral decor reverses normal growth patterns; plants that ordinarily would be green, with a few blossoms peeping through, are a solid mass of bloom with a minimum of green leaves. And a potted azalea, instead of being a mere decoration for a center table, outspans it.

A guest who arrives before noon is greeted by a staff dressed in morning uniforms of starched white cotton. By afternoon they have changed to navy ones with gilt buttons, which are more formally swank.

One is greeted by a tall, dark, aristocratic man in a frock coat and carnation, who represents the Italian brand of public relations. But there is little of Madison Avenue in the way he kisses a lady's hand.

An Italian hand-kiss is anything but a casual brush-off. It is a leisurely affair. The lady's hand is raised quite slowly, and there is always a pause before the encounter, as if the Signore were saying to himself, "This is going to be the most crucial moment of my life"; after which the event takes place. That, in itself, is worth the trip to Italy.

The Signore escorts one to quarters which, avoiding the grandeur of the Pace public rooms, reveal an exquisite sense of balance. Their decor is that of an English country manor where comfort replaces grandeur. Flowers, fruit and wine await one on an antique sideboard.

Once installed for the duration of the cure, there comes a visit from the "Professor," which is the title one accords a doctor in Italy. Professor Pisani, a true man of the world, speaks English, French, German, Danish, Hungarian, and, in later years, Japanese and Arabic. For the Pace draws its clientele from many nations of the world.

The guests are wonderful to watch, for, when all is said and done, it is they who give a hotel its character. In normal life one is lucky to know a few interesting people; at the Pace everybody seems interesting, if for no other reason than they have to be rich, and the speculation of how they got that way is always fascinating.

Any deluxe hotel might have interesting guests, but as a rule they're fairly transient; there is no time to get to know each other. At the Pace, the cure requires two weeks, and to share the common denominator of a cure brings people very close together indeed. Nobody can be snooty while sharing a regimen that places everybody in the same mundane category.

There were always guests of a high cultural degree. I used to have a daily luncheon date with the great Italian historian, Giovanni Papini, who suffered from rheumatism and came every year for the cure. I recall discussions about his literary classic *The Life of Christ;* not so much as the work of art which it is, but because Papini had sold Warner Brothers its motion picture rights for a colossal sum, only to have Jack abandon it. Papini used to muse over the fact that he had fathomed the mysteries of the Gospel, but had never been able to understand the mind of Jack Warner.

An American friend I brought to the Pace myself was Alice B. Toklas, who, because of a cruel arthritis, could only get about with the aid of two crutches. It was a satisfaction when, after her cure, Alice went back to Paris and phoned me: "I threw away my crutches at the airport and walked up the gangplank without help."

Professor Pisani never seemed to run out of fascinating patients from faraway outposts: Iran, Switzerland, Hungary (even a few millionaire gypsies). And a high point of glamour was supplied by the yearly visit of the Orsini Circus, the most extraordinary in the annals of show business. It was a family affair of great tradition and aristocracy, in which the young men were educated at Oxford or Cambridge, and the girls did their stints wearing Paris gowns from Dior. In Italy their fame and status equals that of Sophia Loren.

For many years another guest of the Pace was Mrs. Winston Churchill, generally accompanied by the Duchess of Marlborough, who came not only for the cure but for the game of gin rummy that traveled through the lobbies night and day (just like Damon Runyon's floating crap game on Broadway—but indulged in by dukes, viscountesses and earls).

From Hollywood came Louis B. Mayer and a bevy of yes-men. Louis was generally bent on removing the bend in his oversized middle.

On a more ethereal note, a great dress designer used to show up, generally accompanied by a coterie of his favorite Catholic priests. His gowns were often influenced by a chastity unusual to the fashion trade.

Two mystery guests were blond sisters: beauties of such refinement that we decided they must belong to one of the Scandinavian royal families. But we later found out that one of them was the wife of the then prime minister of Israel.

There were twin Italian countesses who were regular patrons. They escorted the husband of one of them, who suffered from lumbago. But they were such an inseparable trio that we never did pinpoint which one was actually his wife.

Another typical Pace surprise was a modest young American publisher of books from New Haven, Connecticut. I had recently had a best seller of my own, which I mentioned with pride, only to be let down by his announcement that his books, which were printed in Tokyo, ran into editions of several *billion* volumes. They were paperback comic books, printed in twenty-eight languages and edited in the gardens at the Pace because the publisher suffered from a "football" kneecap. The hotel never seemed to accord with normal life.

Whatever the mysteries, speculation and allure of life at the Pace, the main reason for one's visit is the cure. It is prefaced by a visit to the Professor's office, made cozy for Americans by copies of *The National Geographic*. Tests are taken for heart, lungs and blood pressure; prescriptions written out for liver, nose, stomach, throat or martini middle. Those Montecatini waters have something for everyone.

One's day begins after a light intake of coffee and croissants, enjoyed with the birds under the trees in the gardens. Then one has to sip the required quantity of waters, during which a patient is ordered to stroll (never jog) through the maze of parks that surround the Pace, gardens that glow with flowers and sparkle with marble fountains, where the water is served by Tuscan beauties dressed in bright cotton uniforms of wide stripes in royal blue and white. There is a strong touch of red in their cheeks that sparks one's belief in the cure.

Along with sipping the water, one is ordered to take in the beauty of the landscape and the purity of the air; both are supposed to be important to one's psyche. The bitter-salt taste of the water is sweetened by the tones of a distant orchestra playing sentimental Viennese melodies. One discusses with fellow health seekers the tonic values of the Tutticcio Spring as opposed to those of the Tamericci.

But the sublime outdoor clinic must perforce have a ridiculous side; an aspect so unglamorous, my pen balks at describing it. One's halcyon strolls must be interrupted by detours into little cubicles that nestle among the greenery and resemble the toy chalets on Swiss cuckoo clocks. But sometimes while waiting at one of those fancy, trellised doorways, one may be able to strike up a friendship with a real Grand Duchess.

And to get back to the sublime, one will always dine on Lucullan dishes, but as if Lucullus had rounded up a new type of health food: melons from the Pace gardens; wild strawberries gathered from the slopes of the Dardanelles; raspberries as big as crabapples; pasta in variations that are a continuous astonishment. And to make sure that everyone is happy, the Pace manager, Signore Gino Degli

Innocenti, makes the rounds of all the tables three times a day, and every lady there gets her hand kissed.

But finally, alas, a low point of the day arrives with one's afternoon rendezvous with mud, which the Italians call by the more romantic term of "fango." When the clock clicks off one's required twenty minutes, the fango is washed away by giant hoses, in an emulsion of radioactive water that bubbles like champagne; and, once back in civilian garb, one feels as "born again" as any Democratic President, and almost as virtuous.

Roman Holiday

*T*HE Hotel de la Ville stands at the top of Rome's highest hill and from our seventh floor terrace we could overlook the whole city. At first, it was difficult to tear oneself away from this superb view and descend to see the sights at closer range.

Rome spread out below, illuminated around the clock by a series of heavenly light effects, from the pale glow of dawn, through dazzling middays and multicolored sunsets, to the nighttime shimmer of the moon and stars. But something modern had been added: neon lights outlining ancient Rome which, despite one's bias against neon, did create a spectacular view.

Our horizon was dominated by a gigantic dome, but its shape was so delicate and sensitive, even feminine, that it gave the Vatican an aspect of tenderness. And that's an overall impression of Rome itself: the sublime humanized by being quite gentle. Perhaps the patina of hoary age helped to obliterate, or made one forget, the violence and corruption of some stages of Roman history.

It was August and the weather sizzled, but every afternoon around four o'clock a soft breeze began to blow, that fabled *aria da Roma,* which gives the city a daily breather. Generally, we waited for the *aria* before starting out in search of culture, and going down the enormous curving length of the Spanish Steps toward the Piazza di Spagna, and onward.

My friend Diana couldn't wait to show me the Rome she visits every year. She had planned to start our holiday by guiding me through the Etruscan antiquities of the Villa Giulia. But on the way we happened to pass the dress salon of Valentino.

Diana isn't exactly a clothes horse, but she has a fine sense of style, and I'm not immune to fashion either. "Let's drop in and have a look at Valentino's new collection," Di suggested. Well, we'd never get to the Etruscans now, I thought. But she quickly added, it would just be a short detour, and we might not get far past the doorway. "I've been looking for something new at Valentino's every year, but so far I haven't bought anything."

In a vast marble hall we were greeted by a polite but skeptical directrice who welcomed Diana with reservation. "It's too bad that most of the clothes are away in Sardinia," she said. Her excuse seemed plausible because August is the billionaire season in Sardinia; the Agnellis were there, so were the Onassises, the Rothschilds, and a few others who could afford Valentino's prices.

Were any of the new models left behind? Diana asked. The directrice then grudgingly showed us some ruffled and spangled chiffon numbers hung on racks high enough to keep their skirts from sweeping the floor.

Now Diana, who is a famous sex symbol, might have bought out the entire line, but those gowns couldn't easily be crammed into her Jaguar. Anyway, in this mechanical age a Jaguar is much sexier than any robe de style.

Proceeding to the Villa Giulia, we spent the afternoon among the controlled splendors of the ancient Etruscans. "If Valentino had only come here for inspiration," said Di, "I might have bought some of his dresses at long last."

On her anything would look good, even a plain toga. She is aptly named, as handsome, sleek-limbed and graceful as Diana, goddess of the moon and of hunting, whose statue we saw in a Roman temple. Though Di is athletic, she has never gone hunting; but men have always hunted her and often found her as inscrutable as Selene, the Greek moon goddess. The Roman deity was also known as the protectress of women. Well, my pal can protect herself. But I wonder if women's libbers have thought of adopting the Roman Diana as their patron saint.

In the next few days we made the ritual rounds of ancient, medieval, Renaissance, baroque and what-have-you monuments.

As every visitor knows, Rome is like a huge layer cake, with the remains of various civilizations layered on top of each other. It is an inexhaustible city, and exhausting if one is greedy and tries to cram it all in too fast. So, we rested in caffès in piazzas with gurgling be-statued fountains, dined with friends in elegant restaurants, and sampled heartier fare in Trastevere trattorias.

One day a sudden gust of rain was an excuse to seek the nearest shelter, which happened to be a restaurant, the Piccolo Mondo. Voluptuous types like Diana are attacked by hunger without warning at any time of the day or night. "That's where Rome has it all over other cities," she remarked. "Food is available wherever you happen to be." And her gourmet tendencies in these days of skimpy diets have made her a favorite of headwaiters wherever she goes.

The Piccolo Mondo was crowded with TV and film personalities, the most romantic of Rome's bohemia. Daughters of the nobility and plutocracy are known to shack up with them.

The Mondo's proprietor, Luigi, greeted Diana with the ardor that Dante might have shown Beatrice, if they'd ever gotten together.

During lunch Diana and Luigi recalled the war years when she'd been trapped in Switzerland and her daydreams were mostly of food. When hostilities ended, she headed for Rome and the Piccolo Mondo. "Luigi saw me coming through the door, grabbed one of my favorite sausages, rushed to me and popped it into my mouth before we could even say *ciao*. And then we both began to cry." That's what makes a gastronomic love affair.

Diana evoked the same warm emotions in the waiters at the enormous sidewalk caffe in the Piazza Navona. As a folk district the Piazza is overrun with footloose youth from everywhere. Rome is quite different from Paris, which never grants a foreigner the status of a Parisian. Being no snob, Rome is full of instant Romans.

It was from the Piazza Navona that young John Paul Getty III was kidnapped in July. Now, in late August, he still hadn't surfaced. Some cynics claimed his kidnapping was faked, that he might even be dead, perhaps of a drug overdose, and the multimillion ransom demanded of his family only would retrieve a corpse. Luckily, they were proved wrong when young Getty finally turned up, but minus an ear chopped off to hasten his ransom.

By this time the outbreak of Italian kidnapping had become an epidemic. It was not only a political crime practiced by the Red

Brigades but, as black jokesters said, a big profitable business, so the Mafia and other gangsters muscled in. The rich didn't dare venture out without bodyguards, but even guards were gunned down and their charges snatched.

We tourists could feel smugly safe while hearing about the latest snatch with dismay. It reminded us of the old gangster movies made in Hollywood. But screen mobsters had slaughtered each other, not terrorized an entire country as Italian kidnappers did today.

One morning an invitation came over the phone to a party at a villa far out on the Appian Way. The occasion was to celebrate the completion in Cinecittà of Andy Warhol's version of *Dracula*. A strange mix, I thought, of Andy, Dracula, and old Rome.

Diana, always an optimist, thought it might be very interesting and she visualized "a gala in an ancient palazzo." Perhaps we should have bought a couple of those Valentino ballgowns, she remarked.

The moment we drove up to the villa that night, we had our doubts. It wasn't the least bit ancient, not even imitation antique, but a replica of countless slick bungalows in Beverly Hills. Moreover, it proved to be part of a compound built by a shrewd Roman realtor for rental to transients in the movie colony. The grounds were pleasant enough, not lit by klieg lights but by flickering candles along the pathway to the house.

Once inside the premises we suffered another letdown. It seemed that Andy himself had ducked out and suddenly flown to New York, leaving his company manager, Bob, in charge.

From the surrogate host we learned the hazards of giving a movie party in Rome, where for every bona fide actor there are hundreds of would-be's who are expert only in the art of freeloading. They sleep on public benches and spend their waking hours hitch-hiking to any locale offering the whiff of a free hunk of parmigiano or salami, or the hint of a fix.

"When I shaved this morning," Bob told us, "there were three strange creeps cluttering the bathroom. Out in the garden I found at least twenty more in the pool. I booted them off the premises, but those crashers will be back before the party's over."

Was that why Andy had vamoosed? "Could be," Bob replied but added that Andy might soon return because Liz Taylor had offered him a role in the picture she was about to film in Rome.

"What part would Andy play?" I asked.

"A *creep!*" said Bob with evident pride. After all, his boss sees himself as the "Little Father of the Creeps."

As more guests arrived we found that for every girl there were at least ten boys, a ratio usually pleasing to women. But they got little attention from these males. Had Di and I splurged on Valentino dresses, what a waste!

Oddly enough, the boys didn't even seem to be on the make for one another. They lolled about the garden in a state of serene vacuity, saying little, laughing never, and disappearing at intervals into the upper reaches of the villa.

While showing us around the house, Bob had led us into a chrome-and-vinyl kitchen where a fat Italian cook stood dazedly contemplating a mountain of chopped beef. This was to be turned into genuine American hamburgers, Bob said.

Suppertime came, but no sign of hamburgers. As usual, Diana began to feel pangs of hunger. So, we asked a fellow guest when food might be forthcoming. His cryptic reply was "Who knows, dear? These characters don't *eat.*"

It looked as if we weren't going to eat either. For we soon learned that the Italian cook, unable to fathom the classic American snack, had walked off the job.

Well, Di would have to wait until we drove back, as we hadn't spotted a café or snackbar along the Appian Way. Meanwhile, we wondered what was going on upstairs, since guests kept trooping to the second floor. Bob explained that a beautician from Cinecittà was up there, giving pointers on the art of make-up. This seemed a novel party gimmick, so we went to investigate. Then, we saw the make-up artist wasn't a bit concerned with anyone's face; he was jabbing away at lower regions of their anatomies with a hypodermic needle.

One youth of superb beauty, with curly blond hair and static blue eyes, was near collapse from an overdose. He had staggered into the bathroom and fallen against the wash basin with such force that the flimsy plumbing gave way. The bathroom was flooding rapidly, water was seeping into the bedroom, and the whole villa might soon be deluged.

Well, try to find a plumber at midnight on the Appian Way or, for that matter, in an emergency at any time. But from the look of things, the police might soon show up.

We were heading for our car, when we saw the party's most

distinguished guest, Valentino himself, striding across the grounds from his neighboring villa, an historic landmark. The devotion between Warhol and Valentino was then a new Roman legend. Surrounded by a retinue of beautiful boys and sustained by his fame, wealth and good looks, he came to pay obeisance to our absent host. He cut a wedge through the languid assemblage, which hadn't yet been routed by the approaching flood. But we were too unnerved to join the worshipers at that shrine.

Driving back to our hotel, we speculated about the current cult of Valentino. One would think he'd achieved the status of a Roman emperor; indeed he had in the world of fashion. Were the designers of Calpurnia's or Pompeia's gowns equally rewarded and fêted in ancient Rome? Who knows? I couldn't recall if Gibbon had anything to say about such frivolities.

"You know, a young designer can't impress us who are old enough to have worn the dresses of Balenciaga," I remarked.

How would that maestro have felt about fashion today? Cristobal was intensely religious, so he might have said, "God will forgive our barbarities. With all the talent He granted me, I couldn't have created anything more suitable for this crazy era than the blue jeans and T-shirts of the Wild West." But now ruffles and lace were in, as if they were brand new discoveries.

The banquet we'd looked forward to finally took place at the counter of a deserted all-night trattoria known to our chauffeur. The menu consisted of two stale buns, harboring some splinters of prosciutto, and a couple of ice cream cones.

At any rate, we'd been present at a modern Roman orgy. And when we got home, we could dine out on that story. But it might seem tame, except for drugs, lacking certain juicy ingredients— semi-nude dancing girls, a Lucullan feast, wine, sex of every variety—the kind of saturnalia shown in *I, Claudius* on television.

The morning after, we were having breakfast on our terrace when I happened to come cross an interview in the *Rome Daily American,* the comfort and contact with home of wanderers like us. The interviewee was Andy Warhol's director and staunch supporter, Paul Morrissey. "How timely!" said Di. "What does he have to say?"

"A lot about Andy and those movies of his, naturally." Reading the story aloud, I found it provided a new slant on the films, which I'd always viewed as hard-core pornography, and a by-product of drug addiction; with no objective except to be cheap in every way, financially, aesthetically and, most of all, morally.

Morrissey stressed a valid point: to make a movie, any movie at all, requires effort by someone in control who is *not* on drugs. Andy is not, nor are Paul and Bob; but one couldn't vouch for other members of their troupe.

Their films, Paul explained, were meant to achieve complete improvisation, without being planned or written. In other words, "home movies," unhampered by the normalcies of home and with no more sensitivity than Andy shows in painting a can of Campbell's soup.

"Our aim is to reproduce the manner in which people live today," he went on, quoting his boss, "as opposed to the form life used to take when there were moral codes and a sense of guilt as regards sin. . . . We try to reproduce the true essence of our time.

"If Andy discovers that a 'message' has crept into one of his movies, he eliminates it. His film *Trash* was considered by some to be anti-drug, when it's nothing but decadent fluff concerning a world no longer bound by moral codes."

When it comes to reproducing the essence of our time or a decadent world, no one can match Fellini. Of course there is no comparison between Warhol and Fellini; the former concocting amateur underground movies; the latter, a professional genius who pictures his world and its denizens with enormous imagination and power—as in *La Dolce Vita* or *Juliet of the Spirits*. But to give Andy his due, he had no such ambitions and rarely showed his movies in public. Those who got to see them in his loft probably felt like the daring elite and hyped up their reputation.

We couldn't help decrying the trendiness of modern Rome which gave such support to a minor American artist. But we hadn't come here to see or even talk about movies. As refugees from Hollywood, we'd had our fill of them.

For all its splendors Rome showed signs, while we were there, of a series of inglorious events. For one thing, strikes became daily, almost hourly, occurrences. You'd go to a museum and find it shut down because the guards had walked out. Or you'd stop by the post office to send a registered letter and see it was closed by a *sciopero*. Heaven help you if you had to catch a plane and the airport was inactivated by a *sciopero*. That was one word we learned right away. A flash strike with no advance warning was not only frustrating to tourists with no time to lose but, even more so, to Romans struggling through their daily business. Of course the unions purposely struck fast, knowing that sudden disruption of services would make the public so mad that they'd pressure the authorities to yield to labor's demands.

Then too, the old Colosseum began to crumble, due to the madcap pace of Roman traffic. As a result its hippie tenants were banned from this landmark, and a plague of fleas invaded the city in their search for nutriment.

There was also a population explosion of snakes. (A scientific theory held that the trend of Roman ecology had killed off small wild animals which heretofore had destroyed serpents in the city's outskirts.) Now, snakes were creeping into elevators, and frightening kids in classrooms. After that aggravation there was a later outbreak of cholera.

But all this would pass, just as the evils of ancient Rome had passed, while the legacies of some of its most wicked emperors, who built great monuments, remained—even if somewhat the worse for wear. Seeing the grandiose Baths of Caracalla, the Castel Sant' Angelo, the Imperial Fora, and the like, was a salutary reminder that while we invented the most devastating device of destruction we have yet to equal the construction of those old Romans. And then there were the popes, all of whom weren't models of religious rectitude, but who contributed great architecture and art to the Vatican, and kept superb artists like Michelangelo, Raphael, and many others, employed.

Centuries later, a modern ruler fancied himself as a builder, but what did Mussolini build? Years ago I'd met Il Duce and the audience left me very unimpressed; a lot of blubber filled with bombast. His ignominious end, hanging upside down by the feet, after being killed by partisans in World War II, should be an object lesson to would-be dictators—like Hitler's suicide in a bunker. But do we ever learn anything from the follies and horrors of history?

Among Rome's most enjoyable features are the piazzas and gardens. A favorite walk was in the Pincio, near our hotel, where green alleys were lined with busts of Italian patriots, children played around them irreverently, and lovers strolled arm-in-arm. A viaduct led to the Borghese Park, with manicured lawns shaded by ilex, pine and magnolia trees. What could be more refreshing or serene on a hot summer's day?

Contrasting with this serenity was the glitter and jangle of the Via Veneto. Here you watched the fashionable world go by over a capuccino or limonata (if you didn't take stronger refreshment, as I didn't) at a sidewalk caffè. In the early evening this was the ritual, killing time before dinner at eight or nine P.M., by which time Diana was starving. But even the friendliest headwaiter would consider us beneath notice if we tried to dine earlier.

Driving away from Rome in Diana's car, we vowed that we would return some day to catch up on everything we'd missed so far—a vow made, but not always kept, by countless visitors who dropped coins in the Trevi Fountain. What a moneymaker that fountain is for the workers who fish out a mountain of coins every day. Whoever invented the durable myth was a brilliant entrepreneur, exploiting the superstitions of travelers.

What happens if you resist? Will the evil eye keep you from coming back? But why take a chance? Drop a dime into Trevi's basin and consider that you've paid your dues.

Why Girls Go South*

*S*OCIETY note: "Among those who are now flitting Florida-wise is the gorgeous Judith Revell, in this instance accompanied by her aristocratic mother, her father, and her maiden Aunt Mary. Judy always manages to keep well to the fore in the public prints, and the Florida season is sure to be considerably *égayé* by her presence, because where Judy is, there is always action, of one kind or another.

"The migration of the Revell clan adds two of the oldest Knicker-bocker names to the Florida roster, which to date, perhaps, has been made up of a too generous sprinkling of the *nouveaux riches*. But, with the Revells, goes not only the substantial cognomen of Revell *père,* but the much-to-be-conjured-with name of van Tassell, to which Judy's mother was born, and which now is carried by her maiden aunt, Miss Mary van Tassell. If one wanted to write a modern fairy-story, it would seem that one could not imagine a more glamorous heroine than the lovely Judy actually is in real life—truly, 'a girl who has everything.' To be nineteen, outstand-ingly beautiful, talented, and with a magnificent social background, what more has life to offer? Judy's career is going to bear watching."

If Judy's career is going to bear watching, we may as well begin at

---

*This novella first appeared as a three-part serial in *Harper's Bazaar* in 1926, a year after *Gentlemen Prefer Blondes* made its debut in the magazine. To follow up *Blondes'* success in 1925, both as a magazine series and in book form, the *Bazaar* urged Anita Loos to contribute *Why Girls Go South,* in which Lorelei Lee makes a brief appearance.

the beginning of it and let the reader in on a scene that took place one morning last December.

The setting is the red-and-gold salon of the old Revell home in the once ultra-aristocratic Murray Hill district of New York. The atmosphere breathes long-standing tradition, and an elegance which has stood a little too long.

On a Louis Quinze table rests the famous silver-gilt urn, which was presented by the late Czar Nicholas of Russia to the present head of the house of Revell, when he was American Consul General in St. Petersburg. Inside the urn is a dun for repairs on the roof of the house, due since a year ago August. To the left of the table hangs a portrait of Julian Revell the First, founder of the family, self-made millionaire, and head of the New York Anti-Vice League that cleaned Manhattan of sin in 1871, and gave it the push that sent it headlong into its present state of grace. On a gilt console table, underneath this portrait, rests a current copy of the *Daily Views,* with a two-column picture of the present daughter of the house, Miss Judith Revell, doing the Charleston at a lawn fête in Southampton; her underwear, a one-piece step-in, is seen to be edged with exquisite old point d'Alencon. Against the opposite wall stands a Louis Quinze spinet, on top of which is an ormolu jewel box, presented to Judith's mother, Emma, on the occasion of her marriage, by the late Ward McAllister. It contains three soiled aspirin tablets, an autographed photograph of the Grand Duchess Kyril, and a notice to the effect that Emma has been posted at the Colony Club.

It is a high moment in the Revell salon, and the air is tense with dramatic feeling. Those present are:

Ex-Consul General, Julian Revell. The last time he was sober was just before his graduation from Harvard in 1886, and he can remember nearly everything prior to that date, but his mind is a bit hazy as to what has occurred since. He made a record as Consul General in St. Petersburg by investing a fortune in the off-stage activities of the members of the Imperial Ballet, went seriously into the drinking of vodka, and won the non-stop handicap away from a certain Grand Duke who had been trained from birth for the championship, thus carrying the American flag right through to the top. He now leads a regular life, automatically making the Racquet Club by four o'clock every afternoon, but if he ever learns about Prohibition, it is going to go hard with him.

Mrs. Revell, born van Tassell. Emma van Tassell was a great catch for Julian in 1889, a van Tassell being of the finest old Dutch stock, and much too good for a Revell. In fact, it was this match that opened up the last social gates to the Revell clan. Emma, at the present time, is fairly clean without being tidy. In the old days, she possessed a maid who had a genius for being able to keep her stockings from bagging at the ankles, but the maid went the way of other lost luxuries. Emma is wearing a vintage gown of the House of Paquin, with a real lace bertha, and she thinks she is wearing the Revell pearls, not knowing that Julian had them replaced by "Indetectibles," the time he was caught with a blonde in a badger game in Atlantic City.

A third member, and the most important of the Revell conference, is Judith Revell, called Judy, the flower of this fine old stock— beautiful with a beauty that comes only through breeding. It is a matter of social record that when she made her entrance at the famous Cosden ball, given on Long Island in honor of the Prince of Wales, those who stood near His Royal Highness overheard the Prince exclaim, "Hot Dog!" Judy wears an exquisitely simple black Chanel frock for which she owes Vendel $195.00, making her bill to date, $3,434.50.

The fourth and last member of this quaint quartet is Emma's sister, Aunt Mary van Tassell, who is wearing a white shirtwaist and a black and white pepper-and-salt skirt. Aunt Mary, having always had a mind of her own, never seemed to need masculine companionship, and has reached the age of fifty-two, unmarried. As she says of herself, "Up to the age of eighteen I was called a tomboy—after eighteen I became an old maid and, in my day, that was all there was to it. But, if I had been born in this generation, my dear, I should be clipping my hair, dressing like a man from the waist up, and leading a life that only Havelock Ellis could explain." She has had a peculiar history. Twenty-five years ago she deserted New York society because she found it dull, and went to Europe, where she made the rounds of continental pensions for nearly a quarter of a century.

Returning to America only three months ago, she found conditions that amazed and delighted her. Social life, when she was a girl, had meant a succession of polite and respectable gaities that bored her stiff. Today, she finds everything changed for the better. To put it in Aunt Mary's own words: "Why, when I was a young thing, men used to get squiffy only at their clubs or at stag parties. We girls never saw any of the fun. *Now* I find you all getting tight together, right in your own salons, and no end of amusement! And twenty-five years ago, if a man so much as kissed a girl without proposing honorable matrimony, her father and brothers came to the rescue and arranged a military wedding, at the point of a gun. As a result, scandals were scarce and life was anemic. But today I find that even the classic excuse for a military wedding isn't taken so seriously. How amusing!

"And, in my time, people had to stick to their kind and be bored to tears. I can remember how we girls used to hear vague rumors about the matrimonial career of Lillian Russell, and if we were very, very good, mamma took us to a New Year's matinée, and let us look at her across the footlights. What nonsense!

"Today, a deb can go up to the Colony restaurant, have luncheon with Texas Guinan, and get full details of all the fun, first hand. Delightful!"

And so, after twenty-five years of retirement, Aunt Mary has decided to reenter American Society. Aunt Mary's attitude, how-ever, is not shared by Emma, who still sticks to the old traditions. It was Emma who organized this morning's session, the subject under discussion being:

First: That last night Judy was out again till morning.

Second: That having left the house to attend the Henry Abel-Abels' dinner to the Dowager Duchess of Dexter, she did not return until 11 A.M. next day, her evening gown covered by the raincoat of the hatcheck girl at the Hotel Astor.

Third: Emma, feeling that this was a bit thick, had gone through Judy's effects and found in her vanity case a check for two thousand dollars, made out to her daughter, and signed by the name of a strange man.

"Who is this Herman Glickman, and why is he giving you two thousand dollars?" demands Emma.

"Yes, why did he do it, and what's his address?" speaks up the ex-Consul General.

Judy overlooks her father's query, which passes unnoticed, as Father's brain seldom retains long enough to follow up a comeback.

"I can't wait to learn, after all that you girls hand out for nothing, what there is left worth two thousand dollars," says Aunt Mary.

Emma now breaks into tears and turns to her husband.

"Julian," she says, "Julian, do something! Try to realize that your daughter's good name has probably gone beyond recall!"

"Just so," says Julian, and turning to Judy he speaks.

"To think that you, my daughter, should so far forget her fair name as to—as to—as to—"

"Yes, Father, go on."

"What was I talking about?"

"Apple sauce," says Aunt Mary.

"Exactly—best apples in the world—right on the old van Tassell place in Rhinebeck—best hard cider in the—that reminds me—I'm due at the club."

"Sit down, Julian!" says Emma. "We are going to have the truth about last night's business before one of us leaves this room!"

Judy draws herself up to her full height.

"Well—since last night was a turning point in my life," she says, "perhaps it is just as well that you all learn something about it!"

"Go ahead," says Aunt Mary, "but you can't make me believe that Herman got his money's worth."

Judy withers Aunt Mary.

"None of you understands me! I loathe and hate our whole existence! I want to be out in the world among people who do things—but of course you've never seemed to realize that I have temperament."

"How did you find that out?" asks Aunt Mary.

"It's obvious to anyone who really knows me. Why, I go perfectly mad every time I hear jazz! Every boy I've ever danced with has said that I am *full* of temperament!"

"Oh, dear, what is she talking about?" asks Emma.

"You had the same thing when you were a girl," says Aunt Mary, "only in those days we called it by its right name and the man had to marry you."

Judy overlooks her aunt completely.

"Temperament, mother, is what makes people artists."

"Just as often as liquor makes people Edgar Allen Poe," says Aunt Mary.

"What's that? Liquor?" speaks up Julian. "Make mine Scotch."

"Well," says Aunt Mary, "all of these dancing boys say that you are full of temperament—now where does that lead us?"

"What it all means is, that I have simply got to express myself.

But, of course, you can't understand! I never expected to get any encouragement from the family—I had to go to outsiders for understanding and sympathy!"

" 'Outsiders' meaning Herman Glickman, I take it," says Aunt Mary.

"Wherever did you meet a person with a name like that?" asks Emma.

"Mr. Glickman knows Eddie Goldmark, and Eddie introduced me."

Emma all but faints.

"And who might Eddie be, if anything?" asks Aunt Mary.

"Mr. Goldmark is the famous motion-picture magnate," answers Judy.

"Judy," demands her mother, "who dared introduce you to a motion-picture magnate?"

"The Duchess of Dexter."

"And how, may I ask, did this motion-picture person meet the Duchess of Dexter?"

"The Queen of Ruritania introduced her to him in London, and when she came over here, of course she looked him up—"

"Don't tell me that this motion-picture person was at the Abels' dinner to the Duchess last night!" says Emma.

"He was not! If he had been, we might have stuck it to the finish."

"Do you mean to say that you left the Abels' dinner before it was over?"

"Mother dear, that dinner was ghastly! We left before the coffee."

"You walked out of the Abels' dinner to the Duchess! With *whom*, may I ask?"

"With the Duchess."

"What?"

"Mother dear, if you want to hear the Duchess' own words—"

"Oh, yes! Let's hear the Duchess' own words," says Aunt Mary. "She learned some good ones from the late King Edward when she was a girl."

"The Duchess said, 'If I don't get out of this house soon, I'll be all over itch!' "

"Best thing for itch," speaks up Julian, "is a rub with pure grain alcohol—get it in a drug store on Third Avenue—don't even need a prescription—purest alcohol in the world!—can put it right in your stomach!"

"And where, may I ask, did you and the Duchess go when you left the Abels?" inquired Emma.

"We went to a party that Mr. Goldmark was giving to Mrs. Allister Wardley."

"Not the Allister Wardleys of Philadelphia?" asks Emma.

"Of course!"

"And what is an Allister Wardley doing with a-a-a-Goldmark?" gasps Emma.

"She took him away from the Countess Menander," answers Judy.

Emma staggers to a chair.

"I am stronger than you, Emma," says Aunt Mary, "let me go on with this," and turning to Judy she asks what happened next.

"Well, I met Mr. Goldmark, and danced with him, and he told me that I was fairly bursting with temperament. He said that I would register 100 S.A. in Hollywood."

"Yes? And what is '100 S.A.'?"

"S.A. stands for sex appeal, and 100 is the highest they can give you, even in Hollywood—and you know what a compliment Mr. Goldmark paid me, when he only gives Lowell Sherman 75."

Emma wants to know if the above-mentioned gentleman is a connection of the Lowells of Massachusetts and the Shermans of Georgia.

"Mother dear, if you knew anything at all about the drama," says Judy, "you would know that Lowell Sherman is a perfectly divine actor, and when he played Casanova, seven girls were expelled from Miss Blakeley's."

Emma, knowing nothing of the drama, is silenced.

"Well—Mr. Goldmark said that it would be a crime for me not to have a career—and he said that if I could come down to Florida next month, he could give me a part in a movie, but you know how much chance there is for me to get to Florida, where one has to pay bills, unless one goes on a grand scale, which I can't."

"I thought these movie queens were highly paid persons," says Aunt Mary.

Julian awakes with a jerk.

"Movie queens?" he exclaims. "Bring 'em in!"

"They are highly paid after they get started," answers Judy, "and this would be my start. Believe me, Aunt Mary, it's a great opportunity. Just think, I would get twenty-five dollars every day I worked!"

"And how often would you work?"

"Well, Mr. Goldmark says at least one day a week."

"Judy, you are not only chuck-full of S.A. but you're a financial genius besides!"

"I don't understand it at all," says Emma, "but it sounds like Bolshevism."

"Speaking of Russia," says Julian, "best vodka in the world—right over on Fifty-third Street! Sixty dollars a case! Grand Duke Alexis has more customers than he can supply."

Judy yawns and looks at her wristwatch, which so far has been a total loss to the firm of Cartier.

"I've an engagement at one-thirty," she says, "so you'll please make this inquisition as short as possible."

"You're not going one step out of this house," says Emma, "without taking your aunt or myself along."

"Mother, don't be stupid!" says Judy. "The first place I'm going is to the Joshua Aldersons' luncheon for Bishop Small, and Heaven knows nothing could possibly happen to me there!"

Emma cocks her eye at her daughter.

"Judy," she says, "now you are lying to me! I know very well that not even wild horses could drag you to old lady Alderson's!"

"Mother," answers Judy, "you don't seem to realize that last night was a turning point in my life. From now on I am going to accept every stupid, exclusive invitation that comes my way."

"What's all this?" asks Aunt Mary.

"It's perfectly simple," says Judy. "This morning I went to see one of the brainiest publicity women in New York, Miss Steinbach. I told her that I was going in for an artistic career and asked if she would undertake my publicity and she said that she would on one condition, and that was, that I give her something to work on. Because, you see, the only talking point she has on me is a purely social one. So she said that I would have to change my mode of life and go to exclusive parties now and then, so as to give her something to get her teeth into. Because she also handles other artists—Ann Pennington, for instance—and she says that as matters stand now she doesn't see much difference between my career and

Ann Pennington's, except that Ann Pennington knows how to dance."

Emma is too dazed to come out of this tangle of cross-thought without help. So Aunt Mary jumps into the breach.

"Well, Emma," she says, "half the women in society are going in for the—mm—Arts, and as far as I'm concerned, I'm all for it! It makes the world a brighter and funnier place to live in. What if a career *is* only an alibi for being rowdy? At least, it's better than being rowdy without one. And, as I take it, this Steinbach woman is the only person capable of keeping Judy in respectable company for even a small portion of the day. Put your brains to work, Emma, and give it some thought!"

"Oh, dear," says Emma. "I don't know what to think—after all that happened to Judy last night—"

"Well, buck up, Emma," says Aunt Mary, "we haven't yet heard *all* that happened, and it may get worse." Then turning to Judy, she continues. "You have accounted successfully for about half the night. What happened next? I'm dying to know!"

"Well—Mr. Goldmark and Mrs. Allister Wardley and the Duchess and two gentlemen and I—"

"Do I know the two gentlemen?" asks Emma, hoping against hope that they may be in the Social Register.

"They were Damon Giles and Spottiswood Irving," says Judy. "They are interior decorators, and the Duchess adores them!"

"Yes, I know," says Aunt Mary. "When she's out with the two together, she feels she has a man about."

"They are artists, Aunt Mary!"

"Ah, yes—I always forget that we are moving in the realm of Art!"

"Well—the six of us went up to the Love Nest."

"Whose love nest?" asks Julian.

"The Love Nest is a divine cabaret in Forty-eighth Street. Well, by seven o'clock, Mr. Goldmark and I were left alone and we had a long, serious talk."

"What became of the other Art lovers?" asks Aunt Mary.

"Aunt Mary, have you got to know every insignificant thing that happened last night?" asks Judy.

"If anything happened last night that *was* insignificant, go on and tell your mother. It might cheer her up."

"Well, while Mr. Goldmark was out getting more Scotch—"

"Yes—yes—" speaks up Julian.

"A waiter was rude to Spottiswood—"

"And what did the waiter do to Spottiswood?"

"Well, you see, Spottiswood told the waiter to remove an electric candelabra, because he is very sensitive to light effects, and he considered that the Duchess was badly lit."

"Lit!" exclaims Julian. "Good for her!"

"So then the waiter refused and he called Spottiswood a name."

"What name?"

"Well, a name that means a man—who is an interior decorator."

"Oh, dear," says Emma, "I don't know what you're talking about—do we have to go into all of this detail?"

"I wouldn't miss a word of it for money," says Aunt Mary. "And what did Spottiswood do then?"

"Well, Aunt Mary," says Judy, "he got into an argument with the waiter, and if you have got to know every single word of it, I'll try to remember."

"Go ahead," says Aunt Mary, "and don't you hold out on me!"

"Well—Spottiswood was very dignified, but he told the waiter that if he knew anything at all about history, he would realize that every great man who ever lived was an interior decorator at heart."

"What?" asks Aunt Mary.

"Spottiswood knows what he is talking about, because he has gone into the subject thoroughly, and he said that when he visited Stratford-on-Avon, he proved to himself that Shakespeare may have spent his spare time writing the drama, but it was not for nothing that his house looks like a high class gift shop on the Boston Post Road."

"Yes, yes, go on!"

"Well, he also said that one trip to Mount Vernon had convinced him that winning a few battles didn't interfere with George Washington being able to put the right rag rug where it was needed. And as far as Napoleon was concerned, any one who had ever been to Malmaison could see at a glance that he knew where to put a dash of Empire blue to get the effect he was looking for. And then the waiter got rude."

"Oh, goody! And what did the waiter do?"

"Well, he called to one of the other waiters and said, 'Come on over and look at what just said that George Washington embroidered the Constitution on a tea cosy.'"

"Delightful! And what happened then?"

"Well, the Duchess was furious and sent for the proprietor, who was perfectly charming about it all, but he couldn't do anything, because the waiter was the personal representative of the Prohibition officer in that District, so he suggested that as long as Spottiswood and Damon got on the waiter's nerves, we had better go to another place. So the two boys and the Duchess went on to Childs, but Isabel Wardley and I had to wait for Mr. Goldmark to come back."

"And did he bring the Scotch?" asks Julian.

Every once in a while Julian astounds his family by a real feat of memory.

"Well," says Judy, "it finally got late, so we started away, but as we were going out Isabel fell upstairs and strained her scar—"

"Her what?"

"She had her face lifted two weeks ago, and it isn't healed yet. So we had to take her home to put ice on it, and then, Mr. Goldmark and I went to the Astor Hotel for breakfast, and I accepted his offer to work in the movies, but I told him that I would simply have to have money to get to Florida—and then he suggested Mr. Glickman."

"Why didn't this Goldmark person offer to be your banker, since he is rich, and you are so full of S.A.?" asks Aunt Mary.

"Mr. Goldmark said that he would be glad to finance my career, but he is crazy about Isabel Wardley, and she is violently jealous, so he wouldn't dare. And the next best thing was Mr. Glickman."

Emma looks faint.

"If you want to leave the room for the remainder of this, Emma," says Aunt Mary, "I'll get the story myself and break it to you a little at a time."

"No," says Emma, "my great-great-grandmother carried water to the Continentals on Morristown Heights! I can stand it."

"Then go on, Judy," says Aunt Mary.

"Well, after breakfast, Mr. Goldmark said that the one person who could arrange matters with Herman Glickman was a lady who lives on West End Avenue so we—"

"Wait a moment—wait a moment," says Aunt Mary, "even my old brain is beginning to weaken! What did you say this lady was?"

"She is the lady who gets girls in touch with Herman Glickman."

"What's her address?" speaks up Julian.

"But what—" breaks in Emma.

"Emma," says Aunt Mary, "if you had the faintest idea of what is being discussed here, I'd order you from the room."

"I'm just as unhappy when I don't understand," says Emma.

"Well, Judy, what happened then?"

"We started for West End Avenue to see—this lady, and as we were leaving the Astor, the hatcheck girl, who is a friend of Mr. Goldmark's, noticed that I was in evening dress and lent me her coat."

"The hatcheck girl noticed this? And where were your powers of observation?"

"Our minds were on other things."

"That's right," says Aunt Mary. "I always forget that your minds are on Art."

"Well, we picked up this lady at her house, and came back to Mr. Glickman's place—and then Mr. Goldmark had to leave us. So the lady introduced me to Mr. Glickman, and he was perfectly delightful, and in less than ten minutes I agreed to his proposition for two thousand dollars."

"Well," says Aunt Mary, "we may just as well brace ourselves and hear the worst. What was the proposition?"

"I hate to tell you, because you'll make a furious fuss, and it really isn't anything at all."

"No—in these days, I notice it isn't," says Aunt Mary.

"Well, all I had to do was to sign a paper for Mr. Glickman allowing him to use my name and pedigree and photograph in some very high-class advertisements that go only in the best magazines, together with a statement that I had been cured of seborrhea."

"What's—seborrhea?" asks Julian.

"You'll never know," answers Aunt Mary, "because I've read those advertisements and they say that only a mother would tell you."

The discussion gets no further, because Emma has fainted and it takes some time to bring her to. As she regains consciousness, she murmurs instructions to Judy to remember her ancestry, particularly on her mother's side, and finally picks up enough strength to rise to her feet, order Judy to tear up the check, lock herself in her room and spend the remainder of her natural life in prayer.

"I knew exactly what would happen if I told you," says Judy, "and I'm not going to stay here to be insulted by petty minds!"

"No," says Aunt Mary, "why should you, when all the high-class magazines in America will soon be on the job?"

Judy turns to Aunt Mary.

"I must say, I'm surprised at you, Aunt Mary," she says, "I thought that *you* would understand."

Aunt Mary thinks a moment, right through the sobs of Emma and the snores of Julian.

"As a matter of fact, Emma," she says, "I do think you are taking this a bit too seriously."

"Mary," asks Emma, "how could it be worse?"

"Easily," answers Judy, "the advertisement says in plain English that I've been *cured* of seborrhea! Suppose I had to say I have it yet!"

"Exactly," says Aunt Mary. "I'm beginning to be won around."

"And think of the publicity it gives me when I'm starting on a career!"

"Publicity!" gasps Emma. "Publicity! To think that we—!"

"Oh, Mother," cries Judy, "it isn't as though I were the only one who ever did this! How do you suppose the Duchess of Dexter got money to come to America? The only income she has in the world is rent on her flat in London."

"She can't get much for that," speaks up Aunt Mary, "because the view looks smack on the Albert Memorial."

"Of course!" says Judy. "The Duchess signed up for seven thousand dollars. It's frightfully simple. Everybody's doing it."

"But Judy," asks Aunt Mary, "when the Duchess got seven thousand why did you get only two?"

"Well, Aunt Mary, it's all a comparative thing. The Queen of Ruritania gets as much as fifteen thousand, but then, you see, she is royalty. Now, of course, the Duchess of Dexter has a very famous title."

"Plus the O.K. of the late King Edward," speaks up Aunt Mary.

"Of course! But with *our* ancestry, all they would offer me was two thousand." Judy shoots a dirty look at her mother. "That's just the trouble with American ancestry—we all take ourselves seriously because we date back a hundred years or so! The Duchess of Dexter's family goes back centuries, and is really worth money in an advertisement."

Emma looks dazed. Proud of race as she is, she can't seem to think of a comeback to such definite statistics. But a strange glitter begins to light up the eye of Aunt Mary.

"Judy," she asks thoughtfully, "just exactly who is this Herman Glickman?"

"Well, you see, he is very much interested in charities and it's his job to get the debs to sign up for all the different advertisements, so that they can give the money to their favorite charities."

"Ah, yes," answers Aunt Mary. "I met a woman at luncheon yesterday who had sold out to silverware, stationery, bathroom fixtures, dressing-tables, curtains, cold cream, yeast, radios, lace, and radiators. The only thing the public doesn't know about that woman is that she has a lump on her left knee—and all for charity! In fact, she just bought a new Rolls so that she can dash about more quickly from one charity to another."

"But," says Emma, "I don't believe that Judy intends giving her check to charity."

"Of course she does," says Aunt Mary, "only her charity happens to be the Promotion of S.A. in Florida."

"She can't go to Florida," says Emma. "That is final! She can't go to Florida without the family and we can't afford to go."

"I have been doing some thinking," says Aunt Mary, "and I have an idea about that." And turning to Judy, she asks, "What's Herman Glickman's address?"

"Mary," gasps Emma, "you wouldn't—"

"If the name of Revell is worth two thousand dollars the name of van Tassell ought easily to bring five!"

Emma, by this time, is panicky. She goes to Julian, shakes him by the shoulder and says, "Julian, wake up! Wake up! Talk to Mary! She's going to sell the name of van Tassell!"

Julian comes to.

"Where'll she find a taker?" he asks.

Aunt Mary goes over to the console table and picks up a copy of a current magazine. As she glances through it, her eye kindles. The advertising pages are glittering with great names, just like the Social Register—only, better than the Register, they have pictures and give details, not only of a lady's pedigree, but even, in some cases, of her plumbing. Aunt Mary enthusiastically hands the magazine to Julian and explains.

Julian takes it in a trembling hand, and after dropping it twice, finally focuses, finds himself staring into the monthly "spread" of a yeast company.

"What's this?" he says, and he reads out, "Famous man about town regulated by yeast!"

"Oh, yes," says Judy, "I forgot the yeast company, but they only pay five hundred."

"Five hundred for what?" asks Julian.

"For anyone who's been cured by yeast."

"All right," says Julian, "where do I collect?"

Emma, seeing the members of her clan dropping from her one by one, begins to realize that she is on the losing side of a highly successful revolution. "What is society coming to? Where is pride? Where is privilege? Where is prejudice?"

"Where is Herman Glickman?" asks Aunt Mary. "That is much more to the point."

Judy digs his address out of her pocketbook, and goes off about her afternoon's affairs, which are to end in a scientific demonstration of the effect of 100 percent S.A. on the American male at tea time, aided by a 90 proof substitute for tea.

Emma now faces the two remaining members of her house and begs them not to sell out.

"Don't be silly, Emma," speaks Aunt Mary. "I've suddenly made up my mind to see Florida, which I can't do on my income, in its present state. I haven't had much fun in my old life, and I'm not going to overlook anything from now on! Florida must be divine! I haven't been so thrilled since I discovered Boccaccio at the age of eleven! Julian, get your hat, if you're coming with me to Herman's!"

Aunt Mary now picks up the magazine, opens it, turns and addresses her sister.

"Emma, don't be a fool all your life! Here's some magnificent coconut oil, excellent for the hair. All it needs is a life-sized reproduction of that false front of yours to bring it to the attention of every salesgirl that rides the subway. Come on along!"

Emma summons all of the van Tassell dignity and pride.

"Never!" she exclaims, "I've never used anything on my hair in all my life."

"Then it's about time you did," says Aunt Mary. "Don't spoil this beautiful morning by holding out on us. Why, I'm all bucked up! I never thought it possible, in this day and age, that our family could mean so much to the community."

"Why, Mary, our family has always been among the first to help in any movement that—"

"Nonsense," says Aunt Mary, "our family hasn't done a darn thing worthy of anybody's notice since great-grandmother carried water to the Continentals on Morristown Heights—And, here is an opportunity for you to carry oil to those who are fighting just as hard to keep their hair!"

Emma is dazed, but the argument sounds logical.

Aunt Mary continues. "If our family has always been among the first in any great movement of the upper class, how can we lie down now?"

Emma tries to answer, but can't think of anything to say.

Aunt Mary thrusts the magazine into her hands and continues, "Consider your duty toward this excellent coconut oil, which has stood the test of half the crowned heads of Europe! Can we of the American Aristocracy do better than follow their lead? Think hard, Emma, because your answer's got to be good!"

Emma thinks as hard as she can, for this last argument has pierced clear through her armor of pride and prejudice. After as profound a consideration as Emma's brain is capable of compassing, she speaks.

"Well," she says, "I'll tell you what I'll do. I'll go along with you and I will stop at a drug store and *buy* a bottle of the preparation you speak of, and I'll *use* it, and if tomorrow morning my hair looks improved, I may even consider it my duty, as a van Tassell, to tell the world."

Considering that nothing yet invented by the mind of man could make Emma's hair look *worse* next morning, this is as good as a capitulation. And so, keeping her dignity to the last, Emma joins the expedition that is to boost the house of Revell into the forefront of the winter's social life in Florida.

Society note: "One of the favorite sports in Palm Beach these hectic days (and nights) is betting on the outcome of the many activities of the divine Judy Revell. Of course, it was a foregone conclusion that the cinema would make a desperate bid for her, and Judy has capitulated to the extent of lending her beauty and talent to an elaborate production which is now being *tourné*, as they say in France. But wherever Judy is, a certain little god named 'Cupid' is pretty sure to step in and disarrange the best laid plans, and so matters complicate themselves. For a while, it looked as if a gentleman from the Argentine might be the favored suitor, but Judy, of late, has been seen many times in company of none other than our greatest matrimonial prize—the Valentine heir. However, even this may be no indication of the way the wind blows, for Judy is nothing if not eclectic, and is seen quite as often with Count Swazy, who has little wealth, but important listing in the Almanac de Gotha. What will Judy's future be—Art, Millions, or a Title?"

All this sounds great, but it is too much like a real-estate prospectus to be convincing. Anyone reading it would think that Society is a beautiful garden where Judy Revell's only problem is to decide which flower to pick—whereas, the only garden comparable to Society in these days is Madison Square Garden during a lively bout, and Judy, instead of picking a beautiful lily, is much more likely to find herself up against a good sock in the nose.

As to her choice of "Art, Millions, or a Title"—well, that matter, at this very moment, is being thoroughly gone into at a tea, given in her honor at the Palm Beach studio of Damon Giles and Spottiswood Irvine, interior decorators. The studio is a reproduction of a Spanish cloister of the twelfth century, but Damon and Spottiswood are not strictly in the period, being reproductions of nothing that has ever existed on earth before. The spirit of the South has run rampant through their wardrobe. Spottiswood has restrained himself sufficiently to keep to the mauves and purples, but Damon has broken right out into the yellows and reds. The room is lit by fading daylight, filtered through old stained-glass windows, picturing some of the early Christian martyrs. The guests are lit by several rounds of bootleg Bacardi, filtered through a cocktail shaker, and some of them are probably going to be martyrs before the season is over.

Damon and Spottiswood are talking to a girl friend, who wears the same model collar (size 14½) as her hosts, but whose necktie, by way of contrast, is much more conservative in coloring. Her name is Georgie Wilkes, and the newspapers were full of her at the time she renounced beaus and a butterfly life in Society, to go in for settlement work and the Drama. She organized the Toolchest Players in a stable over on West Twelfth Street, and started her task of rescuing neighbors from the vile atmosphere of the open streets, and initiating them into that of the stable and strong sex drama. The three are discussing Judy. Georgie believes that she has talent, while Damon is all for her marrying that great prize, Winnfield Valentine, who is paying her such marked attention.

Winnfield is also present, so the truth may as well be told about him. He is thirty-four years of age and the only unmarried male left in one of the oldest and wealthiest families in America. He was educated at the best school for defectives in Connecticut, and graduated at the very head of his class. Today he is unhappy, because he didn't want to come to the party, and only the fact that Judy is expected was a strong enough lure to drag him away from a new toy electric train that had just arrived from New York. He has found some solace, however, in bringing along an imitation fly, which he has pinned on one coat lapel, the notion being to fool the public into a futile attempt to brush it away. He also has a spool of thread in one pocket, the end of which has been pulled through the cloth of his sleeve in such a manner that anyone trying to pick it off will keep right on unwinding. But fate is unkind, for nobody bites, because his general get-up is so negligée that a piece of thread or a fly more or less on Winnfield would pass unnoticed anywhere. He is dolefully dallying with a cup of tea. He can't drink cocktails, because liquor gives him a rash.

Winnfield, although a great catch, has not yet fully come into his own, because his father still controls the family fortune, and, being a canny old soul, he hangs onto it. However, Winnfield is the recipient of a fairly good income derived from the fortune left him by his mother, which she acquired in an extraordinary manner. It seems that when Winnfield was eighteen, the old man, who was inordinately vain of his reputation for virility, looked his son over one day and offered his wife a million dollars in her own name if she would assure him that nineteen years before she had been unfaithful. Winnfield's mother had not been unfaithful, which anyone could prove who had seen her photograph taken at that period, before medical science had succeeded in harnessing buck teeth. But Mr. Valentine said that the mere empty words would reestablish his morale. So Mrs. Valentine wrote them out, and received the first real money she had ever been able to pry from the old man. From this time on, there had developed a better feeling in the little family, especially between father and son, which in late years has developed to the point where Father can almost endure him. Consequently, since there are no other heirs in this branch of the family, Winnfield has assumed the importance of a great catch.

Also present at the party awaiting the arrival of our heroine, is Count Swazy, scion of one of the noblest houses in Hungary. He is a handsome young giant, an expert at polo, tennis, and all sports, except that, having been brought up on Hungarian Tokay, any

American deb can outdrink him on Scotch. He is a specialist in good manners and the knowledge of when, where, and how to do the right thing. If Europe were not in a jumble, some wealthy European house would have been happy to follow the old established custom in practice among civilized families on the other side, and marry off a daughter to Count Swazy, settling an income on the two of them.

Count Swazy could take his wife into the smartest homes of Europe, teach her how to spend her money charmingly, and point out to her the difference between a Greco of the middle period and a Coca-Cola lithograph. However, his estates are in impoverished Hungary, his money is in kronen, and every wealthy father in America is living in terror, lest daughter get more plastered than usual some night, consent to become his Countess, and drag a fine old American name in the mire.

Count Swazy arrived only recently. He hasn't learned whether Judy Revell has money back of her or not, but the Count never yet allowed business to interfere with pleasure, and Palm Beach is no place to begin.

The third rival for the hand of Judy is Enrico Cadiz. He, unlike Count Swazy, is a self-made man, and an example of what earnest effort can achieve in our democratic America. Coming up from the Argentine five years ago on a cattle-ship, he is today one of the most sought-after bachelors in American Society. He won his way by hard work, starting his career in New York by crashing débutante parties, standing in the stag line and watching for signals of distress from men who had been stuck with undesirable debs. These signals are given by the dancer eagerly eyeing the stag line, and at the same time fingering a dollar bill held in the hand which is back of the débutante. The stag cutting in gets the dollar bill, which is deftly passed while the change of partners is being effected, the whole process being known as "life-saving"! Enrico worked at "life-saving" for months, nobly avoiding the gatherings of the "new line" debs, who were pretty and well supplied with liquor, and going only to the finest old Knickerbocker affairs, where dollar bills were passed most frequently. At one of the most exclusive débuts of his first winter, the ante for "life-saving" was raised from one to five dollars, and business was so good that he picked up a nice little nest-egg. With this as a start, his rise was rapid, and today he is indispensible to any really exclusive affair.

Enrico approached Delicia Dennington, a sub-deb. She was to have come out this winter, but illness prevented. She developed "smoker's throat" right on top of an acute attack of "Charleston feet," complicated by an overdose of acid in the system, due to too much orange juice taken in cocktail form. Delicia is having a "boy and girl" affair with "Stewie" Winthrop, who is hanging over her shoulder. Stewie's father started him out to live up to the fine old family name of Winthrop, but that being a bit difficult, Stewie has compromised by living up to his nickname. There are those who say that modern life makes for inconstancy, yet the little romance of Stewie and Delicia has endured for months. Together, they have been through three motor wrecks, two of Stewie's D.T. attacks, a police raid, and a jail sentence, and still the bloom has not worn off.

Feeling that a pair of lovers will understand his troubles, Enrico comes to them for sympathy. It seems that Judy has been cold to him of late, after being otherwise. He wanted a chance to see her, so he made violent love to old lady Cobb, in order to get an invitation to her treasure hunt, and so be with Judy. But at the treasure hunt, Judy had schemed to be with Count Swazy, so that Enrico was stuck with old lady Cobb, who took everything he had said to her seriously. Enrico is bitter and disillusioned about Judy. He is a Latin and can't understand such American cold blood and calculation.

Delicia allows that it was "perfectly putrid" of Judy, but tells Enrico to cheer up and *"hold everything."* Her words of sympathy are interrupted by old lady Cobb herself, who joins them. She is Mrs. Cornelius Cobb of Chicago—famous for the rope of pearls given her by her father on her marriage. It reached clear to her toes in those days, but increasing embonpoint has lifted its limit to a point half-way between the knee and the hip. She is not wearing it today, however, because her husband is hanging about, and as Mr. Cobb has just had a bad run of luck at Bradley's, Mrs. Cobb has given her pearls to the chauffeur for safekeeping.

The Duchess of Dexter now draws all eyes to the center of the room by giving her well-known imitation of Charlie Chaplin. The Duchess is noted for her imitations and can do almost anyone. If she could only give an imitation of a duchess, her line would be complete.

At this point, Mr. and Mrs. Henry Spoffard of Philadelphia enter the cloister and make their way through the throng to Damon and

Spottiswood. Mr. Spoffard is the great millionaire reformer and his wife is known on the screen as Lorelei Lee. They dropped in to order the decorations for their new home, a late Addison Mizner, and Lorelei's instructions to Damon are that she "doesn't really mind antique furniture so much, so long as a room is full of plenty of maribou."

Mr. Spoffard is looking the party over and becoming uneasy. He nudges his wife, motions her away from Damon and Spottiswood, with whom she is "holding a conversation," and tells her that all of this is very reminiscent of Sodom and Gomorrah. Lorelei says that she never saw Sodom and Gomorrah, but if they were anything like Savoy and Brennan used to be, she thinks he is right. Mr. Spoffard now notices Georgie Wilkes lighting a pipe, and decides that matters have gone far enough. He grabs Lorelei by the arm and heads for the door, where they bump into Judy's Aunt Mary, who is just arriving. Mr. Spoffard stops long enough to tell her that they are shocked at the goings-on, and that he wonders what the next generation is going to be.

"Now, Mr. Spoffard," says Aunt Mary, "don't you worry about the next generation. Why, you'd have to import some Turkish atrocities to get another generation out of this crowd!" And with that, Aunt Mary bounces into the room to join the fun.

By this time, the Duchess has done her stuff, and approaches Damon and Spottiswood, who are biting their nails under a beautiful old thirteenth-century reliquary. They are both annoyed because Judy, for whom the party was given, has not put in an appearance.

"For the love of linoleum," says Damon, "where's Judy?"

"Damon, my dear," says the Duchess, "don't expect too much of the darling child—she never catches up with her dates, dear boy, and she may be detained by that beastly cinema business she's gone in for!" The Duchess is sore on the cinema. She tried to horn into the minor role of an English lady, but the director said she couldn't look the part, and finally gave it to a telephone operator from the Poinciana.

"What's Judy playing in the film?" asks Spottiswood.

"Well," answers the Duchess, "they started her to play a statue that comes to life—but she couldn't stand still as the statue, and she went dead on them when they told her to come to life. So then they made her a guest at a house party, but *my dear,* they expected her to be on the set for *hours at a time*. So, finally they made her a lady who drops in for a cup of tea. They've taken the scene of her dropping in, but she has so many engagements, they haven't been able to pin her down to the cup of tea."

By this time Aunt Mary approaches.

She grabs Spottiswood by the arm and drags him over to the seclusion of an early Spanish prayer bench.

"I hope Judy shows up here," she says. "I never see her at home, and there is something I must find out."

"Oh, do tell what!" says Spottiswood.

"It's a long story, my dear! What we have been through since we came to Florida has surprised even me, and I consider myself shock-proof! You know, we are keeping house in the Gwynn cottage."

"How *ever* did you happen to get a cottage—why, they're scarcer down here than morals!"

"Of course they are, but when we arrived, the local realtor told us that, even though cottages were scarce, one was frequently given up by somebody who had to be moved to the hospital, and from the way Willie Gwynn was bringing liquor in from Key West, his cottage ought to be vacant any time. So we simply went to the Poinciana and waited."

"Clever you!" exclaims Spottiswood.

"Well," continues Aunt Mary, "we had the most dreadful time after we moved into the cottage! We took over all of Willie's servants, and matters started off well enough, when Judy's father came into a check for five hundred dollars, and disappeared."

"And how did *he* ever raise five hundred dollars?"

"He raised it with yeast, my dear!"

"Yeast?"

"He wrote a testimonial for a yeast company. Surely you've seen it in all the magazines. I'm having it framed, because it's the first time in history that it was ever intimated that Judy's father had any insides."

"But where did he disappear *to*?"

"Well, that was the question. If we only had a civilized governmental control of liquor in this country, such as they have in Canada, we should simply have gone to the nearest depot and picked him up. *But,* when you have to comb fifty or sixty obscure liquor stations, it's dreadful! We finally had to go to the police! But, I must say, they were sweet about it. They gave us a complete list of addresses where liquor could be bought, and a charming detective went along with us, but—wait until I tell you what had happened to Julian!"

"Well, tell away!"

"We finally found a certain place—excellent gin, by the way—let me give you the address when I'm finished. Now, at this place they also deal in real estate. It seems that all the bootleggers down here have gone into real estate on the side. So when they learned that Julian had five hundred dollars, they produced the map of a new town called, 'Dolce Far Niente,' with sixty miles of water-front lots, and they induced Julian to put every cent he had on one of them, so he could import his own liquor from the rum fleet, right up to the front gate. Well, as we found out later, Dolce Far Niente was two hundred miles inland, but they *did* have sixty miles of water front, which they achieved by digging a thirty-mile ditch, turning some fresh water into it and marking out lots on either side.

"Well, my dear, this bootlegger's lots were terrible, but his gin was magnificent, and when we arrived at the place, Julian had gotten full of it and started down the ditch in a rowboat, expecting to connect with the rum fleet in the Atlantic Ocean. He had been gone half a day, when a blinding rainstorm came up and washed away the ditch. We finally located him, but by that time the sun had come out, and there was Julian, simply smothered in dust, trying to locate the place where the ditch had been so he could push the boat back!"

"How too precious!"

"But that's only half of the story! Judy's mother and I had to be away for two days, routing out Julian, and while we were gone, something strange happened at home."

"It *did?*"

"Yes, indeed! The evening we left was the night of the Coconut Ball. A number of guests were to meet up with Judy at our house for a cocktail beforehand. Enrico and Judy were going together, both in seventeenth-century French costumes. Delicia, Stewie, Mrs. Cobb, the Duchess, and that dear boy who used to dance at the Reliquary before he met Mrs. Cobb, were also due. As I understand it, the party started at our house about half an hour after Judy's mother and I left, and broke up two days later at the same place, when they heard us returning up the gravel path. The Duchess had started out in a sweet Dolly Varden effect, but by the time we got back, she had changed to something modern—that is, if you want to call Julian's hunting breeches modern. He bought them from Poole in London thirty years ago. In fact, I believe, almost all of the guests had changed to something they found around the house—but Enrico might still have been dressed in the period, because he took French leave out the back way when we came in. However, I may be wrong, as some of the others, who were in this year's bathing-suits, followed his example. Well, we entered the house and surveyed the almost complete wreck of what had once been an Adam interior. You know yourself, Spottiswood, that no Adam interior can keep its simplicity when there are chunks of plaster out of the ceiling that nobody has bothered to pick up off the floor."

"Oh—Miss van *Tassell!*"

"And underfoot, my dear, there was fuzz an inch deep, from large tufts that had been dug out of the carpet."

"Well—that might suggest the Charleston!"

"That's just what I figured! But, wait a moment, you haven't heard anything yet! We finally decided to fortify ourselves with food. So we rang for breakfast. The butler appeared, and said that the servants were all going for a swim, so we'd have to get it ourselves!"

"*Bolshevism*—I'll be *bound!*"

"Of course, I fired him on the spot, at which he raised his hand to his mouth to cover a smile and said I had better ask Miss Judy whether it would be wise to let him out. So we called in the parlormaid to find Judy, which she did by opening the door into the hall and calling up the stairs, 'Hey, Judy, your aunt wants you!' "

"How *horrible!*"

"I told the butler that if we fired them, they could never get another job in Palm Beach, but he only smiled and said they could shake down a job out of any lady who had been at the party. But they had gone over the list and decided to stay with us, because the Duchess had only a hall bedroom at the Poiniciana, the Dennington estate was in the hands of their bootlegger, and they understood that Mrs. Cobb's house had been marked for a jewel robbery.

"Well, Judy finally came downstairs and we talked things over, pro and con, and decided that, after all, we had better not let the servants out—it looks so bad to see a whole flock leave in the middle of the season! However, it's all been very trying, because, as the butler started to go out the door, he turned and said, 'No doubt, Miss van Tassell, you'll be glad to have us here to help out at the wedding!'"

" 'What wedding?' I asked, and he said, 'Well, I mention no names, but we all hope there's going to be a wedding.' "

"Oh, the beast!"

"This business has simply played havoc with our home life! It's not so bad for Judy, because she's never there, but it's very difficult for us! Only this morning, I told the upstairs girl, who is supposed to be 'maiding' me, that my stockings needed mending, and she replied, 'Well, Miss van Tassell, I didn't know that you could mend.' And yesterday, when the Duchess dropped in at tea time, the butler gave her a cup of cold tea that was left over from breakfast, borrowed ten dollars, and told her a risqué story!"

"Well, Miss van Tassell, what are we coming to when the lower class can behave like that to the nobility!"

"Heaven knows! However, people of that type occasionally have a clever idea. We mustn't overlook the fact that genius sometimes comes from the gutter. For instance that butler's notion about a wedding wasn't bad on the whole. Judy would look divine in a wedding-gown. I talked to her seriously about it and finally got her interested, but she said that she had better pick a fiancé from among the boys who had not been at the party. So we finally settled on dear Winnie Valentine. But since then, Count Swazy has appeared on the scene and Judy has been dividing her time between the two of them. I don't want her to let the Count take her mind off Winnie, because, of course, she must marry money. I do hope Winnie proposes before he hears too much gossip, because his bride will have to be a perfect housekeeper in order to manage the Fifth Avenue mansion and if Winnie hears that Judy has no control over servants, it might go against her. You know how fussy some of the old families are."

At this point Judy herself enters. She has grown more beautiful since her sojourn in the South, and radiates a softer and more shimmering loveliness. She has been down on the pier with her publicity agent and a news photographer, posing with a tuna fish for a "better movie" campaign.

Both Count Swazy and Winnfield make a dash for her side, but Winnie gets there first, so Wealth wins out over Nobility. Winnie grabs her by the wrist and leads her straight through the crowded room and out into the garden, hardly giving her a chance to nod a greeting to her friends on the way. Judy's late entrance had given her so much importance, that her almost immediate disappearance into the garden with Winnie makes a sensation. Every one in the room feels that Winnie's action has only one purpose; that social history is in the making, and that, from now on, as the financée of Winnie Valentine, Judy will be legitimate front-page stuff, without having the bother of a bluff about a career.

Winnie steers Judy out into the courtyard, because it has grown shadowy in the cloister and, for a certain reason, he wants the full light of day to shine upon his wooing. He has worn that imitation fly and bit of thread all afternoon, with no results, and he feels that, given half a chance, he can work them now on the girl he loves, because surely she will see, and understand and bite.

He seeks a well-lit spot, and plants himself firmly in front of her.

"Say, Judy," he asks, "do you see anything wrong about me?"

Judy could easily work up a list of several hundred items, but she feels this is hardly the time to do it, so she merely says, "No!"

Winnie drags her into a better light, throws out his chest, to bring into prominence his coat lapel with its imitation fly, and assumes a well-known Napoleonic attitude, which brings his right arm, with its bit of thread, across his chest.

"*Now,*" he says, "do you see anything?"

"Well, Winnie," says Judy, giving him a pretty good look-over, "it seems to me that you've brushed up a bit."

Winnie stamps his foot in impotent exasperation.

"That's the finish," he yells. "I'm through with you, Judy Revell!"

"Why, Winnie!" she exclaims.

"I'm absolutely through! We would never be congenial, because you will never learn to understand me."

"Why, what are you talking about?"

"I'm not going to take the trouble to explain. All I've got to say is that you have no sense of humor and you never think of anyone's pleasure but your own. Here I've gone around with you for days and days, and even drunk cocktails, and gotten all over rash, just to please you, but any time I ask you to put your mind on something for me, you just go right on thinking about yourself. I'm through— absolutely through! And I'm going to order up steam on the yacht and go for a cruise, and I'll never see you again!"

He turns angrily and stalks away. Judy watches him pass through the pergola and become a silhouette against the setting sun, just like the end of a movie. There is no dodging the fact that the divine Judy Revell has been walked out on by the best bet in America.

Judy is stunned. She looks about helplessly and sinks onto a cold marble bench. Winnie's sudden disappearance is terrible! Everybody in Palm Beach will know that something unusual has happened to send him away like that, and, as there isn't a girl in her set who would refuse him, it certainly is going to look as though Winnie had done the refusing himself.

What Judy lacks in brains is made up for by a magnificent instinct for self-preservation, so she puts that to work, and it works like a dog for several moments. Finally it suggests that she reeenter the cloister and start her well-known line about a career, letting them all take it for granted that ART has ousted Winnfield! She gets up, powders her nose, squares her shoulders and sails back into the studio.

Both Swazy and Aunt Mary are waiting near the door for her reappearance. Judy's gaze softens as she sees the Count. He clutches her hand and kisses it, sending a thrill right down to her toes. *Really,* these Hungarians! Enrico, by this time, has moved up. Judy gives him a grateful look for the first time in weeks. After all, he is a comfort, in that he can talk about Judy almost as constantly as she can talk about herself, and only lacks her sincerity.

"Where's Winnfield?" asks Aunt Mary. "Did you throw him in the Wishing Well?"

"Aunt Mary," answers Judy, "I've quarreled with Winnie. He's too tiresome! I can't be annoyed with him, when all my interest is in my career."

Everybody appears to be interested, and so, bolstered up on all sides, little by little Judy's self-esteem starts to return. Delicia, the Duchess, and several others draw up, to hear how life goes on in the movies.

"I simply love my work!" Judy rants on, "even though it is exhausting. Why, the scene they took of me last month, dropping in for a cup of tea, had to be done over *seventeen times,* and you can imagine what that means to a person of my nervous temperament! Why, I told the director . . . and my test was . . . and the scene of myself . . . and I said . . . and he said better than Gloria Swanson . . . and I . . . me . . . myself . . . mine . . . me . . . I . . . I . . . I." (But the only possible way to stand for this line of talk is to be able to look at Judy while she is doing it, and since we can't see her beautiful self, it's best to come down to the meat of it in a few words—*Judy has given her ALL to ART.*)

In the midst of this, a flurry is caused in the cloister by the excited entrance of Miss Steinbach, who is down in Palm Beach handling not only Judy's publicity but that of two Society matrons, a safety razor, a steamship line, a new patent face mud, and a sub-division near Boca Raton.

"Miss Revell," she cries, "something terrible has happened!"

Judy asks what.

Miss Steinbach gasps for breath and continues, "I just passed the railroad station—and what do you think? The entire Acme Motion Picture Company were getting on the train! They've finished. They're going back to New York! You never showed up to take the rest of your scene, and after all our publicity, *you are not going to be in the picture!*"

This announcement is followed by the total collapse of Judy's bluff, by general confusion and by what the French term *brouhaha!*

Miss Steinbach does her best to take the bulk of the blame on her own shoulders by explaining to everybody that she has kept Judy so busy with publicity stunts that she has had no time left to devote to work. A silence falls over the whole group because nobody can think of anything to say—except Aunt Mary, and she decides she had better not speak her mind in public. Count Swazy goes to get Judy a cocktail, but the situation is finally saved by Georgie Wilkes, who takes her pipe from between her teeth, shoots her cuffs a couple of times and stalks up.

"My dear," she says to Judy, "I think you've had a lucky escape. What would you be doing in the movies, anyway? With that coloring—that voice—your place is in the theater!"

"Oh, do you think so?" asks Judy, clutching at a straw.

"Certainly. I'm always looking for talent for the Toolchest Players. We're beginning our spring season next month. It's the opportunity of a lifetime for you! What do you say?"

Miss Steinbach looks at her watch.

"I think," she says, "that I can telegraph the story to New York in time for the morning editions."

"And please tell them," says Judy, "to put two l's in my name. The last time nearly every front page had it wrong. Wouldn't you think that when the newspapers are dealing with people of temperament, they'd try not to do things that send one into a rage?"

And so, Judy, casting her fortunes once more with ART, turns her beautiful face toward a life of endeavor in the best little theater on West Twelfth Street.

Society note: The career of Judy Revell continues to puzzle the soothsayers of Mayfair. Admirers she has in squadrons, but a mere successful marriage is much too easy an accomplishment to interest a deb of Judy's beauty and talent. In fact, she sent Winnie Valentine packing from Palm Beach when every other debbie in Florida would have given her best Charleston step to get him. Since then, she has divided her time generously between Count Swazy and Sherman Bennett, that charming actor of villainous rôles who has thrilled us all with his art as a naughty stage lover. However, even these two beaux have not been able to keep the attention of Judy, and her recent appearance in the revue of the Toolchest Playhouse has added one more notch to her record of varied conquests.

A reception was held in the ultra exclusive Revell home after the opening of the new Toolchest Revue to celebrate Judy's stage début, and for the first time, the *haut monde* and *haute Bohemia* trod together the sacred Revell carpetry, to do reverence to Thespis. Truly, when such goings-on occur, social history is in the making.

Scene: The sacred Revell salon during the reception to celebrate Judy's triumph in the theater.

Judy, flushed and beautiful, is receiving congratulations from all sides. Every one within earshot is praising her extravagantly. Those out of ear-shot are not praising her so much, while a fringe around the outskirts of the crowd are speaking the truth—but they are all speaking of Judy, at any rate.

"Everybody in New York" had come to do reverence to Art, but most of them are leaving early, because a rumor is afloat that a man who occupies a penthouse on a new building in Park Avenue is at the peak of an unparalleled career of scooping out free liquor. Nobody knows who he is, but the Duchess of Dexter believes his first name to be Jake, as she heard one of the waiters call him that the last time she was there. The Duchess, having started the news about Jake, is leaving, taking with her the cream of talent from the Toolchest group.

Judy is not sorry to see these fellow artistes go, because they have put her through a rough ordeal this night. When rehearsals for the revue started, Judy looked over the girls of the cast and realized that she had nothing to fear in the way of rival beauty. A couple of them had a certain distinction, but, take away their monocles, and they lost even that. Thus, feeling secure in the field of girlish charm, Judy had paid little attention to what went on. She disdained the Toolchest wardrobe department, whose creations were being fumbled up out of cheesecloth, radiator paint, and bits of linoleum, and had ordered her gowns from Fifty-seventh Street, studying them with much more care than she did her lines.

Standing in the wings at dress rehearsal, she suddenly saw something that threw her into a panic. As she glanced across the stage, there appeared another brunette so gorgeously lovely that Judy realized something was radically wrong, somewhere. She turned in terror, and bumped into a flaming blonde in a gold and silver *robe de style* that beggared description. Then, in a daze, Judy saw other beautiful girls appear as if by magic, and finally the truth began to nose in on her. The Toolchest Players were no fools. As lookers, the girls of the organization were not so much—but the boys were *magnificent!* So when dramatic necessity called for beauty, the director simply cast the girls as boys, and vice-versa.

The leading blonde, Albert Castlewood, made Judy look like a dim shadow in a bad light—and he had stitched every inch of his costume with his own fingers, whereas Judy's cost so much that she would be annoyed by the bills for years and years to come.

Judy was so vexed that she would have quit right then and there, but she conferred with her publicity agent, who advised that if she quit them, it would only be good for one set of front-page pictures in the newspapers—whereas if she first *opened* and *then* quit, they could land them twice.

But to get back to the party—the departure of Albert Castlewood with the Duchess in a way cools off the evening for Judy's father, Julian. Julian was present at the Toolchest opening—but he fortified himself to bear the disgrace of his daughter's appearing in public on the stage, with a bottle of Mexican mescal (a sort of triple-strength gin) which he bought from a sacramental wine depot in Hester Street, whither he was led by a taxi driver, and which cost him six dollars, a renunciation of the Christian faith, and a quick clasp to the bosom of Judah. As a consequence, he slept through the entire revue and failed to see his daughter disgrace the fine old family name, but as luck would have it, he came to just in time to see the gorgeous blonde make her final exit, and gave three cheers.

An usher succeeded in quieting him, but couldn't convince him that Albert Castlewood was not Peggy Hopkins Joyce, so Julian stumbled out of the theater and into the nearest florist's, where he ordered the most expensive thing they had in stock. As it was a slum shop, this turned out to be a beaded funeral wreath with "Requiescat in Pace" in blue beads on a white bead background. He carried the wreath to the stage door, but by the time he had concluded that bit of navigation, he learned from the door-tender that everybody had left to go to a party at Miss Revell's. So Julian hurried home, hopping off to Hester Street only long enough to bolster up his new faith with the purchase of a two-quart demijohn of sacramental Scotch.

Arrived at his house, he demanded of the butler if there were any Jewish guests present, for Julian had all the enthusiasm of a neophyte and wanted to share his libations with his kind. But receiving a negative reply, he hid the demijohn in the bedroom for his own religious consumption. Had he loosened up and staked the Gentiles to a little snifter, Judy's guests might have been able to stand the party, and there would have been no general exodus to Jake's.

The bead wreath Julian put into his bed for safekeeping, and he has spent the whole evening hovering between the demijohn of Scotch and a search for his charmer, never learning the cruel trick that Fate has played. He finally gives up and goes to bed, to awake next morning with "Requiescat in Pace" picked out in blue and white beads on his back. In fact, Julian has not had such an unsatisfactory evening since the time he hung around the stage door of the George M. Cohan theater for two hours, waiting for Nita Naldi to come out after a running of Cecil deMille's "Ten Commandments," having muffed altogether the great moral lesson which Mr. deMille intended to convey.

Judy, herself, is talking to her latest conquest, Sherman Bennett, that sterling actor who has wrecked the work of so many leading men by making villainy more attractive than virtue. Sherman could not be present at Judy's performance, as he is himself playing in the famous dope drama wherein the hero proves his complete renunciation of the drug forever, by breaking a four dollar vial of heroin. Sherman Bennett has given Judy some coaching. She even stayed away from rehearsal from time to time to get a more direct and professional "line" on her rôle. Sherman's dramatic method with a pupil is simple, yet revolutionary, and requires in the way of apparatus only a full flask, a taxicab, and the use of Central Park. Sherman tells Judy that he hears she was charming, and Judy admits the truth of the rumor up to a certain limit. But there is one point of dramatic technique about which she always meant to ask him and always has forgotten, and that is—what does an actress do when she happens to recognize some friend in the audience?

Judy goes on to explain that she feels as though the smile and friendly nod she tossed off to Delicia Dennington, who sat in the first row, did something to her stage presence.

Judy's Aunt Mary sits in a corner of the room, looking things over with a clear, cold eye. Count Swazy, the delightful Hungarian, gravitates to her side and starts a conversation.

"Your niece—she was charming," he says.

Aunt Mary gives him a long look.

"Swazy," she says, "I helped Judy get into this thing because I'm a fiend for amusement—but I've laughed myself out, so don't try to be funny."

"Oh, but her rôle was a small one, she had no opportunity!"

"Opportunity? Why, Swazy, the part you saw Judy play tonight was merely the one they handed her after trying her out in every other rôle that could be played by a female since Judy joined the troupe."

"But," asks Swazy, "if Miss Revell has no—no—no—sympathy with acting, how did she come to get into this?"

"Well, Swazy," says Aunt Mary, "Judy's talent for the drama was discovered down in Palm Beach by one of the girls who organized the Toolchest Players, and converted the old stable on West Twelfth Street into an Art dispensary.

"This girl, Georgie Wilkes, noted that Judy could invariably take the center of the stage in any roomful people, so she decided that if Judy could do that on her own and unaided, she would be able, with the assistance of grease paint and lights, to make the audiences in their stable stand up and neigh.

"So she made Judy an offer and Judy took her up on it. If you will gaze across the room and note a girl who looks more depressed than I do, that's Georgie Wilkes, who discovered Judy."

"Ah—so!" says Count Swazy, having no difficulty in spotting the dejected Georgie.

"Coming back on the train from Palm Beach," goes on Aunt Mary, "Georgie explained to me the purpose of the Toolchest group. It's a magnificent organization, really! All based on uplift. She read me the play they were to start the season with. It was by a German, named Hasenclever, and was called 'Beyond.' It had nineteen scenes, a cast of only one man and one woman, and Georgie said that if the police let them get by with it, the cause of uplift would flourish right through the spring until time to stage their summer revue.

"Well, we got back to New York and they started rehearsing 'Beyond' with Judy in the leading rôle. Now it seems that this heroine had only one main idea, and all the equipment she needed in order to carry it out was a man. When her husband was shot in the first act, it didn't interfere with her principal notion in the least, because, as it happened the stranger who brought in the news to her was also a man.

"Luck happened to be with the heroine, for this young fellow caught her idea instantly and they wrastled about through nineteen acts, until it began to get on my nerves. No mention was ever made of eating, paying visits, phoning the butcher, or, as a matter of fact, going to sleep.

"I sat around at rehearsals for a couple of days and finally suggested that, just for the sake of variety, they serve a cup of tea in one of the less intimate scenes. So they tried that out, but they couldn't make a go of it without spilling the tea on the couch, and they had to leave it as it was in the German."

"And do you mean to say that Miss Revell had difficulty with that rôle?" asks Count Swazy.

"She did, indeed," answers Aunt Mary. "It's a mystery to me how the child, who is always the life of any tête-à-tête with a beau off-stage, could so freeze up on that leading man behind the footlights. I must say that Georgie was very patient with her, but the stage director was dreadfully irritating.

"He used to scream at Judy and say, 'You're supposed to be *German,* not a *Pole!*' And I didn't like the way he said 'pole.' "

"I wish I had been there!" says Count Swazy, indignantly.

"Thanks," says Aunt Mary, "but Georgie stood up for Judy nobly.

She said that all Judy needed was to be 'brought out' and then it transpired that Georgie had a scheme of developing her talent by getting Judy to come to her apartment, where a crowd of girl friends sit around every evening, talk about the SOUL until three or four A.M. and suffer keenly.

"Judy went once, but some way she couldn't key in, and I didn't blame her because I tried it out myself, and it wasn't even funny after the first couple of weeks. I always think that there is enough toothache in the world to supply a full quota of suffering to every one, without having to worry over a lot of trumped-up agonies of the spirit. Why those girls have to keep in constant touch with Russian literature in order to reach a state of depression where they can't have any fun at all, I don't see. One of Georgie's gang is writing a book to establish their Temperamental Oneness with all the famous women of history and I understand that it is to have a frontispiece of Catherine the Great with a monocle and Queen Victoria shooting her cuffs.

"Well, Georgie thought that a good, thorough course of their brand of self-expression would develop Judy, teach her about Life, and help her to play that single-track German heroine. But about this time, Judy had an offer of the invaluable services of Sherman Bennett in the way of a coach, so she took him on instead. However, Mr. Bennett's coaching was so exacting that it seemed to take all her time, and she finally reached a point where she had to give up the rôle, in order to do justice to the coaching and the Toolchest Players got in some warmer talent to play that heroine in 'Beyond.' But it only uplifted audiences for about two weeks, when it collapsed and let them down with a crash to a little lower than they were before.

"So Judy's talent was finally given an outlet in the bit you saw her do tonight, and I think you'll agree with me that her presence on the stage wouldn't have been noticed if she hadn't worn so many strings of pearl beads that she rattled when she walked."

"Your American girls are so strange," says Count Swazy. "They are never satisfied to be one thing. I should as soon want the Sèvres vase on my mantelpiece to start singing, as to have Miss Revell be anything at all but divine to look on."

"How charming!" says Aunt Mary. "You must say that to Judy. You Hungarians are too adorable! But tell me, Swazy, what does one do in your country when the daughter of a noble house takes up heavy drinking, low company, exhibitionism and general rowdyness?"

"Madame, we spank her."

"Oh—you beasts! No wonder our girls can't put up with you as husbands."

By this time, practically all the guests have left or are leaving. Even Sherman Bennett is having to pry himself away from Judy, as the Duchess exacted a secret promise that he would meet her in the private bar at Jake's at two o'clock. He kisses Judy's hand at parting and leaves, not knowing that trying to break in or out of the crowd in Jake's bar at two A.M. would defeat Houdini.

Count Swazy is last to go, with the exception of Georgie Wilkes, who is waiting to have a final word with Judy. He kisses her hand, with as much technique as Sherman Bennett and with more feeling. Sherman needs liquor to keep his speed up and he had all but died on Judy before he left, whereas Swazy has a non-stop, Hungarian interest in the ladies that never lets down.

With all the outsiders outside, excepting Georgie, Aunt Mary rises, strides to the center of the salon and calls a family council.

"Judy," she says, "go find your father. From the way he's been acting all evening, I think he has a still in his bedroom, and you'll probably find him hanging over it, if he hasn't fallen in."

Judy departs on her errand and Aunt Mary turns to Judy's mother, Emma, who has been present all evening, but crushed by the fact that she didn't know anybody at her party.

"What did you think of your daughter to-night?" asks Aunt Mary.

"I thought she was excellent," says Emma. "She knew almost all her words."

"Emma," says Aunt Mary, "that remark puts you right in line to become dramatic critic on the *Atlantic Monthly*."

By this time Judy returns with Julian, *le nouveau Juif*, in tow. He is more kosher by two quarts than he was at the time of his conversion. The family thus complete, Aunt Mary calls them to order and says:

"After the orgy of palaver that has just been held here, it's about time that somebody spoke up with the truth about Judy's performance, and made a definite stand as to what is to be done next."

"But Aunt Mary," says Judy, "everybody said—"

"Everybody lied like ladies and gentlemen, but this evening has convinced me that so far as Judy is concerned, the mantle of Duse is still on a coat hanger."

Judy had fully intended not showing up at the theater again on account of the success of Albert Castlewood, but Aunt Mary's opposition is exactly what was needed to get her back up, and she announces her intention of sticking.

Aunt Mary then turns to Georgie.

"Georgie," she says, "step in and give us your own expert opinion on Judy's performance this evening."

"Judy was perfectly unformed, lacking in technique, and without a spark of fire."

Julian snaps out of a reverie in time to catch the end of Georgie's criticism, and jumps up in alarm.

"Fire?" he exclaims. "Women and children first!"

"Oh, shut up and sit down," orders Aunt Mary. Then turning and addressing Judy, she demands that she hand in the customary two weeks' notice to the Toolchest Players and date it back fourteen days.

"I'll do nothing of the kind," says Judy. "You have no right to say anything about my performance until you see what the critics write about it."

At this point, Emma breaks into the argument.

"Judy is right," she says. "I sat between two newspaper gentlemen, and from what they said, I understood that Judy lived up to our finest family traditions and did credit to her ancestress who carried water to the Continental troops."

"What did those critics say?" asks Aunt Mary in a cold, hard tone.

"They said her appearance was the greatest act of bravery they had ever seen in the theater."

"Emma," says Aunt Mary, "something tells me that your understanding of the stage is hampered by the fact that you haven't any. You'd better let us thrash this thing out by ourselves."

"I'm not going to quit!" announces Judy.

"Then," says Aunt Mary, "it's up to you, Georgie, in the interest of the drama, to give Judy the gate."

"In the interest of the drama," says Georgie, "that is exactly what Judy deserves! And she hasn't yet heard of the magnificent opportunity she has thrown away by her refusal to take things seriously."

Georgie pauses a moment in order to give her announcement the importance it deserves.

"You were to have been given the leading rôle in a new unpro-
duced play by Hans Pfeffer, who is the important exponent of
modern German Explosionism."

Georgie's audience is hardly arty enough to realize the signifi-
cance of Mr. P's. contribution to modern drama, so Georgie lets it
be known that she is ready and willing to give a brief outline of the
plot.

"If any German plots are going to be spilled here tonight," says
Aunt Mary "let's get the old people out of the room."

Julian, however, has fallen asleep and Emma's face shows a
certain expression which indicates that her brain has knocked off
work for the day, and will not be back on the job for at least twelve
hours. This being the case, Aunt Mary calls for Mr. Pfeffer's plot.

"It's a story of mother love!" says Georgie, "and tells of a young
girl who meets her lover every night in a coal mine and so never
gets to see what he looks like."

"I'd simply adore playing those scenes," says Judy sarcastically. "It
would give an actress such a good chance to wear clothes!"

"Oh, I understand your attitude toward the theater *now*, Judy,
but there was a time when I considered you worthy of a part like
this."

"Well," asks Aunt Mary, " what went on in that coal mine, besides
coal mining?"

Georgie warms to her plot and begins to wax dramatic.

"The lover is killed by a blast, and in the light of the blast, the
heroine sees his face for the first time and realizes that he is a
veritable monster! There's a situation for you!"

"It certainly is," says Aunt Mary, "when you figure that even a
German Valentino isn't so very much to look at!"

"But," goes on Georgie, "this man had a beautiful soul, and the
woman is able to forget his outward appearance until she learns
that she is to have a *child*. Then her lover's hideous face appears
before her every moment.

"When her child is born, not only does it look like its father, but
Fate wills it to be a girl! How about that for tragedy?"

"Simply horrifying," says Aunt Mary, "unless it took after its
father and went in for deep coal mining."

Georgie refuses to be swerved from enjoying herself, now that
she is going good, so she takes a deep breath and continues.

"Finally the mother evolves a plan—the most brutally tender plan that has ever been touched upon in the drama. Do you know what she does?"

"Trains the child for German opera, where it won't be noticed?" suggests Aunt Mary.

Georgie is too het up to be steered from her course.

"No!" says she. "She encases its head in a wooden mold of the head of the Venus de Milo, and feeds it with a straw through a hole in the mold.

"When the child reaches the age of eighteen the mother takes off the mold, and the child is so ravishingly beautiful that she raises the suicide rate, causes several murders, instigates a revolution and is on the verge of wrecking German Kultur, when the mother has to kill her to save the Fatherland!"

"Take my order right now," says Aunt Mary, "for a good seat in the front row."

"If you want to know what *I* think," says Judy, "I think that your German dramatist is an imbecile."

Georgie is aghast.

"Why, you poor simpleton," she exclaims, "that is the greatest rôle that has ever been created. Think of the Soul Crises that heroine goes through! That betrayed girl. That mother without a husband! What agony! What terror! What . . ."

"Oh, Georgie, you make me sick!" says Judy. "You're always dramatizing things and wanting people to get all worked up and into a state."

"Huh! You think a girl could go through all *that* without having her Soul torn to shreds?"

"Georgie," says Judy, "you talk as if getting into a jam simply started a girl running around in four directions at once. You can take my word for it—it doesn't! And I know what I'm talking about—"

"What's all this?" speaks up Aunt Mary with a note of alarm.

"Well—it's about time that Georgie stopped talking nonsense about 'Life' and learned the truth from some one who knows."

"Do you mean to tell me—" breaks in Georgie.

"Oh, of course, a girl worries a little naturally," says Judy, "but I'm certainly not going to get into a state of chronic hysteria—" and then realizing she has said more than she intended, Judy decides not to go on.

A hush falls over the trio. Even Aunt Mary doesn't know just how to pick up the repartee at this point. She finally looks at the clock to suggest a move for Georgie who stands dazed but pat.

"Georgie," says Aunt Mary, "I think our discussion of the art of the drama is pretty well thrashed out. And I believe I have a little matter to talk over with Judy alone, so if you don't mind—"

"Of course, I'll go," says Georgie, and she picks up her Stetson from off the piano.

"Wait a moment," interrupts Aunt Mary. "Before you leave, I think Judy will reconsider and give in her notice. How about it, Judy?"

"Oh, all right," says the recent *associétaire* of the Toolchest Players. "I intended to all along."

Georgie nods her acceptance and leaves.

"What's the matter now?" asks Emma. "After all the trouble Judy took to be an actress—"

Aunt Mary throws her arm about her niece's shoulder.

"Judy and I have got to thinking things over, Emma," she says, "and we've about decided that there's no career so charming for a debbie as that of a wife and mother. And if we can swing things from now on, so that she can manage to be both at the same time, I shall consider that my old life hasn't been wasted."

"I've always wanted Judy to give up other activities and marry," says Emma, "but the great trouble is, that it's almost impossible to find somebody with whom a marriage into our family would not be a misalliance."

Aunt Mary cocks her eye at Judy's mother.

"Emma," she says, "it would be well for you to realize that Judy is just the least bit—uh—handicapped."

"What do you mean?" asks Emma.

"Well," says Aunt Mary, "after all, her name has been mentioned with so many different escorts, that a future husband might feel a bit out of it."

"She is a *Revell*," says Emma, "and I'm not going to consent to her marriage unless we find a man worthy of an alliance with our house. It is perfectly dreadful the way these American débutantes are marrying men who are beneath them!"

"But wait a minute," says Aunt Mary, "let's take stock. Just what have these girls to offer a husband?"

"Why, Aunt Mary," speaks up Judy, "what do you mean?"

"Well—suppose we go over Judy's case and tell a little truth. In the first place, her reputation is in shreds. As a helpmate she would be about as handy in the home as an electric fan that has lost its moorings. As a mother, she will be a practical joke. All we can do is hope that joke isn't sprung too soon. In my way of thinking, any man of her acquaintance is a pretty good catch. I don't believe we can be choosy."

Emma freezes Aunt Mary with a look, and Judy goes over to her mother's side.

"Mother is right," she says, "suitors like Count Swazy and Sherman Bennett are all right to play about with, but there's nothing like marrying somebody with money in our own class."

Aunt Mary is dumbfounded.

"And who do you think this happy man is going to be?" she demands.

"Winnie Valentine—he has everything a girl of my position requires."

"Yes," says Aunt Mary. "I have to grant you that Winnie would be ideal . A brain specialist told me once that he would always have the charming fancies of a child of ten, and he might even believe that little fable about the stork. But Winnie is away on a cruise that was scheduled to last four months and I don't know how you'd get him back in time."

"I've sent for him," announces Judy.

"I'd like to think that would fetch him back," says Aunt Mary, "but I don't believe it will. He took a complete stock of picture puzzle books that will keep him amused until late fall. I don't think that an amorous cable from you, or even a signal of distress would turn him about."

"Don't be silly, Aunt Mary. I didn't send him a 'crush' cable or anything so stupid as that. I merely told him to hurry home in time for his birthday, because I had bought him a set of musical glasses that you play by dipping your fingers in rosin. And I think that will make him change his course."

Aunt Mary gives her niece a searching look that lasts for some long seconds.

"Judy," she says, "I'm beginning to think that perhaps my worries about you are baseless. You may be up to nonsense most of the time, but when it comes to a pinch I guess you'll get along."

"Of course she will," speaks up Emma, "she's a Revell."

Society Note: Memories of the brilliant wedding of Judy Revell to Winnfield Valentine last July have recently been somewhat overshadowed by the illness of the bride, who had to go into seclusion at the Tuxedo estate with her husband during a protracted case of diptheria. Now comes the happy news item: in April, the lovely Judy became "mamma" to a baby boy. This column admits to a bit of snobbery which is gratified by a marriage between our old American families. In these days, when debbies are marrying right and left, and in most cases not doing their duty to Society in the way of offspring, it is refreshing to be able to report the arrival of an heir in whose veins runs the pure unmixed blood of two of our finest clans.